Praise for

THE BRAINBOW BLUEPRINT

"I absolutely loved *The Brainbow Blueprint*! This book covers a wide range of areas—including nutrition, psychotherapy, herbal medicine, and much more. Yet it does so in such a practical and approachable style, complete with tangible strategies to improve your life in a holistic way. Whether you're a client, a therapist, or anyone curious about living a happier and healthier life, you're sure to love this book!"

—**Jonah Paquette, PsyD,** author of *Happily Even After,*
Awestruck, and *The Happiness Toolbox*

"*The Brainbow Blueprint* is a comprehensive and insightful resource for clinicians seeking to expand their therapeutic toolbox with evidence-based integrative and functional medicine practices. Dr. Leslie Korn skillfully introduces complex concepts in an accessible manner, providing a thorough review of the latest research and practical applications of nutrition, mind-body therapies, psychedelic-assisted therapy, and other modalities, accompanied by case studies, treatment protocols, and plenty of user-friendly assessments and worksheets. Emphasizing the importance of a holistic approach to patient care, multidisciplinary collaboration, and genuine compassion for patients' well-being, this book serves as both an informative guide and an inspiring call to action."

—**Linda A. Curran, BCPC, LPC, CAADC, CCDPD,**
author of *101 Trauma-Informed Interventions*

"Dr. Leslie Korn's *The Brainbow Blueprint* fills the gap between traditional mental health training and advancements in integrative treatment methods. Beautifully written and well organized, this book provides the foundations and scripted practices you need to personalize a holistic approach to healing and well-being for your clients. The spectrum of modalities for well-being are supported by scientific and clinical rationale and then translated to practical assessments, self-awareness activities, recipes, client exercises, informative tables, handouts, and more. The reach is broad, inclusive of nutrition, culinary medicine, integration of culture, human and animal relationships, nature, somatics, bodywork, exercise, breathwork, and spirituality. Whether you are a seasoned integrative practitioner or just beginning to explore the possibilities, you will find that *The Brainbow Blueprint* will become your go-to guide."

—**Catherine Cook-Cottone, PhD,** author of
Embodiment and the Treatment of Eating Disorders

"Dr. Korn has written a beautifully illustrated book that is use-full. It can be read cover to cover or used as a resource with tools, recipes, charts, exercises, and forms for both clinicians and clients to use. I highly recommend adding this book to your shelf to be used as part of your daily practice!"

—**Vicki Steine, DSc, LCSW,BCHN, IFNCP**

"*The Brainbow Blueprint* is an integrative masterpiece for any health care provider who is interested in supporting their clients' mental health and wellness. It is a comprehensive guidebook artfully designed with everything you need for your practice in one accessible resource, including scientific summaries, inventories, client worksheets, food- and herbal-based nutrition therapies, clinician handouts, and so much more! This is the culmination of Dr. Korn's decades of clinical wisdom and expertise—an absolutely brilliant resource for busy clinicians!"

—Kathie M. Swift, MS, RDN, LDN, FAND, EBQ, co-founder of
the Integrative and Functional Nutrition Academy

"I love, love, love *The Brainbow Blueprint*. The US health care system is severely ill, and integrative medicine for mental health is desperately needed. *The Brainbow Blueprint* is the perfect prescription."

—Mary Ann Osborne, DNP, FNP, integrative nurse practitioner

"As a psychologist, I find that most of my clients' distress comes from a complex mix of psychological, genetic, somatic, and existential/spiritual issues that cannot be neatly compartmentalized. Treatment for complex situations cannot be reduced to a pill or a quick fix. Therefore, it is more difficult to describe integrated treatments in simple terms. However, Leslie Korn has done it once again. In *The Brainbow Blueprint*, she not only breaks down and integrates the contributing factors of disease, but also offers systematic techniques and practices combined with practical suggestions, making this book uniquely user-friendly. I highly recommend it for both students in training and experienced practitioners of any healing art."

—Ilene Serlin, PhD, BC-DMT, Serlin Institute of the Healing Arts, editor of
Whole Person Healthcare and coeditor of *Integrated Care for the Traumatized*

"*The Brainbow Blueprint* will make it possible for you to fulfill our social work creed to help individuals and families identify and overcome the challenges posed by their physical, social, and economic environments while *primum nil nocere* (doing no harm). *The Brainbow Blueprint* will enable you to work on the clinical level while still maintaining your commitment to the person and environment perspective. The integrative model is the new norm for treatment; gone are the days of just talk therapy and medication. Statistics show that the modern client wants more. So give them more! In these times of Big Pharma and Big Food, we must be advocates for our clients to heal naturally, wholly, and without side effects."

—Ilysa B. Keeley, LCSW, CMHIMP, CPCC

THE
BRAINBOW
BLUEPRINT

A Clinical Guide to Integrative Medicine
and Nutrition for Mental Well-Being

Leslie Korn, PhD, MPH, LMHC

The Brainbow Blueprint: A Clinical Guide to Integrative Medicine and Nutrition for Mental Well-Being
Copyright © 2023 by Leslie Korn

Published by
PESI Publishing
3839 White Ave
Eau Claire, WI 54703

Cover and interior design by Amy Rubenzer
Illustrations by Leslie Simonin
Editing by Jenessa Jackson, PhD

Proudly printed in the United States of America.

ISBN 9781683736387 (print)
ISBN 9781683736394 (ePUB)
ISBN 9781683736400 (ePDF)

PESI Publishing
pesipublishing.com

DISCLAIMERS

HEALTH DISCLAIMER

The publisher and author are not responsible for any specific health needs that may require medical supervision and are not liable for any damages or negative consequences from any treatment, action, or application to any person reading or using the information in this book. References to internet resources are provided for informational purposes only and do not constitute endorsement of any websites or other sources. Readers should be aware that the websites listed in this book may change.

LEGAL DISCLAIMER

Several worksheets offer recommendations for how you can incorporate integrative medicine and nutrition into your clinical practice. None of these worksheets constitute legal advice and should not be used as such. These worksheets are for educational purposes only. This book provides information. Information is not the same as legal advice—the application of information to an individual's specific circumstances. This book does not provide legal advice. Although I try to make this information accurate and useful, you should consult a lawyer to interpret and apply this information to your situation. Readers should retain legal counsel to obtain definitive answers and identify their specific practice needs in their state and within their disciplines, licenses, and certifications.

TABLE OF CONTENTS

15 SPIRITUALITY AND MEANING-MAKING 303

16 ALTERED STATES AND PSYCHEDELIC MEDICINE 319

17 ADHERENCE STRATEGIES 339

18 BRIDGING INTEGRATIVE MEDICINE AND SOCIAL JUSTICE .. 357

19 PRACTICE DEVELOPMENT, COLLABORATION, AND LEGAL SCRIPTS 375

ACKNOWLEDGMENTS

Writing this book was possible only with the help of skilled assistants and contributors, to whom I am grateful. Working with others on this type of project always brings the dynamic of creative collaboration and enjoyment.

Among these collaborators is Gillian Joseph, MA, a budding psychologist who was the organizational anchor through much of this innovative project, working with me directly to organize and manage the oft-unruly material "downloaded" from my mind to the page. Ilyse Keely, a social worker, approached me several years ago with an idea for an advanced practice group for graduates of my certification program. These groups led to the development of some new worksheets, which I adapted for this book. I also listened carefully as she and others expressed the need for more exercises, methods, documents, and information. One of the great joys of my week is meeting with this group of therapists, who bring their unique approaches to integrative medicine and nutrition. Victoria Kvitek arrived as a savvy intern fresh out of college, just in the nick of time to develop several movement worksheets and research the evidence to support many of the methods I propose.

Leslie "Sindos" Simonin, a stellar designer, has now participated in two of my book projects. She provided many of the lovely icons. I am lucky to have Michel Medellin on my team as a designer and artist helping me visualize what otherwise would be just "blocky" charts. I am also grateful to the editors at PESI. Karsyn Morse is always eager to listen to my ideas for book topics and endlessly patient as they develop over time. Jenessa Jackson brought a keen eye to the first draft, and her detailed suggestions made my writing even stronger. Toward the end of the book's development, I was fortunate that Jennifer Russ arrived to help me sculpt and refine my words so they could find their essential clarity. I am so grateful for her contribution. Gretchen Panzer wrangled the final version with a deft editing hand.

Finally, my greatest teachers are my clients, and here you will find some adaptations of their stories. I still remember vividly many of my clients from over 40 years ago and how their own illuminations led to mine. Their challenges spurred me to consider alternatives for them that would help. They have shared with me what works and what doesn't. I have learned from them the importance of treating the person, not the disease.

INTRODUCTION

As you hold this book in your hands, you are embarking on an adventure—one in which you will explore, come to understand, and learn how to implement effective integrative medicine and nutritional methods to help your clients. As you begin this journey, I want to share with you the core guidance that I offer my students and clients alike: If you engage in self-care and undertake the methods I suggest, I promise you will get better. Like nature itself, these methods work slowly but surely, and they rarely have side effects. If you have patience and keep going, you will see results.

I have written this book—based on my own 40-plus years of clinical practice—as a roadmap and a toolkit to use along your journey. Whether you are already working in this field or exploring it for the first time, these methods are the missing piece of current mental health care. They will undoubtedly help your clients and synergize their improved mental health. A bold claim, no doubt, but one that you will prove in your work. That is not to say that everyone is ready for this approach or that it is an easy path. Your task as a clinician is to know what will help a client and determine whether they are ready to engage in the partnership these methods entail.

As you study the methods in this book, you will find that the idea of the "quick fix" is a faulty one that always fails clients. The notion that any one treatment or cure will sustain our mental and physical health is lacking in evidence. The methods in this book are, therefore, designed to support a lifelong and individualized practice. You will help your clients build the skills and tools they need to overcome the challenges they will face throughout their lives.

MY STORY

I want to share my own journey in this work because I know each of you has had a journey that has brought you here.

I did not begin my career as a psychotherapist. I began studying and practicing many of the methods I describe in this book as a route to my own healing. In my teenage years, I was a feminist activist engaged in the early Our Bodies, Ourselves movement in Boston. My peers and I focused on reclaiming our bodies and working within the community to take control of our health and our sexuality as acts of empowerment and social justice. When I was 16 years old, I was also introduced to mantra meditation and yoga, and I began a lifelong personal practice. Both of these experiences continue to inform my work as a therapist and integrative provider.

I completed high school and two years of college, but I longed for adventure. As a child, I had had a vision of working in the jungle. While this early dream was long forgotten, my subconscious drove me toward achieving this goal. In need of healing from a traumatic childhood and determined to find the time and space to write, I set out when I was 20 for Mexico. I landed in an Indigenous village in the jungle where there were no roads, cars, or electricity. The village was accessible only by boat, and mail took three weeks to arrive, if it ever did. I was in heaven! And although I was a stranger, I was welcomed and felt like I belonged. I would stay for 10 years, and over time I would return again and again, for a total of 25 years living and working in this village.

Nature Provides the Medicines

In Mexico, I had finally entered my laboratory of learning and healing. With no conventional doctor or formal health care nearby, I had to rely on myself and the three books I brought with me: *Where There Is No Doctor, A Barefoot Doctor's Manual*, and *Our Bodies, Ourselves*. I also practiced yoga, fasting, and meditation. These proved essential when I became fearful during my numerous bouts of tropical illnesses, and I came to understand the power of the mind to self-regulate. During my first year in the jungle, I also withdrew from nicotine, alcohol, and recreational drugs by engaging in intense aerobic exercise, breathing exercises, and sweats, and I took herbs that target the nicotinic receptors. These actions helped me relinquish the addictions driven by mind and body, and they form the basis of the detox methods I present in this book. I continued experimenting with altered states practices—anomalous cognition, lucid dreaming, kundalini yoga, and Chinese alchemical practices—as I explored transpersonal models of health and healing.

I also grew to have friendships with the local women. They taught me about the jungle's herbs, foods, and medicines—how *mota* (marijuana) can be made into a liniment for pain; that ripe papaya is good for digestion, while the sap from an unripe papaya can be applied to an infected tooth to draw out pus; that coconut water soothes dysentery; that *roselle* brings down a fever. This type of experiential learning would become a central component of my future clinical practice. It taught me about intention, which is a message I share with my students: to allow the process of learning (and practice development) to unfold organically. Yes, create the learning structure, but allow the many unseen forces to guide and align us with our purpose.

During my first year in the jungle, I opened a small middle school and had the opportunity to teach children the way I wish I had been taught. As a kinesthetic learner and dreamer, I was often bored with school and had barely graduated from high school. If I were a child in school today, I would likely be medicated. But at my school, children were invited to learn actively—through dancing, writing poetry, and observing the pollywogs—which reflects an important principle I hold as a counselor: Don't pathologize (or medicate) different learning styles or the various ways children express their distress. Don't try to make the child fit the school, but find the school that fits the child. As you will learn in this book, nutrition—in particular, eliminating food additives that destabilize mood—and expressive therapies will do wonders for children's mental health.

Throughout this time, I continued my study of acupuncture, which I had begun at college, and began a practice in bodywork and "barefoot" acupuncture. I opened a health center, and people arrived from all the surrounding villages. Running this tiny jungle health center gave me the chance to treat people with various problems—pains, insomnia, injuries, anxiety, asthma, stomachaches, dysentery, and even conditions thought by some to be the result of the rising moon. My exposure to culturally defined illnesses broadened my perspective and influenced my understanding of diagnostic categories and how we create meaning out of our symptoms.

I recall one young woman who came to me with what we would call psychotic symptoms, who said she had been hexed with the evil eye. How could I help? I had to learn what I didn't know, and I had to be fearless in the face of the unknown. These experiences informed what became my approach to mentoring and care: Jump in, do, learn, act, and do no harm. The common principles of being present, authentic, and curious become the foundation of healing.

My village clinic bodywork practice was gentle, energy-based work, and while my clients were on the treatment table, they shared their stories of their lives, their traumas. As I touched their physical pain points, rocked them, or stretched their joints to increase range of motion, their memories of traumatic events poured out—memories that had been long forgotten or simply submerged in the pain. There was the young man who had back pain and suddenly remembered being beaten by his father with a belt buckle, the woman who purged to release the tension that built up in her diaphragm, the abuse survivor with chronic constipation. For these clients, the traumatic memory often lived separately, as if behind a closed door of conscious awareness, until it peeked out to join the physical memory that was screaming in pain for recognition and to be reunited with its missing half so that it finally made "sense."

This was my hands-on introduction to dissociation, and what became my profound respect for the requisite coaxing of the memory from behind the door to join the pain it left behind. After ten years in the jungle and thousands of hours of clinical care, I decided to train as a psychotherapist.

Boston, Biochemistry, and Body Psychotherapy

I returned to Boston in 1982, where I interned at a chronic care hospital wellness center—the first of its kind in the country. I practiced bodywork with older women with a diagnosis of psychotic disorders. This helped me understand how to integrate innovative public health methods to help underserved populations, and it set the stage for my later work advocating for the inclusion of integrative health methods in public health policy.

I had wanted to leave my jungle home only in the hope of returning as a better helper and healer to my neighbors. I therefore entered a public health school to study tropical health and herbal medicine. I wanted to know what biomedical science said about why certain herbs and foods worked. But I was soon to learn much more than I had expected. I was a midwife in a sea of scientists. I did not know the language of conventional science or biochemistry, and I had to learn quickly. Many, though not all, scoffed at my interests; after all, they said, these were not "modern" methods I sought to understand.

This taught me a powerful lesson: Learn the language of those you hope to convince of your ideas. Use the language of your colleagues so they can better understand your point of view. Not that the evidence doesn't speak for itself—even today, 65–80 percent of the world uses traditional Indigenous medicine (Pan et al., 2014), not so-called modern methods. And we have seen the unintended consequences of all things modern: antibiotic resistance, cancer from pesticides and fertilizers, the persistent stigma of mental illness. But still, people often won't allow themselves to be convinced unless you use their own language.

Therefore, following public health studies, my next step was to continue my training in psychiatry. Again, I brought my jungle methods and my bodywork into a psychodynamic psychotherapy clinic of the 1980s. I wanted to understand the story of both the mind and the body. I was fascinated to learn that Freud and other early analysts used hypnotherapy and touch to access the terrain of the unconscious in hopes of healing. I studied the history of medicine alongside my clinical training, discovering the use of hydrotherapy to alter mood and the use of colonics to help detoxification in 20th-century sanatoriums. I also practiced psychotherapy and behavioral medicine with a wide range of people with severe mental illness and experienced the benefits and limitations in all our methods, continuing to fine-tune my approach of personalizing interventions.

The introduction of Prozac in 1988 was still on the horizon, and the advent of psychotropic interventions as the first line of treatment brought with it the end of community mental health. Yet we were also entering a revolutionary new model recognizing trauma as a major etiology in mental distress, one that continues to be refined today. During this time, *vipassana*, also known as mindfulness, was being introduced into Western mental health care, although it would take another 25 years before it would be fully integrated and considered de rigueur. This is another key lesson: Gaining acceptance for new methods takes time. While mindfulness is an ancient spiritual practice (hardly "new"), it took decades of work by a growing cadre of forward-thinking clinicians in the 1980s to create the mindfulness revolution in mental health care today. This lesson illuminates a pathway for nutrition and integrative medicine to become incorporated everywhere into mental health.

As a body psychotherapist in Boston, I continued my private practice and incorporated a new specialty practice in integrative post-trauma therapy. I conducted long-term post-trauma therapy for survivors of complex trauma and also developed an approach to working with people with dissociative identity disorder and borderline personality disorder, as well as people who were suicidal. I did not see them as needy or demanding or dangerous, but rather recognized that they were expressing the damaging effects of trauma, the dysregulation of the nervous system, and the inability to reestablish internal rhythms.

My work as a bodyworker emphasized the role of psychobiological rhythms: the rhythm of the breath, the rhythm of day and night, and the rhythmic interpersonal synchrony between therapist and client—even the rhythm of my canine therapists snoring. These all became part of what I defined as somatic empathy. This approach is facilitated by energetic connection and results in psychophysiological entrainment between the therapist and client. Entrainment describes a state in which two or more of the body's oscillatory systems—such as respiration, brain, and heart rhythm patterns—become synchronous and operate at the same frequency (McCraty et al., 2001). Entrainment occurs intraorganism and interorganism, as between therapist and patient and between individuals, groups, and cosmic rhythms (Korn, 2021). This helps restore the rhythmic flow template that is always disrupted by trauma and is the underlying physiological factor in insomnia, anxiety, and depression.

I also integrated canine therapy in my work with children and adults alike, and with the victims of violence and the court system, as a method to restore safe touch and reestablish the capacity to tolerate healthy sensation. I did this work with people who self-harmed and with suicide survivors, and I began to understand these behaviors as the ultimate form of dissociation. I observed faster, long-lasting results when we engaged the body in this type of treatment.

By this point, I had been immersed in Western psychological theory, Eastern medicine, and "jungle medicine" for quite some time. I had worked with a wide variety of people—of different ages, ethnicities, abilities, gender identities, and diagnostic categories. This led me to another lesson: the value of having diverse clinical experiences, across different settings and with different populations. Broad clinical experience leads to a depth of expertise that undergirds the clinical wisdom required for integrative and nutritional therapies.

> "What's the use of their having names," the Gnat said, "if they won't answer to them?"
>
> "No use to *them*," said Alice; "But it's useful to the people who name them, I suppose."

Much like Lewis Carroll writes in *Through the Looking-Glass*, my own breadth of experience taught me to question the limits of diagnostic categories. I rarely rely only on a previous clinician's assessment. Informed by my cross-cultural work, I understand that we often name things to make ourselves feel safer.

The Art and Science of Integrative Mental Health Care

I spent a total of 15 years in Boston, where I continued my private practice, taught at universities, and consulted with the state and federal governments. I received contracts from the Department of Housing and Urban Development to develop multilingual, multicultural, integrative health programs in areas with low-income and middle-income housing throughout Massachusetts. This satisfied my passion for bringing this work into public health and applying it to prevent and treat addictions. I was able to introduce ideas that were still budding in public health.

However, I still longed for my roots (yes, my herbs!) in Mexico and my cross-cultural work. So I completed my doctorate, developed a bi-country practice, and reimmersed myself in the study of mental health nutrition. This revealed yet another lesson: Yes, I could do everything I was passionate about! I just couldn't do it all at once. Gaining competence and expertise takes years, but there are many cycles to our careers—so prioritize, step by step, and keep the intention focused.

When I returned to Mexico in 1997, I recalibrated my practice. I opened my jungle clinic again—which had been reclaimed by vines, armadillos, and snakes in the meantime—and joined my clinic with a nonprofit. I raised funds and conducted research so I could contribute to the evidence of what I had long observed clinically: These methods help and heal, and the therapeutic method of touch heals. Biomedical science is still catching up with and "proving" what Indigenous medicine scientists and healers have long known.

But in 2002, after five years back in the jungle, running my clinic and training programs, I got word that both of my parents, who were still living in Boston, were ill and needed help. I had to walk away from everything; living on Indigenous territory meant that you could build your house—or, in my case, a four-acre retreat center—but you could not own the land or take anything away with you. I moved my parents to Washington state, known for its progressive health care system, where I tended to them and opened my integrative mental health practice.

From this experience, I learned a lot about being a family caregiver for dementia and cancer. It led me to ask: How do we reduce stress in dementia caregivers, and would the type of bodywork I give (and receive) reduce stress in Indigenous dementia caregivers? These questions led to a three-year randomized clinical trial research project on polarity therapy to reduce stress in dementia family caregivers in tribal communities (Korn et al., 2009), which was funded by the NIH. I still joke that there is nothing more stressful than studying stress! The NIH also funded our team to mentor two newly graduated Indigenous researchers.

This work brought still more lessons, including the value of collaboration. I worked with diverse teams from nonprofits, universities, consumer groups, and tribal communities to define a problem and the methods to solve it. Research often brings much-needed funds for clinical care and jump-starts change. But evidence isn't everything, any more than diagnostic categories tell the whole picture. Nevertheless, I had achieved my goals with the dementia project: We identified evidence for an important intervention that also provided our tribal community partners with a basis for opening massage clinics and defining more specific funding needs for family caregivers. One of the most important challenges of researching integrative medicine and nutrition is that there is no cookie-cutter approach. We maximize results when we tailor our methods to each individual.

Following the conclusion of several successful research projects and my parents' deaths, I returned to Mexico, where I now devote myself to teaching, mentoring, and the clinical care of clients. I continue to split my time between Mexico and the United States, and I have a satisfying and overly full practice. (Take note, budding integrative medicine and nutrition mental health practitioners!) This is a burgeoning niche, and there is great demand for this work. All the while, I continue to be a lifelong learner.

My goal as an integrative practitioner is to help children and adults engage their innate capacity for healing, self-regulation, and self-care. To help them claim their ability to actualize the lives they want. To help them center their healing power within themselves as they seek out expert guides. And I support clinicians to follow their heart and passion for these methods.

Our clients seek more than the alleviation of their symptoms—they also seek integration. They want to understand how all the various symptoms they experience fit together into a coherent story. Reaching this understanding is healing in and of itself. It can reduce the shame of chronic mental distress and illness, which clients have often internalized from the culture and media around them. Countless times clients have said to me, "I never understood that my experiences during childhood were contributing to my mood today" or "I never knew that my chronic stomach pain was related to the fighting I endured during mealtime in my home."

Too often, health care is segmented. Clients see clinicians who know one part of the body, or another, or perhaps only the "mind." This puts the onus on the clients to figure out how all the puzzle pieces of their mind and body fit together, when in fact, we as clinicians are in the best position to help them do so. We must develop the capacity see how all the apparently disparate parts fit together as a whole. To achieve this, we must continue to learn—to study, research, and reach out for collaborative support across multiple disciplines. This is the foundation of integrative medicine and nutrition.

In my own practice, I draw upon all the diverse experiences and forms of knowledge that I have gained throughout my personal journey. I integrate psychotherapy and behavioral medicine with Indigenous people's traditional and cultural science and wisdom, sprinkled with biomedical science. And I use every one of the methods that I present to you now in this book. These powerful interventions will help you give your clients the integration they seek, while alleviating their anxiety, depression, and pain.

WHAT IS IN THIS BOOK

The chapters in this book follow the categories of the **Brainbow Blueprint**®—a set of modalities that provide clients with a more integrative medical approach to their mental health care.

Chapter 1 introduces integrative medicine and nutrition for mental health, as well as the Brainbow Blueprint. It's the place to get your bearings in this emerging, revolutionary field of natural methods, self-care, and clinical practice.

The remaining chapters focus on specific areas of the Brainbow Blueprint. Though the different areas harmonize and can overlap with each other—the focus is integration, after all—each chapter explores one area of Brainbow practice.

Chapter 2 explores the art and science of **bioindividuality**, which can help guide your work by allowing you to personalize interventions based on each client's cultural and genomic profile. Since our individual needs are based on our ancestral heritage, incorporating genomic data that illuminates an individual's metabolic functioning, detoxification capacities, and nutritional needs will allow you to treat with greater confidence (and your clients will experience better outcomes). This is especially essential because, as you will see, there are several specific genomic profiles that influence mental health and responses to medications.

As an integrative practitioner, your work involves tracing how the varied parts of a client's life fit together to tell their story, not only emotionally and cognitively, but also through their physical symptoms. Therefore, in **chapter 3,** I explain how **integrative assessment** supports your work. I include a comprehensive integrative assessment that you can use as a model as you start to incorporate integrative methods into your practice.

In **chapter 4,** you'll learn the latest science on **biological rhythms and hormones.** Most mental illnesses, including bipolar disorder, post-traumatic stress disorder (PTSD), depression, and seasonal affective disorder, are a major response to the disruption of biological rhythms, like our circadian and ultradian rhythms. Reestablishing these rhythms is an essential tool in restoring mental wellness. Because rhythms drive hormones and hormones drive rhythms, in this chapter I will also explore some basic information about stress hormones and sex hormones, and how these influence mood and well-being at all stages of life.

Our very first medicines came from nature. We remain interdependent with the earth, and we benefit from it in countless ways. Therefore, **chapter 5** introduces the role of **nature** in integrative mental health care and includes an array of ecotherapy techniques that can help virtually anyone in search of healing or reconnection. Simple outdoor activities are a surprisingly powerful means of decreasing anxiety, depression, and stress.

Chapter 6 sheds light on another area that can provide deep healing for people with mental health or physical challenges: **human-animal relationships.** Here I focus on the science of interspecies connection and discuss how animals can help people heal from the most traumatic experiences. This chapter provides exercises and information to help you learn about different kinds of animal assistants as you consider whether and how you might work with clients who may benefit from this type of intervention.

Chapter 7 provides simple exercises that help you connect the dots between stress, food, **digestion,** and well-being. In counseling therapies, the aim is to nourish clients with new information and help them "digest" and absorb their insights. The fact that digestion is metaphorical in this way, as well as a literal process, suggests why improving digestion improves mental health. It's more than mere coincidence that most clients have co-occurring digestive issues!

Once your clients have made the connection between digestion and mental health, **chapter 8** focuses on **culinary medicine.** Here I provide you with the tools to help clients choose food that improves mood and functioning. The benefit of the Brainbow approach to food is that there is no one right diet for everyone, nor is this method ideological. It is based on the science of mental health nutrition and the individual's needs, rather than the latest fads. This approach espouses body positivity, as all sizes matter.

For clients with underlying nutrient deficiencies or genetic predispositions to certain mental health conditions, culinary medicine works best in concert with **nutritional supplementation.** Therefore, **chapter 9** explains the benefits of using supplements in mental health care and provides guidance on how you can help clients select high-quality supplements as well as check for drug-supplement-herb interactions. I include a template for "supplement smoothies," for clients who can't swallow pills, and I provide guidance for parents and providers who want to offer nutritional supplementation for children.

Herbal medicine is considered the "mother" of allopathic medicine and pharmaceuticals. The biochemical effects of herbs are well-documented, but learning to incorporate them into your practice is an organic process. **Chapter 10** provides an informational overview of each category of herbs, from adaptogens to stimulants, with information regarding which herbs benefit which client populations and which symptoms. I include reference to a modern drug-herb-nutrient interaction database, along with recipes you can begin to use safely.

While much of this work is concerned with finding ways to better nourish the body and mind with wholesome foods, natural herbs, and select supplements, you must rid the body and brain of problematic toxins and pathogens in order to fully optimize health. Therefore, **chapter 11** introduces effective and often enjoyable practices in the area of **hydrotherapy and detoxification,** and provides a multipronged protocol for clients seeking to reduce their dependence on psychotropic medications.

Chapter 12 is devoted to **exercise.** Here I provide guidance on how you can better understand the range of associations that clients have with movement and exercise, as well as the range of ways you can better support the inclusion of exercise in integrative health care. I review the five major types of exercise and which kinds are best for which symptoms. I also include a collection of fun, at-home exercises to help clients at a variety of fitness levels and with various wellness targets.

Our bodies are our closest lifelong companions. Yet tuning in to their needs is often quite a challenge because the majority of us are quite used to dissociating and distracting ourselves from the stories our bodies are trying to tell us through symptoms. **Chapter 13** provides a set of simple **somatic and bodywork** practices that can help clients reconnect with their bodies to ground, energize, and deeply relax. I also include recommendations for different kinds of bodywork and how these can vary based on client diagnosis or wellness target.

Breathing is an ever-present, though usually unconscious, aspect of human life. Disordered breathing often co-occurs with mental distress, so in **chapter 14,** I focus on the **breath.** I provide a brief assessment for disordered breathing, as well as a range of symptom-specific exercises that have the power to transform mental distress. Healing breathing disorders by making the breath conscious is a potent mental health intervention.

Our beliefs have a foundational power to either heal or worsen our outcomes. In **chapter 15,** I explore **spirituality and meaning-making,** including how to engage your clients' belief systems to catalyze profound psychobiological change. I include exercises that tap into the power of myth and art, the wisdom of dreams, the practice of meditation, and the possibilities of post-traumatic growth.

Chapter 16 discusses **altered states and psychedelic medicine.** Here I examine the research on a range of psychoactive compounds, provide guidance on harm reduction, and discuss how to educate clients on safely exploring altered states, including dissociation, with the goal of increasing their self-regulation. The burgeoning interest in psychedelic medicine for mental health requires you to become educated about these substances' medical, psychological, and ritual uses so you can provide evidence-based guidance to clients interested in them.

Even the most well-laid-out Brainbow Blueprint program will not work if the client does not engage in it consistently. Therefore, in **chapter 17,** I discuss five significant barriers to program adherence and provide you with several **adherence strategies** to help clients tackle these barriers in a focused, lighthearted, and shame-free way. These strategies will allow you to support clients in defining their priorities, goals, tasks, and timelines.

Given that illness often occurs in the matrix of community (where clients may be exposed to pesticides, pollutants, poor-quality food, poverty, and other factors), in **chapter 18** I discuss how to bridge **integrative medicine and social justice.** I explore how to magnify your impact by making inroads at the community level and provide guidance, drawn from my 45 years of community health care work, to help you provide more personalized care to clients in the context of individual sessions. I also explore large-scale research projects that address the social and political underpinnings of access to integrative health and nutrition.

Finally, **chapter 19** focuses on **practice development, collaboration, and legal scripts.** In this chapter, you will find sample forms and procedures that can support your work and provide a legal and ethical foundation for a healthy practice. You may adapt these as needed in your particular state; note that you may also require consultation with an attorney. I include a sample client protocol and a clinician self-evaluation in this chapter to help you assess your own competency as you decide on a timeline to launch your integrative practice.

HOW TO USE THIS BOOK

I have structured this book in a way that I hope will allow you to navigate with ease and joy the revolutionary changes that you are helping your clients to make. You are your own laboratory, experimenting with and exploring these methods. Use this book in the way that best serves you. You might read it from front to back, home in on the chapters that are most useful to you, or pull out a specific form or worksheet that grabs your attention.

At a Glance

In each chapter, I compile a table of recommendations for treating different diagnostic categories of distress, which appear with the heading "At a Glance." This includes categories such as depression, anxiety, obsessive-compulsive disorder (OCD), insomnia, chronic pain, substance use, and digestive disorders.

When working with clients, identify the health and diagnostic challenges they want to recover from, and consider how the interventions discussed in each chapter might be applied to their dis-ease category. (I place a hyphen in the word *dis-ease* to remind us what *disease* means—to be out of ease—and that we support our clients to come back into ease.) Then put together a protocol, drawing from all the applicable Brainbow Blueprint methods listed in each table. However, these recommendations are a guide, not written in stone. Use them as a jumping-off point, bringing your creativity and client attunement to create your own protocols.

The Icons and Their Meanings

Icons appear throughout the book to denote types of worksheets and activities, the areas of the Brainbow Blueprint, and other key concepts. Here is a key:

BRAINBOW BLUEPRINT ICONS

Bioindividuality

Hydrotherapy and Detoxification

Integrative Assessment

Exercise

Biological Rhythms and Hormones

Somatics and Bodywork

Nature

Breath

Human-Animal Relationships

Spirituality and Meaning-Making

Digestion

Altered States and Psychedelic Medicine

Culinary Medicine

Adherence Strategies

Nutritional Supplements

Bridging Integrative Medicine and Social Justice

Herbal Medicine

Practice Development, Collaboration, and Legal Scripts

GENERAL ICONS

 Resources made for use by **clinicians**

 Resources made for use by **clients** (these might be completed as homework and brought back to the clinician or used simply as a form of personal reflection and practice)

 Resources made for use by **clinicians and clients** together

 Recipes for physical and mental health

 Exercises, which include movement, breathing techniques, meditations, and more

 Worksheets to be printed and filled out

 Handouts to be printed and read

 Clinical pearls, which are words of wisdom about clinical practice from me to you

 "Did you know?" callouts, which provide additional context and tips

 Client stories that illustrate the Brainbow in practice

1

THE BRAINBOW BLUEPRINT

UNDERSTANDING INTEGRATIVE MEDICINE AND NUTRITION

Integrative medicine and nutrition for mental health plays an essential role in helping clients on their journey to recover and mental well-being. Yet this approach may be new to many of your clients—and perhaps to you as well. To help you get your bearings in this emerging, revolutionary field, this first chapter provides the background you need to incorporate integrative methods into your practice and to introduce these methods to your clients.

Integrative medicine and nutrition incorporates the fields of counseling, somatic work, and talk therapy with a range of mind-body-spirit methods that address the needs of the whole person. This approach does not separate the presenting symptoms of mind and body but, instead, puts these manifestations of distress and strength together, as one does a jigsaw puzzle.

The Academic Consortium for Integrative Medicine and Health defines integrative medicine as the practice of medicine that "reaffirms the importance of the relationship between the practitioner and patient, focuses on the whole person, is informed by evidence, and makes use of all appropriate therapeutic and lifestyle approaches, health care professionals, and disciplines to achieve optimal health and healing."

An important part of this definition is *informed by evidence*, meaning that integrative medicine and nutrition is no less scientific than conventional medicine. It asks two questions: (1) What works? and (2) What evidence is there for it based on biomedical research? Integrative medicine and nutrition looks at this available evidence to address the root causes of imbalances that contribute to mental and emotional illness, as well as to identify interventions that draw from the four major fields of health care to help clients come into balance. Central to this approach is ensuring that the interventions you propose are consistent with the client's belief system.

Integrative Medicine and the Four Major Health Care Models

Let's take a closer look at the four areas of care:

- **Naturopathic and functional medicine.** Naturopathy is a distinct system of primary health care that emphasizes prevention and the self-healing process through the use of natural therapies. The focus is on whole-patient wellness through health promotion and disease prevention, while addressing the underlying cause of the patient's condition. The guiding principle is *vis medicatrix naturae*, a Latin phrase meaning "the healing power of nature."

  There are two types of naturopaths: licensed and traditional. Licensed naturopaths are licensed as primary clinicians in more than 25 states in the United States. Not all states require licensure to practice naturopathy; however, the scope of practice is very different. Licensed naturopaths can diagnose and prescribe medicines.

  Functional medicine is a systems biology-based approach that determines how and why illness occurs. It focuses on identifying and addressing the root cause of disease.

- **Complementary and alternative medicine.** These terms indicate whether conventional approaches are also being used. If a practice is used together with conventional medicine, then it's complementary. If a practice is used in place of conventional medicine, it's alternative.

- **Allopathic or conventional medicine.** These terms are synonyms. They refer to a system in which medical doctors and other health care professionals treat symptoms and diseases using drugs, radiation, or surgery.

- **Traditional or cultural medicine.** This is the sum total of the knowledge, skills, and practices that are based on the theories, beliefs, and experiences indigenous to different cultures, whether explicable or not, used in the maintenance of health as well as in the prevention, diagnosis, improvement, or treatment of physical and mental illness.

When adopting an integrative approach into your practice, you have an advantage due to your training as a mental health professional. You understand the complex etiology of mental illness, and you are skilled in various methods to help clients overcome emotional and social obstacles to success, whether it's cognitive behavioral therapy (CBT), eye movement desensitization and reprocessing (EMDR), internal family systems therapy (IFS), or other methods. While knowing about different treatment methods is necessary, it is not sufficient.

That's because integrative medicine and nutrition is not just about methods, though methods, techniques, and culinary interventions can be applied to help your clients. Integrative medicine and nutrition is also about you: It starts with you becoming integrated as a clinician. This means that you must unlearn the compartmentalization of your educational training to access all the ways of knowing, analyzing, and understanding the whole human: soma and psyche combined.

As humans, we are born with the natural capacity to integrate our experiences, and our brain has dominant ways of perceiving and knowing the world. As we grow, these innate tendencies are influenced by the type of educational experiences we receive, and we then gravitate toward careers and specializations that reinforce these tendencies. Some may focus on applying CBT and behaviorism; others may embrace art therapies, EMDR, and narrative methods. The utility of the integrative methods I propose here is that they complement all of these treatment modalities. Whether you are analyzing nutrient protocols, assessing whether a client benefits from more right- or left-nostril breathing, or facilitating the moment-to-moment awareness engendered by shavasana and mindfulness, there is no limit to the methods that you can incorporate.

Therefore, when applying this approach, your clients will benefit the most if you are deeply integrated yourself, using all parts of your knowing to assist them in their next steps to recovery. Your own integration process allows you to best help clients by undoing the systems that separated out all your functions to begin with. When your clients pick up on your integration, it allows you to serve both as a guide and a role model. In this role, you are ideally situated to help your clients understand how all the aspects of their mind and body fit together—and how they can use this knowledge to achieve healing and empowerment.

THE BRAINBOW BLUEPRINT

The Brainbow Blueprint is my framework for integrative health and nutrition for mental health. It is a full set, or palette, of modalities that can be used in the context of any or all of the four major health care models.

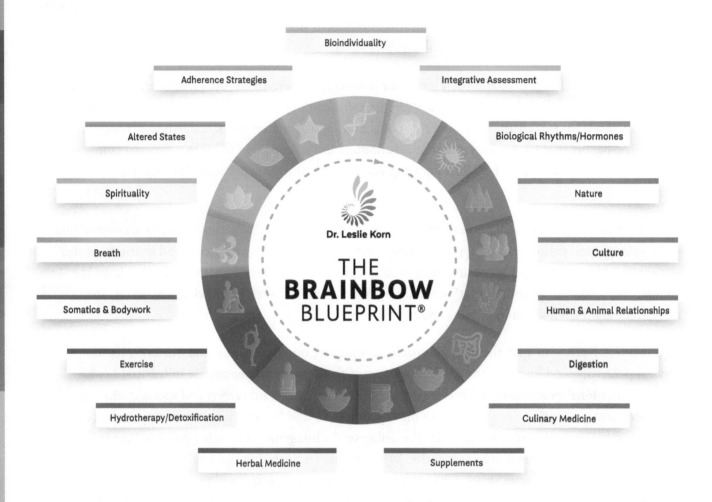

Each area of Brainbow practice will be the focus of its own chapter, with the exception of culture. Because culture, ethnicity, and identity infuse everything we do, I have incorporated these ideas throughout all the chapters. (For a more focused discussion of culture and diversity, see my *Multicultural Counseling Workbook* [2016a]).

The following handouts will guide you as you introduce the Brainbow Blueprint to your clients. First, I provide a clinician handout with questions for you to consider and sample dialogue you can use with clients. This is followed by an exercise that will help your clients get in touch with deeper ways of knowing and become integrated within themselves—an essential first step in their journey toward integration and healing.

INTRODUCING THE BRAINBOW BLUEPRINT TO CLIENTS

PURPOSE

As a clinician, you must be able to explain your methods in a way that your clients will understand. This handout provides a sample dialogue for explaining the role of the Brainbow methods to your clients. Practice this language, or feel free to substitute your own.

BACKGROUND

Consider your audience when tailoring your explanation. For example:

- Would this client benefit more from a general overview or from having details specified for their unique situation?

- How would the description of culinary medicine change for someone who is eating lots of sugar and fast food versus a client who is already nutrition savvy?

- What metaphors or imagery might you use when working with more visual learners?

- Do you want to cite recent research if working with a skeptic or a scientist?

- How might you adapt this language for other purposes (e.g., when describing your clinical practice, facilitating a group, teaching a class, or creating written materials for your clients)?

SAMPLE DIALOGUE

I am so excited to learn of your interest in integrating a variety of helpful methods to bring about balance in mind and body. These methods are called "integrative" because we combine many methods together; we know they work well together with psychotherapy or as stand-alone methods. They synergize with each other based and with my expertise to help you achieve your best health and wellness. I want to explain what these methods are. Feel free to ask questions as we proceed.

Bioindividuality

Bioindividuality is our core philosophy of personalized health. It recognizes that we are individuals and that there's no one "right" diet or intervention for everyone. Consider how the nutritional needs of people living in the Arctic are different from someone living in Mexico. Your cultural heritage and ethnicity—and all the aspects of your identity—are potent resources for resilience and growth.

You are a bioindividual, so let's find out what works best for you. There is no cookie-cutter approach to enhancing health, so we may do genomic testing to understand how your genes affect your health. We might also explore your ancestral wisdom: the culinary and health practices of your forebears. We can then personalize methods to what your body and mind need by understanding who you are and how you respond to all the methods available.

Integrative Assessment

Because the mind and body are interconnected, we will do comprehensive assessment to explore all the aspects of your physical, mental, emotional, and spiritual well-being. We will explore the causes of your symptoms and how they may be related. We will go at your pace. I know that sometimes assessment questions can be upsetting, at which point we can always take a break. I'll rely on you to let me know how you're feeling during this process. If tests are called for, I will recommend those and tell you what they will tell us, and you can decide about those as well.

Biological Rhythms and Hormones

Some of the most exciting research on mental health is about how natural rhythms influence our health and how we can improve our sleep and mood by balancing these many rhythms. For example, the light and dark cycle of the day and night has important influences on our mood, appetite, and more. When we balance these rhythms, we function better, so we will explore your rhythms to enhance your health.

Hormones are also part of our rhythms, and they affect our health and mental well-being at all stages of life. We will ensure that your hormones are balanced as a foundation for your mental health and well-being. This may include referral to a hormone specialist at some point in our work together. I suggest only the use of bioidentical hormones, never any synthetic hormones.

Nature

Natural medicine recognizes the body's inherent ability to heal itself. We respond to the rhythms and sensations of nature—the morning dew on our bare feet; the sun and the moon influencing our brain and mood; the repetitions and variations of colors, like the blue-green of the ocean, sky, and forest; and so much more. Finding ways to touch and engage with nature enhances all aspects of our wellness.

Nature puts things in perspective and allows us to engage with something greater than ourselves, especially when we don't feel well. It can embrace us in a profound moment of awe, gratitude, and connection, such as when we take in the view from the top of a mountain or spy a rainbow after the storm.

Culture

In the Brainbow Blueprint, *culture* refers to individual and collective values and practices, ethnic heritage, and all other aspects of personal identity, including sex and gender. Culture intersects with physical and mental health, both as a protective, resilient influence and as a risk factor (such as when we experience discrimination and cultural trauma). It influences bioindividuality and genomics. It also affects the meaning we make of symptoms and potential interventions.

The word *culture* comes from the Latin *cultus*, which has meanings ranging from "tilling of land" to "adoration." Cultural practices root us in the earth, even as we reach toward the sky.

Human-Animal Relationships

All our relationships are vital to our mental well-being. Our relationships with other humans and animals enhance our sense of connection and bonding, and they have profound effects on the physical body. Did you know that caring for animals like dogs or cats can lower our blood pressure, decrease pain, and reduce anxiety? In our work together, we'll explore how humans and animals can play an even more significant role in your life and health.

Digestion

Where there is mental distress, there is poor digestion. We will explore the different diet options available and discover how you best digest. Some people respond best to a diet higher in carbohydrates, vegetables, fruits, and grains. Others will feel best on a wide variety of animal and plant proteins and fats.

We will also explore your need for enzymes and the effects of medications and stress on your digestion. Digestion takes place in a state of relaxation. Regardless of your diet, your ability to practice mindfulness, gratitude, and relaxation will aid in your digestion. We will explore how to best support your digestive process so you will get the benefits of nourishment.

Culinary Medicine

There is substantial evidence that what we eat affects our mood. For example, the fats and sugars in fast food can contribute to depression, anxiety, and attention-deficit/hyperactivity disorder (ADHD). We can reduce and eliminate many of the causes of our distress by changing our diet.

Culinary medicine is a new, evidence-based field in medicine that blends the art of food and cooking with the science of medicine. Culinary medicine helps people make good decisions about accessing and eating high-quality meals that help prevent and treat disease and restore well-being.

It's not always easy to make dietary changes, but we will go at the pace that feels right to you. I promise you will see results with some of these changes. As we proceed in our work together, I will have recommendations for you, or we can also bring in a nutritional consultant to ensure that you have all the options available.

Supplementation

There is substantial evidence that nutrients and nutritional supplements enhance physical and emotional balance. Even some pharmaceuticals now include vitamins, like B6, because they potentiate the action of drugs more effectively.

Your unique genetics may require more of certain nutrients or certain forms of nutrients; we can explore that via tests if you wish. We will address any nutrient deficiencies that may be affecting your health and engage any nutrition specialists if necessary.

If you want to reduce or even eliminate medications you are taking, supplements will be an important part of helping you do that successfully.

Herbal Medicine

An herb is any plant or plant part that is used for its culinary or therapeutic value. Herbal medicine is the art and science of using plants to support health and wellness. Many pharmaceuticals derive from natural sources like herbs. We can explore many options for enhancing your mental and physical health using herbal teas, compresses, and extracts. We will discuss any recommendations with your prescriber to see if they would interact with your current pharmaceutical regimen.

Hydrotherapies and Detoxification

Hydrotherapy is the use of water to treat a disease or to maintain health. This can include hot, cold, wet, or dry treatments to alter mood and decrease pain in the body. These are simple self-care methods that you can do at home, and they are very soothing and enjoyable.

Detoxification is a method of enhancing the elimination of waste from the body that can be impairing your physical or emotional function. Different organs—especially the skin, liver, kidneys, and colon—have specific detox jobs. Did you know that every night when you sleep, your brain goes through a detoxification process?

Detoxification will involve both decreasing exposure to toxins, like household cleaning products or pesticides in foods, and aiding your body to eliminate waste, just like when you empty out the garbage bin. As you enhance your detoxification, your physical and mental well-being will improve.

Exercise

Exercise is essential for mental and physical well-being. It improves sleep, mood, and cognitive function, and it reduces pain. I am eager to work with you to explore suitable types of exercise that will help you find the balance you are seeking. We can explore all kinds of exercises together—including yoga, aerobics, weightlifting, tai chi, and balance—to define the best options for you. Each type of exercise has different benefits, and we will match your interests and abilities to your health goals.

Somatics and Bodywork

Somatic therapies look at the connection between your mind and body. When we can't find the words to express our feelings, the body often tells us of its distress through physical symptoms. Somatic therapies will help you listen more closely to and interpret the messages of your body. These therapies feel good and help you remember the pleasure of your body, especially if you are in pain. Somatic approaches may involve just the body, or they may integrate psychotherapy and physical therapies as well for holistic healing.

There are also many forms of bodywork. Some involve gentle touch, while others involve a deeper working out of muscle tension. Some can be done with clothes on, and others with or without oil. There are many types of acupuncture as well, with evidence for its success in addiction recovery and pain. If this is an area of interest to you, or if I believe this will benefit you, I can discuss ways I can teach you some self-care methods and make a referral to a licensed practitioner.

Breath

The breath is the rhythm of life, and restoring this rhythm is a doorway into restoring mental health. I will show you how to use different breathing methods to alter your focus and attention, enhance relaxation, and reduce depression and anxiety. These are simple methods that you can do at home, at work, or anywhere to enhance control over your health and well-being. Did you know that breathing changes the gas mixture in our blood, and this directly affects our mood? This gives us so much power to control how we feel!

Spirituality

I believe spirituality can play a vital part in the healing process, and many spiritual practices also incorporate methods inherent to integrative medicine. I'm very interested to learn more about how you feel spirituality supports your well-being. Please feel free to share more, and we can incorporate this, if you wish, into our evolving plan.

(**Note:** If the client has previously indicated that spirituality is of no interest to them, skip this section.)

Altered States of Consciousness

There are a variety of experiences that can facilitate altered states of consciousness, such as drumming, dancing, chanting, prayer, meditation, fasting, and psychedelics. Sometimes these experiences benefit us, and other times they can make us feel out of control. We can explore this as an integral part of our work together to help you feel grounded and also to explore experiences that transcend the self. We can discuss how you may be using substances to alter your consciousness and whether those benefit or detract from your health.

(**Note:** Depending on the laws in your area, you may be able to offer to discuss and assess the potential benefit of interventions such as psychedelic medicine.)

Adherence Strategies

We have discussed various methods of the Brainbow Blueprint, an integrative, whole-person program. However, knowing all the best practices doesn't mean much unless we actually use them!

I always make sure that we take time to identify what you need to carry out these methods so they make sense for you. In my clinical experience, adherence strategies are as individual as the types of interventions themselves. I will work with you to identify what works for you, supporting and coaching you. Together, we will be creative so you can be proactive and successful in any program we develop.

Client Exercise

PURPOSE

Intuition, trusting our "gut," and cognitive flexibility are all critical to our experience and to making good decisions. These three forms of what can be called "self-communication" can guide us and allow us to be more in touch with our mind and body. The following exercises will help you enhance your intuition. Just like we stretch our bodies to be more flexible, so can we stretch our brain/mind.

BACKGROUND

Intuition is the feeling of knowing something without having conscious reasoning behind it. Intuition is often negatively affected by a history of emotional distress. We might doubt or second-guess ourselves as intuition filters into our awareness.

Intuition is different from the **gut feelings** we may have. The gut, also called the "second brain," is linked via neurochemical pathways to the first brain. The churning in the gut when something isn't right, or a sense of it being precisely right, truly comes about because you "feel it in your gut."

Cognitive flexibility is an executive function that includes our ability to adapt to our constantly changing environment and think about many ideas simultaneously.

Engaging the right side of the brain helps all of these self-communication capacities, because the right side of the brain acts as a parallel processor, connecting and processing everything simultaneously. For this reason, the right brain is essential in increasing intuition, our "gut sense," and cognitive flexibility. In turn, this helps us make good decisions about our lives.

Try the following exercises to activate the right brain and synchronize it with the left.

BUMBLEBEE BREATH

Bhramari pranayama, or bumblebee breath, is an enjoyable yogic breathing technique that involves humming. It opens up the right brain, reduces anxiety, and enhances nitric oxide function—and thus improves heart health, psychological well-being, and longevity. The practice also enhances blood flow to the brain and ventilates and drains the sinuses.

1. Sit comfortably and close your eyes. Place your thumbs in your ear canals to gently block them. Place your index fingers over your eyebrows, and let the rest of your fingers rest over your eyes, covering them.

2. Take a deep breath in, then exhale slowly through your nose while making a loud humming sound in your throat and focusing your attention on the area between your eyebrows. Repeat this five times.

3. As you continue to practice, build up to 5–15 minutes once, and then twice, per day.

THUMB CHANGE

1. Sit comfortably. With both hands out in front of you, start by opening your left hand with the four fingers up and the thumb pointing at the center of your hand. Your right palm should be closed with only the thumb outside pointing to your left.

2. Now, slowly make the change from one hand to the other, closing your left hand, thumb outside, and opening your right hand with the four fingers up and the thumb inside, pointing at the center of your hand.

3. Keep alternating these movements for 45–90 seconds.

DID YOU KNOW?

Long-term meditation is linked to improvement in attention, working memory, and cognitive flexibility. Enhancing cognitive flexibility is a key factor in improving symptoms of anorexia nervosa, OCD, and learning disorders (Fabio & Towey, 2018).

BIOINDIVIDUALITY

There is no one right diet for everyone, just as there is no one right dose of medication, herb, or nutrient. Some medications, herbs, and foods will not be appropriate for some clients. This is the essence of bioindividuality, which is also called personalized nutrition or precision medicine, and it informs your work at all stages as you support your clients on their unique healing journeys.

Bioindividuality is both a science and an art. The science involves understanding the personalized needs of each individual that coexist alongside the universal needs of all individuals. The art of bioindividuality is in its careful, client-centered application.

THE SCIENCE OF BIOINDIVIDUALITY

Our differences are rooted in the intersection of biology and genetics and the environmental and cultural milieu that shapes us. Dr. Roger Williams—a biochemist and nutrition researcher who discovered folic acid, pantothenic acid, vitamin B6, and lipoic acid—coined the term *biochemical individuality* when he recognized that individuals varied significantly in their nutritional needs. Long before the mapping of the human genome, he confirmed genetic variations and their contributions to mental health.

Williams and other clinician-researchers observed what nature and culture suggest: Some people are carnivores, like the peoples who live in the northern climes and survive on animals of the land and sea, with few carbohydrates, while other people are vegetarians, such as those who live on tropical foods like grains, legumes, fruits, and vegetables, along with nuts and some lean animal proteins. Migration and the subsequent exchanges of foods, spices, and herbs have been going on for millennia, yet we know that, just like the engine in a car, some bodies and minds combust almost any food, while others need the specific octane supplied by protein or carbohydrates.

Therefore, when considering the nutritional approaches that will best serve a particular client, it is important to always evaluate their specific needs. For example, while the benefits of the ketogenic diet are well-documented for some, not everyone will benefit from saturated fats, such as individuals with one or two copies of the APOE4 alleles. This allele inhibits cholesterol transport and raises the risk of Alzheimer's and heart disease. Twenty-five percent of the population have one copy of this allele, and three percent have two copies (Gharbi-Meliani et al., 2021).

Bioindividuality also extends beyond diet to encompass the body's—and particularly the liver's—capacity to detoxify waste, leading to the need for more or less specific nutrients. Williams was among several researchers who identified the unique need for B vitamins by people with alcohol addiction, as well as the link between celiac disease or gluten sensitivity and depression or schizophrenia (Levinta et al., 2018).

The different rates at which bodies can detoxify waste also explains why everyone does not metabolize caffeine in the same way. For example, people who metabolize coffee quickly may tend to drink more of it, while those who metabolize it more slowly may still be affected by it later in the day, even though they drink it early in the morning. Genomic influences aside, it is also important to consider how caffeine can impact a client's existing mental or physical health symptoms; caffeine may be a mood booster for someone who is depressed but contraindicated in someone with insomnia or heart problems.

There are several main genomic tests you can order that illuminate mental health specifically. For example, given that the APOE gene is associated with accelerated cognitive decline, you might test for this gene when working with people exhibiting cognitive impairment. You might test for the MTHFR or COMT gene to assess clients' genetic propensity for mood disorders or deficits in detoxification pathways. You might also test for pharmacogenomics, which provides a fine-tuned assessment of beneficial or detrimental reactions to selective serotonin reuptake inhibitors (SSRIs), opiates, proton pump inhibitors, statins, and more. All these tests enable you to tailor your approach to each individual client.

THE ART OF BIOINDIVIDUALITY

I follow a three-stage process when addressing bioindividuality with my clients. First, I listen to their self-reported experiences of digestion—what energizes them, what makes them sleepy, what they feel is the ideal protein/carbohydrate/fat ratio in a good meal—and I ask them about their food likes and dislikes. Intuition plays an essential role in what nourishes us. (But note that cravings are not necessarily the result of intuition—something else is at work if a client thinks they should eat lots of sugar, for instance.) If your clients have not yet had the opportunity to pay close attention to the effects of their food on their mood, this is where you begin. This serves two purposes: It raises awareness, which is the foundation of any modality but especially counseling, and it leads to charting connections heretofore unseen.

Next, I inquire about the client's cultural heritage and ethnic roots. We know that genomic variations evolved in diverse environments, and migration does not change those genomic influences. Most people have a mix of cultural influences, and some dominate over others genetically. For example, just as I might have my father's eyes and my mother's hair, one of their influences will dominate with my digestion. Exploring this is not an exact science but more of an illuminative link to a client's ancestral connections. In this stage, I may have the client do informal experiments to help them deepen their experiential understanding of what nourishes them optimally.

Finally, I conduct testing. Conventional, functional, and integrative medicine for mental health all explore bioindividuality through testing. In addition to genomic testing, I may test blood, feces, urine, and saliva for various insights. Some clients complain of adverse reactions to foods or medications; they may have allergies, sensitivities, or greater needs for nutrients. This level of information cannot be intuited, yet knowing helps me pinpoint the foods, medications, or supplements a client will benefit from including in their self-care regimen. Through this process, I can increasingly broaden my understanding of the factors contributing to a client's distress that extend beyond the "nurture" focus to include the "nature" aspect as well. This rounds out all potential options for interventions.

You might choose to engage in all three stages at once or go step by step, following the client's interests and needs. The following chapter will help you to guide your clients in exploring the genomic, cultural, and environmental influences on their health and well-being. Understanding your clients' bioindividuality will allow you to optimize care, identify potential indications and contraindications of foods and nutrients, and better support your clients' nutrition, detoxification, and exercise efforts.

Bioindividuality at a Glance

WELLNESS TARGET	RECOMMENDATIONS
Depression	• Ensure plenty of anti-inflammatory foods • Carnivores can limit magnesium and citrus, which can be depressing in abundance; check genomics, especially MTHFR and COMT genes
Anxiety and panic	• Ensure the gut is functioning with plenty of fermented foods and GABA support (see chapter 9) • Add vinegar and consider animal proteins if on a vegetarian diet
OCD	• Vulnerable to drops in glucose during the day; may benefit from several small meals • Ensure right-brain activation, inositol intake, and plenty of fats for the brain, especially hemp and fish oils, and chia seeds
Bipolar disorder	• Rule out other causes of mood lability and sleep dysfunction like PTSD; rule out secondary effects of psychotropics • Requires circadian balancing (see chapter 4), often phase-delayed rhythm • Recommend lithium orotate and enact strict sleep hygiene
Insomnia	• Differentiate based on frequency (acute or chronic); type (sleep onset, maintenance, or early morning wakening); and presence of contributing factors (mixed or comorbid) • More common in women; identify influences of life stage and hormones on the client
Stress, trauma, and PTSD	• Identify whether the trauma is acute, chronic, latent, or complex • Assess for the presence of adverse childhood experiences (ACEs) • The number and types of exposures, coping methods, and substances used will inform the brain's needs for amino acids and the client's biological and psychological resilience
ADHD	• Rule out stress, ACEs, poor-quality diet, highly refined carbs and sugar, low protein, and sedentism • Assess learning styles—may require more kinesthetic activities, outdoor education, adequate light

WELLNESS TARGET	RECOMMENDATIONS
Chronic pain	• Associated with depression; reduce inflammation and eat blue, purple, and red anti-inflammatory foods • Assess for fibromyalgia and sleep disorders, structural or functional pain, and history of accidents or abuse; apply mindfulness and herbal analgesics; assess chronic NSAID use and effects on gut and liver function
Substance use disorder	• Apply self-medication theory of addiction and then assign; principle of nutrient substitutions; ask what the brain needs; supplement with amino acids, fats, and nootropics; treat HPA axis function • Resolve ACEs and trauma symptoms, which often contribute to addiction
Cognition and memory	• Check APOE status for gene risk—this guides bioindividual diet • If APOE4 positive: reduce saturated fats and increase intensive aerobics; enhance blood flow and amino acids; reduce hard alcohol; explore Mediterranean diet
Autism spectrum and neurodivergence	• Eliminate gluten, casein and refined sugar for 3–6 months and reassess effects • Assess for low cholesterol levels and increase if necessary • Increase brassica vegetables or glucoraphanin
Body image and eating disorders	• Assess disorder type, including orthorexia, avoidant restrictive food intake disorder, and body dysmorphia • Assess for ACEs, bulimia, SAD, and PMS • Use amino therapies, 5-HTP, herbal sedatives, and core and weight training for self-image
Digestive disorders	• Reduce stress, and enhance liver and gallbladder function with bitter greens, beets, lecithin, and virgin olive oil • High-stress, sympathetic types are prone to acid reflux, anxiety, and inflammatory bowel disease; integrate chewing and mindfulness with a simple diet • Look for any food allergy links • Reduce highly refined carbs • Increase fermented foods or prebiotics

CLAIM AND NAME: A SELF-AWARENESS ACTIVITY

PURPOSE

As you prepare to analyze your diet and make choices for mental wellness, it is helpful to practice claiming and naming your unique needs.

BACKGROUND

We are not often encouraged to explore our needs for fuel, especially when they differ from those of our family, our friends, or others around us. We often get messages that there is something wrong with us or that we have something to feel shame about if we eat certain foods. These cultural/ethnic or social influences can contribute to orthorexia, a focus on eating "just the right way" that becomes unhealthy.

Ultimately, what we eat is about what fuels us and what doesn't; what enhances our sense of well-being and what doesn't. When we approach eating with this awareness, we recognize that we have many options for fuel, and our choices may change over time as we stay in tune with our needs. The first step to being self-aware about how food is fueling your brain, mind, and body is to chart your energy, focus, and mood.

INSTRUCTIONS

The following questions will help you assess what is working—and what is not working—in your diet and nutritional self-care. You will start to notice the connections between what you eat and how you feel. Then name and claim and (if necessary) release the shame.

Take a moment to reflect on how you intuitively feel about different foods. First, name five foods that you intuitively feel are best for you.

_____

_____

_____

Now name five foods that you feel are not good for you.

_____

_____

_____

Food is fuel. Do you think that you are getting the right fuel for your brain, mind, and body? How would you know? What are the criteria that are important?

_____

_____

_____

_____

_____

_____

Have you been hesitant to make changes to your diet because of what your family, friends, or others might say? Or perhaps they have already said something. First write what they are saying or what you imagine they might say. Then craft a response.

_____

_____

_____

_____

_____

_____

Do you feel better when you eat animal protein or plant-based protein? Can you break these categories down even further—how do different types of animal proteins, plants, or legumes make you feel?

_____

_____

_____

_____

_____

What foods make you feel focused or energized?

_____

_____

_____

_____

What foods make you feel relaxed or sleepy?

_____

_____

_____

_____

What foods are addictive for you?

_____

_____

_____

_____

What feelings arose for you during this exercise? Did you notice yourself having thoughts about what you "should" or "shouldn't" do or think? Did you experience a sense of shame or perhaps listen to conflicting voices within you?

_____

_____

_____

_____

_____

_____

Embrace all these feelings, beliefs, and voices that influence your self-nourishment. Let them rise to the surface and welcome them as a jumping-off point for self-awareness.

Client Worksheet

WEDDING OUR CULTURAL AND ENVIRONMENTAL HERITAGE TO OUR FOOD CHOICES

PURPOSE

This exercise encourages you to define your cultural and environmental heritage and to reflect on your ancestral foods as a doorway into exploring your dietary needs.

BACKGROUND

The best fuel for your body is often genetically determined, and that reflects where your forebears are from. Therefore, understanding your cultural and environmental heritage helps you determine which foods are most nourishing for you. It also deepens your connection to yourself and your family and provides you with numerous ways to strengthen your resilience, both emotionally and biologically.

INSTRUCTIONS

Answer the following questions to help you define your own cultural and environmental heritage.

Where are you from? Who are your people, and where are they from? What are your cultural influences? Is there a dominant influence you have always sensed or experienced?

_____

_____

_____

_____

_____

What did (or do) your people eat traditionally? What kinds of food and herbs?

_____

_____

_____

_____

Can you name a recipe from your ancestral culture? What are the ingredients? Does it nourish you?

_____

_____

_____

_____

_____

Do you have any relatives, community elders, or other people you could seek out and learn more from? If not, are there any other resources you could use, such as historical archives?

_____

_____

_____

_____

_____

DID YOU KNOW?
Prior to colonial contact, there were no pigs, cows, or wheat in the Western hemisphere. Foods from these resources came only in the 15th century.

Client Worksheet

HOW DO YOU METABOLIZE FOOD?

PURPOSE

This worksheet will help you determine how you metabolize food by identifying the type of oxidizer that you are. This will help you better understand how to fuel your "engine"—your brain, mind, and body—and lead you to informed decisions about what ratios and types of foods make you "hum." Keep in mind that your needs may change temporarily based on illness or stressors.

BACKGROUND

Oxidation is the rate at which people burn carbohydrates or glucose. Some people burn carbohydrates faster than others, and some burn them slower than others. There are three main types of food oxidizers: fast, slow, and mixed. When studying the world's diverse peoples, Dr. Weston Price (1939) discovered that nutrient-dense foods were the key to health and that there were a range of diets that reflected the environment in which people evolved—some with more plant proteins and fats and others with more animal proteins and fats. Generally, the farther north people lived, the more fat they required in their diets.

INSTRUCTIONS

Read through the following characteristics and check off the ones that reflect your own experience.

1. ❑ I'm usually not hungry in the morning.

2. ❑ I love sweets and caffeine.

3. ❑ I'm vulnerable to hypoglycemia, mood swings, and fatigue.

4. ❑ I can easily feel cold and tired.

5. ❑ I do best when my diet includes moderate carbohydrates, vegetables, fruits, legumes, and grains; lower fat; and moderate protein.

6. ❑ I can feel burned out easily.

7. ❑ I tend to go for the fruits and vegetables.

8. ❑ I don't feel as well if I eat a lot of purine-rich foods (e.g., organ meats, sardines, anchovies).

9. ❑ I do well with a balance of all foods.

10. ❑ I digest foods easily.

11. ❑ Sometimes I enjoy a nap in the afternoon, but not generally.

12. ❑ I enjoy having lots of flexibility in my diet and it makes me feel good.

13. ❑ I sometimes eat more meat, more vegetables, or more fruits.

14. ❑ A Mediterranean diet works well for me.

15. ❑ I love both sweet and salty tastes.

16. ❑ I do not do well with prolonged fasting.

17. ❑ I generally have a strong appetite.

18. ❑ I need to eat frequently.

19. ❑ I'm often hungry if I eat more carbs.

20. ❑ I usually want to eat when I wake up.

21. ❑ I crave fatty foods.

22. ❑ I experience weight gain with grains.

23. ❑ Low-calorie diets don't work for me.

24. ❑ I notice I don't feel as well if I eat a lot of citrus fruits.

Use the key below to determine which type of oxidizer you most likely are. You may find that you score highly in both the slow and fast categories, which could indicate a mixed oxidizer type. Note that illness or stress can cause a temporary shift in your rate.

❑ Items 1–8: Slow ❑ Items 9–16: Mixed ❑ Items 17–24: Fast

The following chart shows the ideal food intake percentage for each oxidizer type.

OXIDIZER TYPE	PROTEIN	CARBS	FATS	SUMMARY
Slow	25%	50%	25%	More carbs; less fat
Mixed	30%	35%	35%	Balanced mix of carbs, protein, and fat
Fast	35%	15%	50%	More fat and protein; less carbs

REFLECTION

Think about the types of meals you typically eat. Do these meals match your ideal food intake percentage? If not, will it be a big change to begin eating according to your oxidizer type?

_____

_____

_____

_____

Are there any obstacles that you anticipate on your journey to achieving better nutrition for your oxidizer type? List them here, then identify actions you can take to overcome each obstacle.

OBSTACLE	ACTION

List five meal ideas that would fulfill your ideal food intake percentage. If you need help coming up with ideas, a sample recipe for each oxidizer type is included next. For a more complete repertoire, see the cookbooks _The Good Mood Kitchen_ (Korn, 2017b) and _Eat Right, Feel Right_ (Korn, 2017a).

_____

_____

_____

_____

Client Recipe

Slow Oxidizer Meal:

Organic Slow Baked Beans

This soothing recipe is perfect for a slow oxidizer. These beans are tasty and exceptionally nutritious with the addition of organic blackstrap molasses and anti-inflammatory spices. Blackstrap molasses is rich in B6, magnesium, calcium, and potassium, all of which combine to produce a very calming and uplifting meal.

Ingredients

- 2 cups dried organic pinto beans
- 1 onion, diced
- 1 clove garlic
- 2 tbsp. olive oil
- ½ cup organic blackstrap molasses
- 1 6-oz. can tomato paste
- 2 tbsp. yellow mustard

- 1 tbsp. smoked paprika
- ¼ tsp. cayenne
- 1 tbsp. grated turmeric root
- 1 tbsp. Worcestershire sauce
- 1 tbsp. organic apple cider vinegar
- 6 cups water
- Sea salt and pepper, to taste

Directions

Wash, rinse, and soak the beans overnight. In the morning, rinse the beans and place in the slow cooker. Sauté the onion and garlic in the olive oil and add to the slow cooker along with the rest of the ingredients (save the salt and pepper until the beans are finished cooking). Cover with the water and cook on low for 4–6 hours. Add salt and pepper to taste. Serve with coleslaw or a chopped green salad with a vinaigrette.

Mixed Oxidizer Meal:

Lamb with Balsamic-Glazed Vegetables

The mixed oxidizer does well with all kinds of foods—both animal and vegetable proteins, and a moderate amount of fats and carbohydrates. This recipe combines lots of nutrients from proteins, fats, and carbs and satisfies a solid appetite.

Ingredients

- 1 tsp. salt

- 1 tsp. freshly ground black pepper

- 1 tsp. ground coriander

- 2 tsp. dried rosemary leaves

- 1 tsp. dried mint

- 1 tsp. dried thyme

- 1 tsp. ground fennel

- 3 lb. lamb roast, deboned and trimmed of excess fat

- 1 large red onion, cut into eighths

- 1 large parsnip

- 2 medium new potatoes, quartered

- 3 tbsp. balsamic vinegar

Directions

Combine the salt, pepper, coriander, rosemary, mint, thyme, and fennel in a small bowl. Rub the seasonings all over the lamb roast. Place the onion in the bottom of the slow cooker and add the lamb roast. Add the remaining vegetables. Drizzle the balsamic vinegar over the vegetables. Cover and cook on high for 1 hour, then turn to low for 10–12 hours.

Fast Oxidizer Meal:

Steak and Roasted Brussels Sprouts with Capers

Capers are nutrient dense. They reduce inflammation, enhance liver health, and stabilize blood sugar levels. Capers are typically salted and pickled, giving them their distinct, sharp taste and intense aroma. Anchovies and steak are purine rich, making this a satisfying recipe for a fast oxidizer.

Ingredients

- 1 lb. brussels sprouts

- 1 tbsp. olive oil

- Salt and pepper, to taste

- 4 tbsp. butter

- 4 cloves of garlic, minced

- 1 oz. anchovies, minced

- 2 lemons

- 3 tbsp. capers

- 1 rib eye or fatty steak, any size

Directions

Preheat the oven to 400°F. Rinse and cut the brussels sprouts and toss in a large bowl with the olive oil, salt, and pepper. Roast for 30 minutes. In the meantime, melt the butter in a small saucepan, add the garlic and anchovies, and let them soften. Add the lemon juice and capers. Once the brussels sprouts are caramelized and a bit crispy, remove them from the oven, transfer to a serving dish, add the sauce, and toss. Serve as a side dish with a steak prepared according to your taste.

THE CAFFEINE GENE

PURPOSE

Each of us responds differently to caffeine. This worksheet will help you identify your caffeine "sweet spot," as well as any changes to your current caffeine rituals that may benefit you.

BACKGROUND

Do you have the "caffeine gene"? Our genetics play a significant role in how we metabolize caffeine. In just the right amount, caffeine boosts energy, mood, and focus, but too much leads to anxiety and insomnia. Caffeine, like many drugs, can also cause dependence. Canned energy drinks appear to serve as a gateway to other forms of drug dependence; they accelerate and magnify the cycle of caffeine intoxication, dependence, and withdrawal, especially in teens. Trying to reduce your caffeine intake too suddenly can cause withdrawal symptoms such as headaches and fatigue (Reissig et al., 2009).

Caffeine is primarily metabolized in the liver by the enzyme known as CYP1A2. Because specific genes are responsible for CYP1A2 expression and activity, caffeine metabolism is largely heritable. Several consumer genomics services now offer tests to determine which variant of the CYP1A2 gene you carry and, consequently, whether you are a slow or fast caffeine metabolizer.

Even without genomic testing, you can learn much about your caffeine sweet spot by reflecting on your caffeine consumption habits and your physical and mental health symptoms. The following questions will help you to do so. You can also share these questions with one or more biological family members to see whether the "caffeine gene" runs in your family.

This activity may be helpful to repeat throughout the caffeine cessation or reduction process, if that is something you decide to pursue. (Guidelines for caffeine detox can be found at the end of this worksheet.)

DID YOU KNOW?

Caffeine can be found in some surprising places, including chocolate and cocoa, decaffeinated coffee or tea (which is not the same as caffeine-free), and even certain pain relievers. You may discover that you have been consuming more caffeine than you realized.

INSTRUCTIONS

Think about your caffeine consumption, both now and in the past. Have you ever had a consistent habit, ritual, or dependence involving caffeine? For example, some people drink coffee every morning. Note how you have consumed caffeine and when and why you've chosen each form (e.g., coffee, tea, soda, energy drinks, pills).

_____

_____

_____

_____

_____

_____

_____

_____

For each period that you maintained a caffeine ritual, think about what was going on in your internal and external life at that time. What connections do you see between these circumstances and your caffeine rituals? Why do you think you use caffeine?

_____

_____

_____

_____

_____

_____

_____

_____

When you were growing up, did any of your family members or caregivers have their own caffeine rituals? Take a little time to jot these memories down. What connections do you see between the rituals you observed and your own rituals?

_____

_____

_____

_____

_____

_____

_____

_____

_____

_____

_____

_____

_____

_____

_____

Read through the following indications and contraindications for caffeine consumption. Do any of these apply to you?

- **Depression, ADHD, or mild cognitive impairment:** may benefit from moderate daily coffee consumption (1–2 cups)

- **Anxiety and panic:** should avoid coffee and caffeine

- **Insomnia, sleep disturbances, or heartburn:** caffeine can contribute to these symptoms

If you currently consume more caffeine than what is recommended for your physical and mental health symptoms—or if you're simply interested in seeing how you would feel if you cut back—the following detox guidelines will help support you in this process.

CAFFEINE DETOX

Since caffeine is often consumed as part of a ritual, to successfully reduce or eliminate caffeine from your diet, you will want to create a replacement ritual. This involves two parts: (1) finding another substance to alter consciousness (lift mood, energy, and focus) with fewer side effects and (2) finding a replacement behavior that will satisfy the ritual of caffeine consumption, which will help you regulate your caffeine intake.

Describe your current caffeine consumption. Include the time of day, quantity, associated rituals, benefits, and challenges.

_____

_____

_____

_____

_____

_____

What do you want to change (the time of day, number of drinks, type of drink, etc.)?

_____

_____

_____

What are some possible replacement behaviors? (For example, you might decide to take a walk outside, do a short mindfulness practice, or complete a daily game or puzzle as your new energizing ritual.)

_____

_____

_____

_____

_____

What would be a satisfying substitute for the caffeinated drink or food item? (Some options are listed below.)

_____

_____

_____

_____

- **Café de capomo:** Also known as *café de Ramón*, this drink is made from roasted breadnut, a plant endemic to the coasts of Mexico, the Caribbean, and Central and South America. It is rich in B vitamins, amino acids, and folate. It lifts mood and is a galactagogue, increasing breast milk production.

- **Carob tea:** Carob powder can be mixed with water (1–2 teaspoons per cup of water) to create a calming beverage with a rich taste reminiscent of coffee.

- **Herbal energy sources:** Licorice root, rhodiola, ginseng, schizandra, cacao, and maca are caffeine-free herbs that energize and stimulate. Yerba mate, green tea, and matcha (green tea powder) have chemicals that counteract the negative effects of the caffeine they contain, producing a relaxed-and-alert effect, rather than a jittery one.

Experiment with these different substitutes until you find a ritual that suits your taste and your energy needs.

DID YOU KNOW?

One of the common side effects of coffee is acid reflux. This is due to the tannins and acids in coffee. An alternative to hot-brewed coffee is cold-brewed coffee, which reduces the acid levels and enhances the flavor profile (Rao & Fuller, 2018). Cold-brewed coffee may still be heated up afterward if you prefer.

CAFFEINE CESSATION SCHEDULE

You can gently wean yourself off caffeine in just a few weeks using any of the following methods. These examples assume that coffee is your preferred form of caffeine, but you can apply the same principles to any beverage or food—simply find a healthy, caffeine-free substitute and gradually switch over to it.

Decaf Coffee Method

- **Week 1:** Brew three-fourths regular coffee and one-fourth decaf coffee.

- **Week 2:** Reduce the ratio to half regular coffee and half decaf.

- **Week 3:** Now brew just one-fourth regular coffee and three-fourths decaf.

- **Week 4:** Brew decaf coffee only. There is still a small amount of caffeine in decaf, but you've virtually eliminated caffeine from your brew!

Lowered Caffeine Method

- **Week 1:** Replace your coffee with a substitute that contains less caffeine, but still some caffeine (e.g., black or green tea).

- **Week 2:** Reduce the serving size of your caffeinated substitute by half, and drink half a serving of a completely caffeine-free substitute (e.g., herbal tea).

- **Week 3:** Completely replace your caffeinated drink with the caffeine-free choice and thank yourself for overcoming the addiction!

Quick and Easy Method

- **Week 1:** Reduce your coffee serving by half, and drink half a serving of a caffeine-free substitute (e.g., herbal tea).

- **Week 2:** Brew just one-fourth of your original coffee intake, and drink three-fourths of a serving of your caffeine-free choice.

- **Week 3:** Drink only the caffeine-free beverage and be free of caffeine!

Clinician Handout

PURPOSE

To assess the potential benefits of genomic testing for your clients, and to guide them through this process, you will need to understand the fundamentals of genomic testing and identify where you can access testing services. This handout provides the key information you will need.

BACKGROUND

Genomics is defined as the science of our genes and their influence on our health. Pharmacogenomics is a type of genomics that studies how genes affect the body's response to medicines. This field helps us understand:

- How our personalities interact with and are influenced by our early life experiences

- Cultural and ethnic diversity and the dynamic interactions that result from intergenerational influences

- How we digest food, and what foods "fuel our engine"

- What medications might help (or hurt) us

- What nutrients we need more of, or perhaps can't use very easily

- And so much more!

Personalized mental health (also called precision mental health) focuses on using an individual's genetics to determine drugs and their doses. Applying this lens helps us decide whether a specific psychotropic medication should be used or avoided, and it recognizes the diversity of possible responses. Personalized methods focus on helping the individual, not on the dis-ease per se. These methods suggest that there may be many causes and many treatments for the same dis-ease, and they require deep inquiry from a whole-systems lens with each person.

Personalized nutrition is defined by where our ancestors evolved and flourished; how we carry that history in our bodies, minds, and genes; and how we nourish ourselves optimally. **Nutrigenomics** is the study of how foods interact with our genes. It explains our individual genetic differences—each of us may require different amounts of vitamins, minerals, and food compounds. Our genetic individuality determines how we absorb, metabolize, and detoxify.

Epigenetics refers to chemical tags that attach to the exterior of the genome. This changes how your cells respond to and express your genes. The difference between DNA and epigenetics is like the difference between nature and nurture. DNA is your roadmap, not your final destination (or destiny). Genes are nature and do not change, even with social or epigenetic influences. However, foods, stress, psychosocial status, sleep patterns, environmental exposures, exercise, and other aspects of our lives affect how our genes act. This gives us the power to influence many responses in the body and mind.

GENOMIC TESTING

The same medicine may have very different effects in different people. Genomic testing has confirmed that genetic variations affect both the efficacy and adverse effects of psychotropic medications, in children and adults alike. Assessing genomics or referring for pharmacogenomic testing is recommended when considering any pharmacotherapy. This is especially important for the use of escitalopram and sertraline. Note that while some insurance companies cover this testing, others do not.

Pharmacogenomics testing provides information about how our genes affect our drug response. Testing is used in both integrative and conventional psychiatry. It may give genetic predictions about drug response, and it can help explain a failure to respond. Some of this information is well-established—for example, the cohort of nonresponders to statins or those may react adversely to certain antibiotics.

Genetic responses to SSRIs and tricyclic antidepressants and antipsychotics are the focus of current tests. Such tests can assess efficacy and adverse reactions, such as the propensity for weight gain or tardive dyskinesias.

Of particular importance is the role of detoxification enzymes in the liver and their effects on medications. Some people may process and eliminate medications very quickly or very slowly. This function is essential when considering the use of herbal supplements, as many supplements—including berberine, Oregon grape root, and goldenseal—affect enzymes that help the liver detoxify.

Genetic responses to pain and pain medications are well-established. Tests that identify pain sensitivity and the potential for efficacy or adverse reactions to different pain medications also provide insight into the best approaches to managing chronic pain, including opiates, antidepressants, and NSAIDs.

Accessing Genomic Testing

When referring clients to genomic testing, I suggest using a pseudonym to maintain anonymity. Most genomic tests relevant to mental well-being are available to both consumers and clinicians. Although some labs provide analysis, it is advisable for consumers to work with a clinician trained in genomic testing to interpret their tests. Of clinical and emotional importance is the difference between tests that may help confirm risk factors for conditions already present and those that may reveal increased risk for *potential* clinical outcomes, as the following case illustrates.

Marcy's Story

Marcy's mother, father, and paternal grandfather all died from complications of Alzheimer's disease. Her older brother was showing symptoms of cognitive decline at age 67, and Marcy wanted to test to see if the risk might be associated with the APOE gene. Marcy was 54 and experienced chronic depression and attentional challenges. She was also a worrier, which can be associated with the COMT gene. I asked Marcy if she would be willing to spend a session exploring the meaning of the testing and suggested that we consider an array of tests, including COMT, MTHFR, and APOE, and work to address her stress cycle by checking her cortisol levels.

We explored the potential outcomes, what they might mean, and how she would feel with any of the potential outcomes. I emphasized that test results do not determine or define the outcomes and that the role of testing is to have specific lifestyle options to reduce risk. We explored Marcy's hopes and fears, and she decided to go forward with testing. She said, "Information will empower me to make good choices."

Can I Order Tests for My Clients?

There is no simple answer to this question; it depends on variables such as your license, the type of test, the lab you select, and the state in which you practice. Some large test consolidators make this easier for you by having a physician on hand to sign for the tests. This enables practitioners and clients alike to order tests directly. Some states, like New York, prohibit direct access testing.

Can Clients Order Tests for Themselves?

Direct access testing (DAT) refers to consumer-ordered testing. The National Academy of Medicine has called for consumers to have complete access to all their health information, and this has driven the changes in access to test ordering. Thirty-seven states and the District of Columbia permit DAT in some form, either with or without restrictions.

- **States permitted to perform DAT with no limitations:** AK, AR, DC, DE, IA, IN, KS, LA, MN, MO, MS, MT, NC, ND, NE, NM, OH, OK, SD, TX, UT, VA, VT, WA, WI, WV

- **States permitted to perform DAT with some restrictions:** AZ, CA, CO, FL, IL, MA, MD, ME, NJ, NV, NY, OR

- **States where DAT is prohibited:** AL, CT, GA, HI, ID, KY, MI, NH, PA, RI, SC, TN, WY

With consumer-purchased tests, payment is most often out of pocket, in contrast to when a licensed provider orders them. Many functional health tests are not paid for by insurance regardless, and there is some debate about types of tests and measures, especially related to accurate measurements of hormones and useful measurements of cholesterol and lipids.

Which Labs Offer These Tests?

Clinicians can order tests from the following labs:

- Kashi Lab (https://kashilab.com)

- Genesight (https://genesight.com)

- PharmGKB (https://www.pharmgkb.org)—for both clinicians and consumers

Major testing consolidators include the following labs:

- Life Extension (https://www.lifeextension.com)

- Direct Labs (https://www.directlabs.com)

- LabTests Plus (https://labtestsplus.com)

- Quest Diagnostics (https://www.questdiagnostics.com)—for some tests

What Are Some Common Genetic Markers to Test For?

Understanding clients' genetic markers can inform personalized nutritional, supplemental, and exercise routines. Here are a few key markers for reference:

- **APOE:** Involved in clearing harmful plaques that form around nerve cells. These plaques are a hallmark of Alzheimer's disease and consist of damaged proteins called amyloid ß, which stick together to form the toxic plaques. There are at least three slightly different versions (alleles) of the APOE gene: E2, E3, and E4.

- **COMT (Val158Met):** Central to dopamine metabolism and highly associated with a propensity for worry. It is a possible risk factor for bipolar disorder, panic disorder, anxiety, obsessive-compulsive disorder (OCD), eating disorders, and attention-deficit/hyperactivity disorder (ADHD). It also affects morphine dosage requirements and perceptions of pain.

- **MTHFR (C677T, A1298C):** Needed to maintain levels of activated folate, which may aid in preventing depression.

- **Vitamin B12 (FUT2):** Affects optimal B12 levels; deficiency is a depression risk factor.

- **Vitamin D (GC, NADSYN1/DHCR7, CYP2R1):** Levels are highly heritable. We obtain vitamin D (which is really a neurohormone) from sun exposure and through food and supplementation. These gene SNPs (single nucleotide polymorphisms) may contribute to the need for more supplementation.

Note that COMT, MTHFR, and the vitamin markers can explain present symptoms, while APOE can explain future risk. For guidance on how to supplement with these vitamins if a deficiency is present, see chapter 9.

3

INTEGRATIVE ASSESSMENT

UNDERSTANDING THE MIND-BODY RELATIONSHIP

Integrative care requires you to prioritize the process of assessment so you can illuminate the relationships among the client's varied symptoms. The assessment process sets the stage for success. With a comprehensive intake, you can begin to understand how all the varied parts of a client's life fit together and tell the story. This includes not just the story of their emotional and cognitive symptoms, but also their physical symptoms and the meaning assigned to these symptoms.

In fact, as a clinician, the most important learning you can do during the assessment phase is to study the physical body and its story, including its symptoms of distress, the history of illness, and exposures to stress and trauma. Knowing the relationship between seemingly unrelated symptoms—complex trauma and autoimmune disease, thyroid medicine and panic attacks, acne and depression, anxiety and constipation, PTSD and acid reflux—enables more effective intervention. Listening to and eliciting the whole story is like putting together a puzzle: Some pieces come together quickly while others are unclear and may require more time and testing. Some pieces may appear to fit, but then do not. The process requires that you understand the complex relationships between mind, body, and behavior.

The first step in this process is to become comfortable asking questions, collecting information, and understand that assessment, whether focusing on mental or physical symptoms, is interventional in and of itself as the client explores connections and begins to make meaning.

Let's assume you are working with a client who presents to you with depressive symptoms, including fatigue, lack of energy, and anhedonia. Here are just a few new types of questions you might ask as you start the assessment: Is the client's complaint of fatigue due to depression or chronic stress and adrenal exhaustion, resulting in hypothalamic-pituitary-adrenal (HPA) axis depletion? Suppression of mitochondria due to long-term SSRIs? Inborn errors, like MTHFR and COMT variations? Low vitamin B12 levels, a chronic virus (like Epstein-Barr), post-COVID-19 syndrome, mold exposure from a "sick" building, or eating too many refined carbohydrates and not enough protein? Or is it a function of some, many, or even all these influences? And if so, how do you prioritize how to proceed?

While it is not necessary for an integrative mental health clinician to be an expert in all these areas, or to know how to test and evaluate these diverse causes, it *is* essential to know that these influences on mental health do exist and to know when and how to make a referral.

Sage's Story

Sage and I had worked together for 18 months to address anxious depression. She had made good progress in creating the social life and work life she wanted. Her mood was stable, with very occasional dips when she experienced a sense of abandonment due to early life trauma. Nevertheless, she was doing so well that she was preparing to change her schedule with me from once weekly to every eight weeks.

Then, almost without warning, Sage's mood took a deep turn downward. She would start sobbing but could not identify any cause or trigger. During one session, we explored almost every possible factor—work, friends, triggers, fears, her menstrual cycle—all without identifying a significant cause. Because Sage lived in Seattle, where vitamin D levels tend to be low, I wondered if that might be related. I suggested that she get her levels checked right away. Her results showed virtually no measurable level of vitamin D. We immediately suggested supplementation according to Dr. Holick's protocol (a leading authority on vitamin D), and within three days Sage was feeling better.

Time and again I have learned that while it is common to miss the emotional cause of distress, it is also easy to miss the physical cause. Whether you work independently or collaboratively, expanding your knowledge base of mind and body functions allows you to make effective recommendations or referrals.

Everything an individual experiences in their mind and body is related. The process of integrative assessment helps you see these relationships, which leads to more effective treatment. Like a just-opened jigsaw puzzle, all the pieces are there; it is a collaborative effort to see how they fit together.

The resources in this chapter include a comprehensive mind-body assessment and tools to help your clients track their mental health symptoms so you can begin to identify potential causes. Before using these interventions with a new client, I recommend trying them yourself, practicing with a volunteer, or asking an existing client if they are willing to try a new approach that may benefit them.

Integrative Assessment at a Glance

WELLNESS TARGET	RECOMMENDATIONS
Depression	• Evaluate multiple factors: leaky gut, inflammation, neurotransmitter dysfunction, low essential fatty acids (EFA) levels, oxidative stress, mitochondrial dysfunction, traumatic brain injury, trauma history
Anxiety and panic	• Use the Nijmegen scale to identify symptoms of hyperventilation syndrome
OCD	• Assess for low omega-3 and high trans fat with a blood spot test; assess nostril dominance and increase forced left-nostril breathing
Bipolar disorder	• Rule out trauma history, hypoglycemia, and misdiagnosis • Address and treat circadian rhythm disruptions
Insomnia	• Identify the types of sleep disruption occurring using the Automated Morningness-Eveningness Questionnaire (AutoMEQ) or the Pittsburgh sleep quality index (PSQI)
Stress, trauma, and PTSD	• Apply the scale of body connection • Assess waking and evening salivary cortisol levels
ADHD	• Assess for a highly refined carbohydrate diet, food sensitivities, and too little dietary fats • Assess for sedentism; explore kinesthetic learning needs • Rule out chronic stress or developmental trauma
Chronic pain	• Conduct a visual analog pain assessment; test cortisol-DHEA ratio and high-sensitivity C-reactive protein • Assess for vitamin D, mold exposure, trauma history, fibromyalgia, excessive NSAID use, and gut function
Substance use disorder	• Identify self-medication strategies and whether these are linked to imbalances in certain neurotransmitters • Assess the psychobiology of cravings, which are most often linked to a trauma history

WELLNESS TARGET	RECOMMENDATIONS
Cognition and memory	• Check blood and oxygen flow • Support brain health, synapse communication, and lubrication with essential fatty acids and phospholipids • Conduct an age-appropriate evaluation • Consider co-occurring disorders, gum inflammation, B-12 levels, PTSD, TBI, and APOE status • Consider referrals, a functional MRI, or neuropsychological testing
Autism spectrum and neurodivergence	• Check for casein and gluten sensitivity • Explore somatic and body-based methods
Body image and eating disorders	• Conduct a zinc taste test • Assess for body dysmorphia, nutrient deficits, and hypoglycemia
Digestive disorders	• Assess for food allergies and sensitivities • Check for H. pylori, acid reflux, and stress levels • Assess for autonomic hyperactivity • Encourage mindfulness

CLIENT INTAKE FORM

Client Worksheet

Client name: _____

Date: _____

CLIENT INFORMATION

Address: _____

City: _____ State: _____ Zip: _____

Phone: _____ Additional phone: _____

What form of communication do you prefer? ❑ Video call ❑ Phone call ❑ Email ❑ Text

Date of birth: _____ Gender: _____ Pronouns: _____

Employer: _____ Occupation: _____

Marital status: ❑ Single ❑ Married ❑ Partnered ❑ Divorced ❑ Separated ❑ Widowed

Spouse/partner name: _____

EMERGENCY CONTACT

Name: _____

Phone: _____ Additional phone: _____

OTHER HEALTH PROVIDERS

List any health providers you are currently seeing.

Name: _____ Phone: _____ Email: _____

Name: _____ Phone: _____ Email: _____

Name: _____ Phone: _____ Email: _____

I give my therapist permission to consult with these health care providers regarding my health and treatment.   ❑ Yes   ❑ No

Comments: _____

_____

Signature: _____   Date: _____

BLOOD TESTS

Along with this intake form, please submit the following tests, which a primary care physician can authorize:

❑ Comprehensive metabolic/blood tests

❑ Vitamin D

❑ Other: _____

If you don't have current tests (within the previous 3 months), we can discuss making arrangements for these tests.

ANIMAL THERAPY

❑ I welcome working with a therapy animal in the office.

❑ I prefer not to work with a therapy animal in the office.

I am allergic to:

❑ Dogs   ❑ Cats   ❑ Other: _____

CURRENT HEALTH INFORMATION

Height: _____   Weight: _____

Ethnic identity(ies): _____

Natural hair color: _____

Do you use hair dye?   ❑ Yes   ❑ No

Do you use a special shampoo?   ❑ Yes   ❑ No

HEALTH CONCERNS

Primary: _____

    ❑ Mild   ❑ Moderate   ❑ Disabling   ❑ Constant   ❑ Intermittent

Do your symptoms get better or worse with more activity?

    ❑ Get worse   ❑ Get better   ❑ No change

Do your symptoms get better or worse with less activity?

    ❑ Get worse   ❑ Get better   ❑ No change

Treatment received: _____

_____

Secondary: _____

    ❑ Mild   ❑ Moderate   ❑ Disabling   ❑ Constant   ❑ Intermittent

Do your symptoms get better or worse with more activity?

    ❑ Get worse   ❑ Get better   ❑ No change

Do your symptoms get better or worse with less activity?

    ❑ Get worse   ❑ Get better   ❑ No change

Treatment received: _____

_____

Have you ever received energy therapy before?

    ❑ Yes   ❑ No   Frequency: _____

Have you ever received manual/massage therapy before?

    ❑ Yes   ❑ No   Frequency: _____

Have you ever received psychotherapy before?

    ❑ Yes   ❑ No   Frequency: _____

What kinds of practitioners have you worked with around food, diet, and nutrition? (Include both formal and informal practitioners—e.g., a dietitian, health coach, or nutritional therapist.)

_____

_____

_____

_____

List all conditions currently monitored by a health care provider.

_____

_____

_____

_____

_____

_____

DAILY ACTIVITIES

Work hours and schedule: _____

_____

Do you now, or have you ever, worked the night shift?　❑ Yes　❑ No

If so, please explain: _____

If currently, what are your hours? _____

Check any of the following activities that are affected by your condition(s):

❑ Sleep　❑ Washing　❑ Dressing　❑ Fitness

❑ Other home/family activities: _____

❑ Other social/recreational activities: _____

How do you reduce stress?

_____

_____

_____

_____

_____

How do you reduce pain?

_____

_____

_____

_____

_____

What are your health goals?

_____

_____

_____

_____

_____

_____

_____

_____

_____

HEALTH HISTORY

Include dates and treatments. Add pages if necessary.

Surgeries:

_____

_____

_____

_____

_____

Accidents:

_____

_____

_____

_____

_____

Major illnesses:

_____

_____

_____

_____

_____

_____

IF APPLICABLE

Last Pap smear: _____   First day of last menstrual period: _____

Marital/partner history (years married): _____   Number of children: _____

Ages of children: _____   Number of pregnancies: _____

Complications: _____

_____

Abortions or miscarriages: _____

_____

Use of contraceptive: ❑ Yes   ❑ No   Type(s): _____

TRAUMA HISTORY

A history of trauma affects both physical and emotional health. This is why it is important for me to understand your trauma experiences. However, if you do not feel comfortable sharing them on paper or with me verbally, I understand. Please feel free to omit this section. If you find that in the future you would like to share your experiences, I am always open to listening and responding to what will be beneficial for you.

Please describe your trauma history as best as you can, providing your age at the time of the trauma and the type(s) of trauma or adverse event(s) you experienced. Include anything you want me to know.

_____

_____

_____

_____

_____

_____

_____

Have you ever been diagnosed with PTSD, complex trauma, or borderline personality disorder?

_____

_____

_____

_____

Have you ever experienced head trauma (e.g., concussion, sports injuries, whiplash)?

_____

_____

_____

_____

❑ I feel comfortable discussing my trauma history with you.

❑ I do not feel comfortable discussing my trauma history with you at this time.

EXERCISE ACTIVITIES

Please list each type of exercise that you do. For each activity, indicate the amount of time you typically spend doing each activity and how frequently.

EXERCISE ACTIVITY	TIME SPENT (HOURS/MINUTES)	FREQUENCY (NUMBER OF TIMES PER WEEK)

FAMILY MEDICAL HISTORY

For each relative, please give their age and list any illnesses. If they are deceased, include the cause of death and age of death.

Mother: _____

_____

_____

Father: _____

_____

_____

Siblings: _____

_____

_____

_____

_____

_____

Maternal grandparents: _____

_____

_____

_____

Paternal grandparents: _____

_____

_____

_____

CURRENT DIETARY HABITS

Please list any specific diets that you are currently following (e.g., vegan, vegetarian, Atkins, paleo, DASH, raw, GAPS):

_____

_____

ALLERGIES AND SENSITIVITIES

❑ Wheat allergy   ❑ Dairy allergy   ❑ Mold allergy

❑ Wheat sensitivity   ❑ Dairy sensitivity   ❑ Chemical sensitivities

Please list any other known or suspected food allergies and sensitivities.

_____

_____

_____

Are there foods you could not give up? If so, which ones?

_____

_____

_____

CURRENT FOOD PREPARATION METHODS

Who's doing the shopping?   ❑ You   ❑ Family member   ❑ Friend   ❑ Other

Do you typically eat with other people or alone?   ❑ People   ❑ Alone

How often do you eat out?

❑ Never   ❑ Less than once a month   ❑ Monthly   ❑ Twice monthly   ❑ Weekly   ❑ Daily

What kind of places do you eat out at?

_____

_____

Do you prepare your own food? ❑ Yes ❑ No

Do you enjoy cooking? ❑ Yes ❑ No

How do you feel about food preparation and cooking?

_____

_____

How much time do you spend preparing food each day?

❑ None   ❑ 1 hour   ❑ 2 hours   ❑ 3 or more hours

EATING BEHAVIORS

Briefly describe your mealtime and snack patterns:

_____

_____

_____

_____

_____

_____

MEANING OF FOOD

Please describe in a few sentences what food means to you. There may be both positive and negative associations. There is no right or wrong answer. For example, is food important to you? Are you preoccupied with it? Does it feel nourishing? Does food cause fear or discomfort?

_____

_____

_____

_____

_____

CHILDHOOD HISTORY

Were you breastfed?   ❑ Yes   ❑ No   If so, until age: _____

Were you fed formula as a baby?   ❑ Yes   ❑ No

Did you experience ear infections as a child?   ❑ Yes   ❑ No

Have you used antibiotics as a child or adult?   ❑ Yes   ❑ No

Please list any other childhood illnesses and the age at which they occurred:

_____

_____

_____

_____

_____

Please list any digestive complaints you recall having as a child (e.g., stomach pains, diarrhea, constipation, gas):

_____

_____

_____

_____

Please list any other physical complaints you recall as a child (e.g., fatigue, headaches, pain):

_____

_____

_____

_____

Did you have acne as an adolescent?   ❑ None   ❑ Mild   ❑ Moderate   ❑ Severe

Do you have a history of fasting?   ❑ Yes   ❑ No

Did you experience any eating disorders during adolescence?   ❑ Yes   ❑ No

If so, please describe:

_____

_____

_____

_____

_____

_____

Briefly describe your family's eating habits and meal times. Did you eat together as a family? Did you eat at the table or in front of the television? Did you fend for yourself? Were foods prepared from packages? Was there fighting at mealtime?

_____

_____

_____

_____

_____

_____

_____

_____

_____

_____

_____

MEDICATIONS (CURRENT AND PAST USE)

Please list any medications, including pharmaceuticals and antibiotics, that you are currently taking or have previously taken.

MEDICATION	PRESCRIBED FOR	DOSAGE	FREQUENCY	DATES/ DURATION

Please note here any side effects you have experienced from any of the listed medications:

_____

_____

_____

_____

_____

_____

USE OF NONPHARMACEUTICAL SUBSTANCES

	Current	Past	Times per week	Comments
Tobacco	❏	❏	_____	_____
Alcohol/drugs	❏	❏	_____	_____
Caffeine	❏	❏	_____	_____
Other: _____	❏	❏	_____	_____

Are you in recovery from substance use disorder?   ❏ Yes   ❏ No

Do you have a history of drug or alcohol abuse?   ❏ Yes   ❏ No

Long-term use of prescription drugs: ❏ Yes   ❏ No

If yes, how often and in what form? _____

_____

_____

_____

_____

Long-term use of recreational drugs: ❏ Yes   ❏ No

If yes, how often and in what form? _____

_____

_____

_____

_____

Do you use artificial sweeteners?   ❏ Yes   ❏ No

Type: _____

_____

USE OF NUTRITIONAL SUPPLEMENTS/HERBS/MINERALS

Please list any supplements—including vitamins, minerals, herbs, amino acids, and hormones—that you are currently taking or have previously taken.

SUPPLEMENT	MANUFACTURER	DOSAGE	FREQUENCY	DATES/DURATION

DETOXIFICATION

Please list any detoxification methods that you are currently using or have used previously. Such methods include skin brushing, coffee enema, liver flush, juice fast, colon cleanser, Epsom salt (magnesium sulfate) bath soak, salt and baking soda bath, vinegar bath, sweats or saunas, castor oil packs, and master cleanse.

METHOD	FREQUENCY	DATES/DURATION	DESIRED/PERCEIVED BENEFITS

PAIN/DISCOMFORT

Please check off each area of pain and describe the experience of that pain.

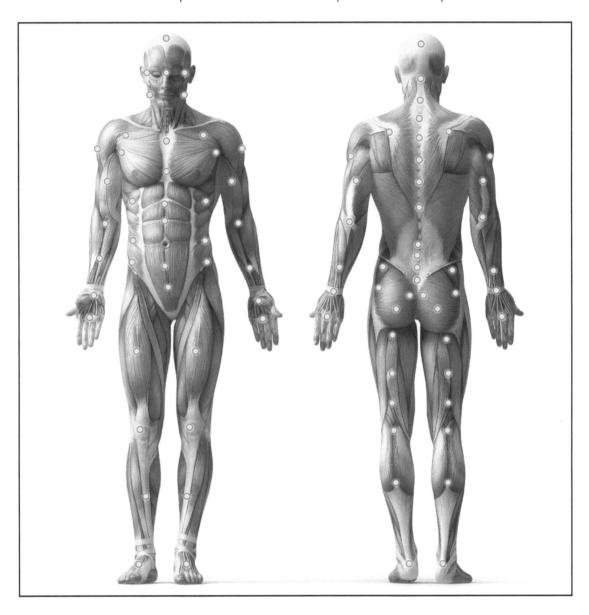

_____

_____

_____

_____

Rate your stress level as of today:

| 1 | 2 | 3 | 4 | 5 | 6 | 7 | 8 | 9 | 10 |

Low ⟵⟶ High

CURRENT AND PREVIOUS HEALTH CONDITIONS

Check all current and previous health conditions (please explain).

General

	Current	Past	Comments
Headaches	☐	☐	_____
Sleep disturbances	☐	☐	_____
Fatigue	☐	☐	_____
Infections in the ear	☐	☐	_____
Fever	☐	☐	_____
Sinus problems	☐	☐	_____
Other: _____	☐	☐	_____

Skin Conditions

	Current	Past	Comments
Rashes	☐	☐	_____
Athlete's foot, warts	☐	☐	_____
Other: _____	☐	☐	_____

Allergies

	Current	Past	Comments
Scents, oils, lotions	☐	☐	_____
Mold, pollen, dander	☐	☐	_____
Detergents	☐	☐	_____
Airborne allergies, hives	☐	☐	_____
Sinus congestion, "stuffy head"	☐	☐	_____
Other: _____	☐	☐	_____

Muscles and Joints

	Current	Past	Comments
Rheumatoid arthritis	❑	❑	_____
Osteoarthritis	❑	❑	_____
Scoliosis	❑	❑	_____
Broken bones	❑	❑	_____
Spinal problems	❑	❑	_____
Disk problems	❑	❑	_____
Lupus	❑	❑	_____
TMJ, jaw pain	❑	❑	_____
Spasms, cramps	❑	❑	_____
Sprains, strains	❑	❑	_____
Tendonitis, bursitis	❑	❑	_____
Stiff or painful joints	❑	❑	_____
Weak or sore muscles	❑	❑	_____
Neck, shoulder, or arm pain	❑	❑	_____
Low back, hip, or leg pain	❑	❑	_____
Other: _____	❑	❑	_____

Nervous System

	Current	Past	Comments
Head injuries, concussions	❑	❑	_____
Dizziness, ringing in the ears	❑	❑	_____
Loss of memory, confusion	❑	❑	_____
Numbness, tingling	❑	❑	_____
Sciatica, shooting pain	❑	❑	_____

	Current	Past	Comments
Chronic pain	❏	❏	_____
Depression	❏	❏	_____
Chronic fatigue/fibromyalgia	❏	❏	_____
Other: _____	❏	❏	_____

Respiratory/Cardiovascular System

	Current	Past	Comments
Heart disease	❏	❏	_____
Blood clots	❏	❏	_____
Stroke	❏	❏	_____
Lymphedema	❏	❏	_____
High or low blood pressure	❏	❏	_____
Irregular heartbeat	❏	❏	_____
Poor circulation	❏	❏	_____
Swollen ankles	❏	❏	_____
Varicose veins	❏	❏	_____
Chest pain, breath shortness	❏	❏	_____
Asthma	❏	❏	_____
Palpable heartbeat in abdomen	❏	❏	_____
Sinus infections	❏	❏	_____
Other: _____	❏	❏	_____

Digestive/Elimination System

	Current	Past	Comments
Bowel dysfunction	❏	❏	_____
Gas or bloating	❏	❏	_____
Bladder/kidney dysfunction	❏	❏	_____
Colitis or Crohn's disease	❏	❏	_____
Belching within 1 hour of eating	❏	❏	_____
Bad breath (halitosis)	❏	❏	_____
Unpleasant body odor	❏	❏	_____
Feel like skipping breakfast	❏	❏	_____
Feel better if you don't eat	❏	❏	_____
Sleepy after meals	❏	❏	_____
Stomach pains/cramps	❏	❏	_____
Diarrhea	❏	❏	_____
Alternating constipation/diarrhea	❏	❏	_____
Undigested food in stool	❏	❏	_____
Pain between shoulder blades	❏	❏	_____
Stomach upset by greasy foods	❏	❏	_____
Nausea	❏	❏	_____
Light or clay-colored stools	❏	❏	_____
Gallbladder attacks	❏	❏	_____
Gallbladder removed	❏	❏	_____
Hemorrhoids or varicose veins	❏	❏	_____

	Current	Past	Comments
Pulse speeds up after eating	❑	❑	_____
Crave carbohydrates	❑	❑	_____
Anal itching	❑	❑	_____
Fungus or yeast infection	❑	❑	_____
History of antibiotic use	❑	❑	_____
Use over-the-counter pain medications	❑	❑	_____
Other: _____	❑	❑	_____

Endocrine System

	Current	Past	Comments
Thyroid dysfunction	❑	❑	_____
HIV/AIDS	❑	❑	_____
Diabetes	❑	❑	_____
Other: _____	❑	❑	_____

Reproductive System

	Current	Past	Comments
Pregnancy	❑	❑	_____
Reproductive problems	❑	❑	_____
Painful, emotional menses	❑	❑	_____
Fibrocystic cysts	❑	❑	_____
Cancer/tumors	❑	❑	_____
Other: _____	❑	❑	_____

MOTIVATION FOR MAKING CHANGES

How would you describe what is motivating you right now to make changes in your lifestyle?

_____

_____

_____

_____

NUTRITIONAL CHANGES

Identify three reasons to improve your diet:

_____

_____

_____

Identify three obstacles to improving your diet:

_____

_____

_____

Identify three goals to improve your diet:

- 3-month goal: _____

- 6-month goal: _____

- 12-month goal: _____

Identify three goals to improving your food preparation:

- 3-month goal: _____

- 6-month goal: _____

- 12-month goal: _____

PERCEIVED BARRIERS TO MAKING CHANGES

❑ Family: _____

❑ Finances: _____

❑ Difficulty swallowing pills: _____

❑ Lack of time: _____

❑ Belief system: _____

❑ Organization abilities: _____

❑ Other: _____

BELIEFS

Do you have specific religious, spiritual, or cultural beliefs? If so, please describe.

_____

_____

_____

_____

_____

_____

_____

Do you have a religious or spiritual practice? If so, please describe.

_____

_____

_____

_____

_____

_____

_____

Do you have beliefs about why you are experiencing specific health problems?

_____

_____

_____

_____

_____

_____

_____

_____

OTHER

Is there anything else you want to share with me about your health, well-being, or history?

_____

_____

_____

_____

_____

_____

_____

_____

_____

_____

FOOD-MOOD DIARY

PURPOSE

The two templates in this worksheet will help you keep a record of what you eat and how you feel afterward, both emotionally and physically. This is valuable information that will guide you in finding the best ways to nourish your body and mind.

BACKGROUND

Research shows that what we eat affects our mood. If you do not pay enough attention to this food-mood connection, you can fall into eating habits that contribute to depression, anxiety, insomnia, addictions, and other issues. Observing your current diet, your emotions, and your physical responses will reveal the patterns in your self-nourishment. You can then use this information to make changes in your diet that can alleviate your physical symptoms, stabilize your energy level, and boost your mood. Defining, exploring, and meeting your own needs for nourishment is an essential form of self-care and self-agency.

INSTRUCTIONS

Food-Mood Diary

Please write down everything you eat and drink for three days, including all meals, snacks, and beverages (even water). Include approximate amounts and the time you consumed each item. Describe any digestive responses you experienced. Also indicate if your energy level and mood increased (↑), decreased (↓), or stayed the same (=) after consuming the item.

Energy-Mood Clock

To better understand how your mood and energy levels fluctuate throughout the day, use this chart on the same days that you complete the Food-Mood Diary. Record your energy level (1 = very little energy, 5 = very energetic) and your mood (happy/sad faces) for each hour of the day.

Make as many copies of these templates as needed (at least three of each).

Food-Mood Diary

Please write down everything you eat and drink for three days, including how it affects your digestion, energy, and mood.

Date: _____

Time of waking: _____

TYPE OF MEAL, SNACK, OR BEVERAGE	AMOUNT	TIME	DIGESTIVE RESPONSE	ENERGY LEVEL (↑, ↓, OR =)	MOOD (☺, ☹, ETC.)

Energy–Mood Clock

Record your energy level (1 = very little energy, 5 = very energetic) and your mood (happy/sad faces) for each hour of the day.

Date: _____

A.M.

P.M.

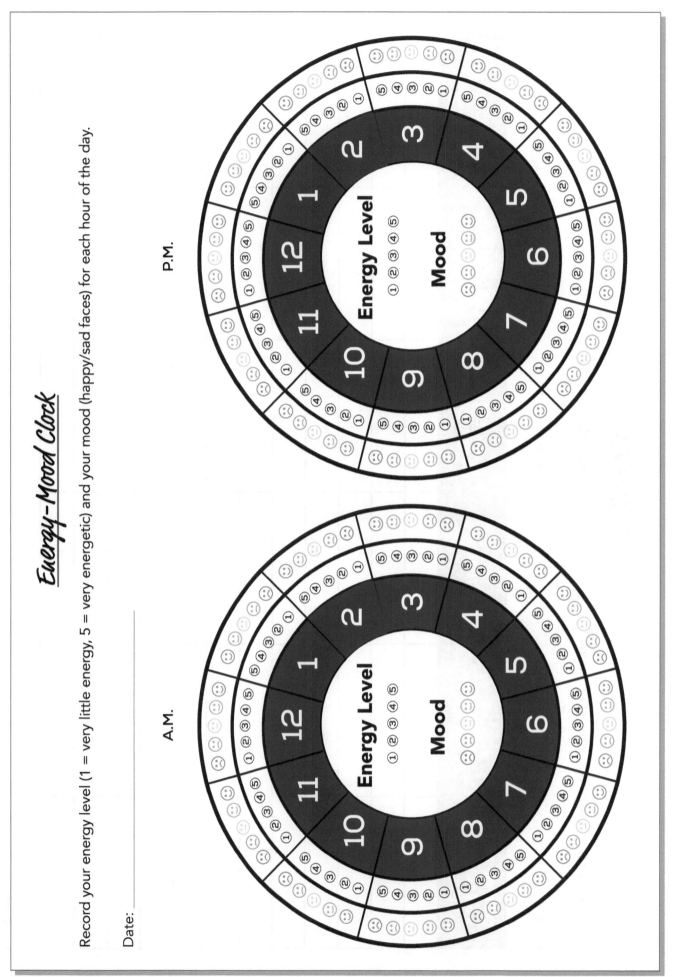

FOOD-MOOD DIARY ANALYSIS

Clinician Worksheet

PURPOSE

Use this worksheet as a guide as you analyze the client's responses in their Food-Mood Diary (p. 68).

BACKGROUND

Review the client's diary, and use their responses to answer the questions in the following table. The right column provides guidance for educating the client based on their status.

QUESTION	ANSWER/NOTES	GOALS AND RECOMMENDATIONS
1. How much time passes between when the client awakens and when they eat breakfast? Is the client eating breakfast?		Most people benefit from eating breakfast, containing at least 3–4 ounces of protein, within 30–60 minutes of waking, for blood sugar balancing.
2. How much water is the client drinking throughout the day?		Water intake should be about 50% of body weight every day, in ounces (e.g., if the client weighs 160 pounds, they should be drinking 80 ounces of water daily).
3. How often is the client eating? How many hours are there between each meal or snack?		Food should be eaten every 3–4 hours if there is hypoglycemia and mood swings. This might include 3 meals per day and 2–3 snacks.
4. How many servings of vegetables is the client eating per day?		At least 3 servings of vegetables should be eaten every day. A serving equals 1 cup.

QUESTION	ANSWER/NOTES	GOALS AND RECOMMENDATIONS
5. Is the client eating raw vegetables and fruits?		At least 1–3 servings of raw fruit or vegetables should be eaten every day.
6. Is the client eating enough protein?		Proteins help stabilize energy and balance mood; they should be emphasized during the daytime hours.
7. Is the client eating enough fats?		Fats help stabilize energy and balance mood; they should be emphasized during the daytime hours.
8. How many servings of starchy carbohydrates is the client eating and at what times of day?		Starchy carbohydrates are best emphasized in the afternoon and evening for relaxation.
9. What is the quality of the food the client is eating (freshly prepared vs. canned or prepackaged foods)?		Recommend whole, fresh, organic foods over packaged and canned foods. Teach about reading labels for additives and sugars.
10. Is the client eating enough soluble fiber?		Soluble fiber is found in foods like oat bran, nuts, beans, lentils, psyllium husk, peas, chia seeds, barley, and some fruits and vegetables. About 30–35 grams, at a minimum, should be eaten per day.
11. Is the client eating enough insoluble fiber?		Insoluble fiber is found in whole grains, oat bran, seeds and nuts, brown rice, flaxseed, and the skins of many fruits and vegetables. Eat about 25-40 grams per day.

BRAINBOW FOOD DIARY

PURPOSE

This worksheet will help you track how many foods you are eating that belong to each color group. This is an easy way to monitor your palette and your palate!

BACKGROUND

The "Brainbow" of colors is the foundation of a healing diet. The (natural) color of a food reflects different nutrients and chemicals that enhance health. Tracking your intake by color will therefore help you identify any nutritional imbalances in your diet and provide insight into new food types you can incorporate.

INSTRUCTIONS

Use the following template to track your eating habits for three days (make as many copies of the template as you need). Record the number of servings you eat for each different color food group (fruits, vegetables, or herbs/spices), and at the end of the day, add up the total number of foods for each color. Then note how many of the food items you listed were consumed raw or cooked.

After three days, review your record to identify any gaps:

- Are any colors of the Brainbow missing?

- How do you balance your raw and cooked foods?

- What foods, colors, preparation styles, and recipes would you like to explore in your future meal planning?

You might like to highlight or make additional notes in your record while reviewing it.

Brainbow Food Diary

Record the number of servings you eat for each different color food group (fruits, vegetables, or herbs/spices), the total number of foods for each color, and the total number of raw versus cooked items.

Date: _____

COLOR	FOOD GROUP				FOOD PREP	
	FRUITS	VEGETABLES	HERBS/SPICES	TOTAL (ALL FOOD GROUPS)	RAW	COOKED
Red						
Orange						
Yellow						
Green						
Blue						
Purple						
White						

Notes: _____

THE CULTURAL FORMULATION INTERVIEW

PURPOSE

This worksheet will help you understand how to use the Cultural Formulation Interview (CFI), which is a key assessment tool that explores cultural identity and beliefs as they relate to mental and physical health.

BACKGROUND

One of the best tools to integrate into your intake is the CFI. It is part of the DSM-5, and it offers a user-friendly and client-friendly series of questions that can lead to deep explorations about culture, identity, and the meaning of health and illness. You can select sections or use the whole interview.

Lest you believe that only "others" have a cultural identity, think again—everyone, including you, will benefit from using this interview. Our cultural identities inform our lived experience of health and illness, so it is vital for anyone interested in providing integrative mental health care to understand the culture(s) that they themselves, as well as their clients, have been shaped by.

INSTRUCTIONS

Download the core CFI and the supplementary modules from the American Psychiatric Association (APA) website: https://www.psychiatry.org/psychiatrists/practice/dsm/educational -resources/assessment-measures. (These resources are available free of charge.)

Find a colleague with whom to exchange interviews. Establish confidentiality and safety for the purpose of mutual learning. Begin with the core module, then progress through the supplementary modules to become familiar with the purpose and structure of each. During or after the interview process, reflect on the following questions:

- What is one belief you hold about your health—whether emotional or physical—that is linked to, or may derive from, your culture, ethnicity, or spirituality/religion?

- Are there any kinds of help that you receive or seek that you may not always share or feel comfortable discussing?

- Are there any areas of the interview that made you feel uncomfortable personally?

- Are there questions that you would have a challenging time exploring with clients? Why is that so, and what might you need to find more ease?

When you are finished going through the CFI together, take some time to explore each other's perspective on medication use. Attitudes about medications vary within and across cultures, religions, and belief systems, and there is perhaps no more fraught discussion than the role of psychotropics in treating dis-ease. As a clinician, your values shape your attitudes and influence your work with clients. Perhaps you take medications yourself and therefore feel others should, or you have experienced side effects and therefore warn others off. By exploring your attitudes openly with a colleague, you can better clarify what is important for you to keep in mind when working with clients. With your CFI partner, explore the following questions:

- What is your personal attitude about psychotropic medications?

- How do you feel about psychotropic medications for children? Adults?

- When you consider a medication referral for a client, what criteria do you consider?

- How do you ask your clients how they feel about medication?

- Do your clients feel they require medication? Do they believe they will not get well without it?

- If a client is interested in alternatives to psychotropic medications, how do you handle taking that approach?

4

BIOLOGICAL RHYTHMS AND HORMONES

BALANCING CIRCADIAN, ULTRADIAN, AND HORMONAL RHYTHMS

Biological rhythms both drive and reflect our physical and emotional well-being. Therefore, one of the most crucial series of interventions you can offer clients to improve their health is to restore and balance their biological rhythms, including their circadian, ultradian, and hormonal rhythms. In my clinical practice, I have found time and again that balancing these rhythms brings about foundational and lasting change.

As humans, our well-being is entrained by the rhythms of the natural world, especially the light of the sun and the dark of the moon, called the **circadian rhythm**. It is scientifically well-established that the symptoms experienced in bipolar disorder, depression, PTSD, insomnia, and premenstrual syndrome (PMS) are rooted in circadian rhythm imbalances (Geoffroy & Palagini, 2021). Because many other rhythms are driven by the circadian rhythm, the clinical term for this emerging field is chronotherapies.

An additional layer of rhythm was recognized first by yoginis and yogis, who discovered that we alternate brain hemispheric dominance every 90–120 minutes. Modern science calls this alternation **ultradian rhythm**. This alternate brain dominance also reflects contralaterally in nostril dominance. Clinically, this provides us with insight into how specific breathing exercises can be used to affect the function of our right and left brain hemispheres, leading to changes in mood, relaxation, and sleep. Cognitive function and focus are also rooted in brain hemispheric dominance and respond to simple methods that anyone can use.

Finally, **hormonal rhythms** also affect our physical and emotional function. Hormones flow in cycles; the most well-known are the 28-day menstrual cycle and the 24-hour cortisol cycle that links to our circadian rhythm. Even vitamin D, a hormone, has cycles in the extreme northern and southern hemispheres, where it is higher in the summer and lower in the winter. Hormonal excesses or deficits contribute to various imbalances, including endometriosis, PMS, fibroids, insomnia, and depression. Our thyroid hormones can contribute to anxiety (if too high) or fatigue and depression (if too low). The flow of oxytocin—the "love hormone"—appears to be reduced in people with complex trauma; the administration of oxytocin is a promising intervention (Donadon et al., 2018). The natural shifts in sex hormones as we age (lower testosterone in andropause or lower estrogen, progesterone and testosterone in menopause) are treated integratively with diet, herbs, and bioidentical hormone replacement therapy.

Most of the interventions in the Brainbow Blueprint can influence circadian, ultradian, and hormonal rhythms. This evolving science is especially effective for treating affective disorders, as it integrates the use of sunlight, nutrients, hormones, exercise, yoga, and timed food intake in order to reestablish biorhythms and restore the foundation for mental health.

There are many biological systems and factors to consider when exploring biorhythms. The complex interactions of the endocrine, immune, and neurological systems influence one another with the ebb and flow of hormones in response to the external rhythms of nature, and these influence the inner rhythms of our biology in turn. Therefore, this chapter includes material on the role of selected hormones that are essential to address for mental health, along with exercises that will help you to reestablish biological rhythms in your clients and provide foundational support for their mental and physical health recovery.

Biological Rhythms and Hormones at a Glance

WELLNESS TARGET	RECOMMENDATIONS
Depression	• Assess for low waking cortisol, a marker of biological depression • Reduce use of sunglasses • Eliminate night shift work; consider 24-hour sleep deprivation • Check for low testosterone
Anxiety and panic	• Disruption of circadian rhythm by jet lag can affect anxiety • Explore history and onset of symptoms to determine the origins of the pattern disruption • Check for a drop in progesterone and estrogen
OCD	• Enhance circadian rhythms to reduce symptoms of OCD • Balance ultradian rhythm with left-nostril forced breathing
Bipolar disorder	• Assess for lithium mineral • Regulate sleep by moving bedtime five minutes earlier every few days or by week
Insomnia	• Sleep in complete darkness and in a cool room (60–65 degrees) • Get exposure to bright light before 10 a.m. • Consider oral progesterone in peri- and post-menopausal women, or testosterone in men • Eat a small meal before sleep

WELLNESS TARGET	RECOMMENDATIONS
Stress, trauma, and PTSD	• Use 24-hour diurnal cortisol to assess acute vs. chronic stage • Consider bioidentical hormone therapy • Assess DHEA levels
ADHD	• Use blue-light-blocking glasses at night; eliminate screen time two hours before bed • Avoid excessive topical or inhalant lavender exposure before and during puberty
Chronic pain	• Linked to depression bidirectionally, often early morning waking depression • Only use NSAIDs during the day (as they affect circadian rhythm and slow the healing process when used at night)
Substance use disorder	• Assess 24-hour cortisol levels • Avoid alcohol (disrupts the sleep cycle) and benzodiazepines (suppress REM sleep) • Assess for disrupted hormones, which can exacerbate mood and self-medication behaviors
Cognition and memory	• Use light therapy for early stage cognitive decline • Brain shrinkage can occur as a result of TBI, excessive stress, depression, and trauma
Autism spectrum and neurodivergence	• Assess 24-hour cortisol levels • Assess for rocking for sleep enhancement and brain spindles
Body image and eating disorders	• Often linked to PMS, depression, or a phase-delayed cycle; ensure exposure to bright morning light
Digestive disorders	• Assess for rhythm of digestion and peristalsis during the day and evening • Encourage larger daytime meals, lighter evening meals, and no food 4 hours before sleep; consider a light meal at night and the main meal at midday

UNDERSTANDING YOUR CIRCADIAN RHYTHM

PURPOSE

This worksheet will help you find your optimal circadian rhythm, which is an important part of your overall health.

BACKGROUND

The degree to which you are attuned to the rhythms of the natural world affects your health and well-being. In particular, your circadian rhythm—how your body responds to the cycle of sunlight and darkness—has a large impact on your physical and mental health. Understanding your personal circadian rhythm is a good first step to recover from depression, PTSD, and more.

INSTRUCTIONS

For the next 7–14 days, use the template that follows to keep track of your circadian rhythm. In the first row, record your current wake time and bedtime. Make sure to also record your energy level (1 = very little energy, 5 = very energetic) and mood (1 = feeling low, 5 = feeling great) when you wake up and go to sleep. In the notes section, write down how you feel overall, and any changes that you wish to see in your mood and energy levels.

Next, identify any adjustments you would like to make to your sleep schedule. For example, if you feel that you're not getting enough rest, you might set a goal of going to bed earlier so you can get more hours of sleep. For most people, restful sleep occurs when they go to sleep before midnight, between 9:30 and 11:30 p.m., and wake up 7–9 hours later. Changes to your bedtime should be made slowly, in increments of 10 minutes per day.

As you make these small adjustments each day, continue to keep track of your mood, energy levels, and any other effects on your body and mind.

Tracking Your Circadian Rhythm

Record your current wake time and bedtime in the first row, along with your associated mood and energy level. In the remaining rows, continue tracking this information each day to see how the changes you are making to your sleep schedule are affecting you.

DATE	WAKE TIME			BEDTIME			NOTES
	WAKE TIME	MOOD (1–5)	ENERGY LEVEL (1–5)	BEDTIME	MOOD (1–5)	ENERGY LEVEL (1–5)	

Client Exercise

PURPOSE

This exercise will teach you how to identify which side of your brain is dominant at any given moment, as well as how you can intentionally activate either side of your brain.

BACKGROUND

Did you know that we alternate brain hemispheric dominance every 90–120 minutes? This alternation is called our *ultradian rhythm*, and it is reflected contralaterally in nostril dominance. That means you breathe more through your left nostril when your right brain is dominant, and you breathe more through your right nostril when your left brain is dominant. You can use breathing exercises to intentionally change which side is dominant, giving you more control over your consciousness, mood, and energy level.

INSTRUCTIONS

Step 1: Assess Nostril Dominance

Begin by assessing which nostril is more clogged and which is more open. Do this by alternating closing off each nostril and seeing where the flow is almost effortless. The more open nostril correlates to the opposite side of the brain: If the right nostril is more relaxed, then the left hemisphere is more active, and if the left nostril is more open, your right hemisphere is more involved.

When the left hemisphere is more active, we tend to be more focused and attentive—in "learning mode." When the right hemisphere is more active, we are more integrative, creative, and relaxed, perhaps even spacey or dreamy.

Step 2: Shift Brain Dominance

Now, decide whether you want to stay in your current mode or shift it. If you're going to learn something new, activate your left hemisphere. If you wish to relax and become more creative, activate your right hemisphere. The first time you try this exercise, I recommend activating your left brain to prepare for the information ahead of you.

- **To activate the right hemisphere:** Cover your right nostril with your right thumb to close it, and breathe in and out through the left nostril only. Continue breathing this way for five minutes.

- **To activate the left hemisphere:** Cover your left nostril with your right index finger to close it, and breathe in and out through the right nostril only. Continue breathing this way for five minutes.

Step 3: Practice Alternate-Nostril Breathing

In Sanskrit, alternate-nostril breathing is called *nadi shodhana*, which means clearing the channels of circulation. This essential breathing exercise brings about deep relaxation, alters mood and cognition, and achieves balance. To practice this technique, use the following steps:

- Find a comfortable place to sit and close your eyes. Let your breath relax, and feel your heart open.

- With your left palm resting in your lap, bring your right hand up to your nose and close your right nostril with your thumb.

- Inhale through your left nostril slowly and steadily. Then close your left nostril with your index finger and slowly release the breath through your right nostril.

- Pause briefly at the end of the exhale, then inhale through the right nostril slowly.

- Close the right nostril again and exhale through the left nostril. This completes one cycle.

- Repeat for five cycles. Allow yourself to focus on the sensations of air moving in and out of the nostrils, paying attention to the movement.

- As you continue to practice, slowly build up to 10 cycles daily.

NASAL IRRIGATION

Client Exercise

PURPOSE

Here, you will learn how to use a neti pot. Not only can it improve nasal health and reduce the effects of respiratory allergies, but it also can enhance both mental and emotional well-being.

BACKGROUND

Nasal irrigation using the neti pot began as a traditional yogic practice to strengthen breathing and to balance the right and left hemispheres of the brain. The word *neti* is Sanskrit for "nasal cleansing." The traditional neti pot looks like a small teapot. I recommend using a ceramic pot at home and a light, unbreakable plastic pot when traveling.

MATERIALS REQUIRED

- Neti pot (these can be found online or in drugstores)

- Distilled water or water that has been boiled for 3–5 minutes and then cooled (water that is not distilled or previously boiled can contain microorganisms that can be dangerous to your health when flushing your nasal cavity)

- Saline mix (you can usually buy saline packets from the same supplier as your neti pot; noniodized salt would also work)

INSTRUCTIONS

- Add the saline packet or ¼ teaspoon noniodized salt to the neti pot. If the salt is coarsely ground, use ½ teaspoon. (Don't skip the salt! Without it, the water may cause a burning sensation in your mucus membranes.)

- Pour the distilled or previously boiled water into your neti pot. Allow the salt mixture to dissolve by gently swirling around the neti pot a few times. (To avoid contamination, do not put your finger into the neti pot.)

- Bend over a sink and gently insert the spout into your right nostril. Open your mouth slightly. Tilt your head to the left, allowing your right arm and hand to raise slowly so that the neti spout stays slightly inside your nostril. Keep your mouth open.

- You should feel the saline water running through your nasal cavity on one side and out the other. Keep your mouth open in the event a little water exits through your mouth. If you don't get a water flow, tilt your head ever so slightly until you reach the appropriate angle.

- Maintain this position, with the saline water running out of your left nostril, until the neti pot is about half empty. Then tilt your head back upright, remove the spout from your nostril, and gently blow your nose.

- Switch the spout to the other nostril (left), and tilt your head the opposite way (right). Repeat what you did on the opposite side, allowing the saline water to run out of your right nostril this time.

- For the next several minutes to hours, you may experience excess water exiting your nose or running down your throat into your mouth. This is normal. Blow your nose, gently, as needed.

- For best results, repeat the neti pot process daily. Use it twice daily if pollen levels are high or if you have a cold. With colds, one nostril and sinus is often more congested, and you may only be able to pass the saline solution via one side.

Clinician Handout

PURPOSE

Although many mental health clinicians are not medical prescribers, it is still important to have a basic understanding of how hormone imbalance disrupts mental and physical well-being. This knowledge allows you to fine-tune referrals and ensure a well-rounded health plan for your clients. I always encourage clinicians to establish collaborative relationships with holistic or integrative prescribers, especially those who are knowledgeable about hormones.

BACKGROUND

Hormones are chemical messengers that circulate in the bloodstream. Our endocrine system produces numerous hormones that regulate nearly all our body functions, including blood pressure, salt balance, inflammatory response, sex drive, fertility, and blood sugar levels.

Hormone imbalances affect all aspects of mental and physical well-being. The main hormones affecting mental health include cortisol, dehydroepiandrosterone (DHEA), vitamin D, melatonin, the thyroid hormones (triiodothyronine and thyroxine), and the sex hormones (progesterone, estrogen, and testosterone). Hormonal imbalances can affect clients of any gender and at any stage of life, resulting in symptoms such as increased fatigue, depression, brain fog, cognitive decline, insomnia, and anxiety. A particular area to keep in mind is thyroid dysfunction, as a hyperactive thyroid can cause anxiety, while a hypoactive thyroid can contribute to depression and brain fog.

Holly's Story

I received a call from a colleague whose client, Holly, was experiencing a significant increase in anxiety. In spite of using all the methods they knew, the anxiety did not abate. I asked Holly to come in for a consult, took a comprehensive history, and reviewed her medications list. Upon seeing that she had recently increased her thyroid medication, I asked her to contact her prescriber immediately to assess her blood levels. The levels came back as too high, contributing to hyperactivity of the thyroid, which can cause extreme anxiety. I was very glad that my working knowledge of medications and hormones allowed me to make an appropriate referral. Sometimes the causes of psychological states are purely physical.

A hormonal assessment is always warranted for clients with PMS, polycystic ovary syndrome (PCOS), postpartum depression, perimenopause, menopause, or andropause. It's also important to note that many transgender and nonbinary people take hormones as part of their gender-affirming care.

BIOIDENTICAL VERSUS SYNTHETIC HORMONES

Bioidentical hormones are chemically identical to the hormones that humans naturally produce in the body. However, most types of hormone replacement therapy (HRT) covered by insurance use synthetic hormones. (The one exception is the availability of bioidentical progesterone, called prometrium.) Both synthetic and bioidentical hormones are generally available only through prescription.

Research suggests that bioidentical hormones pose fewer risks than synthetic hormones. For example, bioidentical estrogens and progestins/progesterone have been found to carry a lower risk of breast cancer, cardiovascular disease, and blot clots than their synthetic counterparts, while also driving fewer complaints from those taking them (Moskowitz, 2006).

Therefore, in my clinical opinion, and that of many practitioners, synthetic hormones should be avoided whenever possible (Beans, 2009). Instead, I help my clients reduce their exposure to exogenous hormones from food and the environment, and I encourage them to consider alternatives to HRT or, when HRT is needed, bioidentical hormones. To reduce clients' exposure to exogenous hormones, I focus on their diet and other environmental factors. Food can influence hormones, especially when the food has been treated with pesticides or fertilizers, or when these same substances contaminate the water supply. Due to their interference with our endocrine and hormonal systems, they are called endocrine disruptors.

I also encourage clients to explore all the treatment options for their symptoms. Hormones will change over the course of life, such as puberty, the "peri," and the "pauses." Conventional medicine frames these changes as problems—for example, referring to the natural decline in testosterone that begins for most men by their late 20s as "low" testosterone—but these are natural, typical changes that can generally be navigated with lifestyle adjustments, including diet, exercise, herbs, and the judicious use of bioidentical hormones. In my clinical experience, severe symptoms of PMS rarely occur without additional complex influences, including sedentism, high levels of sugar, and poor-quality fats in the diet. Symptoms of hormone disruption are always a sign to explore medical causes, of course, but often, to explore lifestyle.

I do have clients who take hormones, including many of my transgender and nonbinary clients. In these cases, I encourage the client to consider bioidentical hormones. Unfortunately, since most bioidentical hormones are not covered by insurance, this can make the option inaccessible for many clients. When referring clients for bioidentical HRT, skilled licensed prescribers and compounding pharmacists are required for the best effect.

5
NATURE

THE HEALING POWER OF NATURE

There is extensive evidence for the healing power of nature. We take trips to the ocean, engage in the Japanese practice of forest bathing, and practice earthing to relax, feel better, and connect. Earthing (also known as grounding) is a therapeutic practice that involves physically connecting with the earth—for example, by walking barefoot on grass, sand, or dirt. This practice stabilizes our physiology by restoring body contact with the earth's natural electric charge (Chevalier et al., 2012). Earthing is a practice that our ancestors experienced but never needed to consciously undertake. Our bodies directly contacted the earth until the age of concrete, steel buildings, and rubber-soled shoes.

One of the benefits of being in nature is the effect of light and color on the brain. Nature's most prominent colors—found in the oceans, rivers, sky, and forests—are in the green to blue-green range of the light spectrum, which happens to be the most critical wavelength for serotonin and melatonin. This spectrum boosts mood and cognitive function and enhances sleep (Wahl et al., 2019). Loss of contact with blue-green light often happens when we live in urban settings due to overexposure to pavement and buildings, and the destruction of trees.

Similarly, have you ever wondered why you feel so relaxed at the ocean? In part, it is because we are exposed to high concentrations of negative ions in the ocean breeze. A negative ion is a molecule that contains an extra electron. These negatively charged particles are created naturally by the sun, wind, and moving water. They make the air cleaner and fresher. Exposure to negative ions also increases serotonin levels in the brain and has a positive effect on mood, learning, and our perception of pain (Della Vecchia et al., 2021). Negative ions reduce irritability and depression in seasonal affective disorder, suggesting why getting outside daily during the winter months is essential (Harmer et al., 2012).

There are countless ways to help your clients connect with the natural world, and this can improve virtually everyone's well-being. You can help them recognize their natural rhythms (as I discussed in chapter 4) and explore how they connect to the rhythms of nature. You can encourage them to absorb the light of day on their skin, which synthesizes the hormone vitamin D, stimulates the brain, and brightens mood. They can pick an orange from a tree and squeeze it for its juice, rich in vitamin C. Engaging with nature can be as gentle or as wild as someone requires for their health and well-being—clients can stroll through the park or ride the whitewater rapids! Your role as a clinician is to help clients identify their particular interests and obstacles related to ecotherapy to set them up for success.

Part of this work involves recognizing that your clients' ability to access nature is a sociopolitical issue, as tree cover is related to socioeconomic status in the United States. We know that a "green view" improves health, stress, and brain function. However, aerial images of populated areas in the United States have revealed a correlation between the relative socioeconomic status of each area and its tree canopy's density: Lower-income communities live among fewer trees, while affluent communities are more likely to be immersed in everyday green views, as their tree canopy cover is 65 percent denser (McDonald et al., 2021). This research must inform your work with underserved and urban populations.

Ultimately, immersing oneself in nature is good for a broad range of wellness goals, so in this chapter, I explore the ongoing role of being in nature and the gifts it provides us as resources for healing. While the suggestions in the following table are categorized by particular wellness targets, any client can undertake whatever activity they feel drawn to. The resources that follow invite clients to explore a variety of ways to experience the healing power of nature.

Nature at a Glance

WELLNESS TARGET	RECOMMENDATIONS
Depression	• Encourage sunlight exposure to enhance vitamin D, especially before noon, for depression, seasonal affective disorder, cognitive decline, and dementia • Exposure to terpenes in forests and jungles works as an antidepressant
Anxiety and panic	• Going outside immediately in the morning and walking barefoot in the dew is great for waking anxiety
OCD	• Weeding and sculpting garden beds can satisfy urges to do focused, detail-oriented work
Bipolar disorder	• Plan nature activities for earlier in the day to help move late waking to an earlier time
Insomnia	• Remove sunglasses while in nature to help regulate circadian rhythm
Stress, trauma, and PTSD	• Nature activities done in pairs or groups, such as adventure therapy (ropes courses, hiking) enhance resilience, attachment, and trust
ADHD	• Combine high-intensity aerobics in natural surroundings with blue-green light to release and channel energy
Chronic pain	• To combine mindfulness and yoga for chronic pain, go on a retreat in mountain air and reduce pain by engaging in gentle movement in nature • Swimming in an ice-cold stream or lake is also beneficial

WELLNESS TARGET	RECOMMENDATIONS
Substance use disorder	• To help restore purpose and meaning, combine intensive partner or group exercise while in nature and access awe-inspiring nature experiences
Cognition and memory	• Encourage early morning light exposure, which stimulates the retina and enhances brain function • Do activities involving "tricky" footwork, such as challenging wooded walks, to enhance balance and brain function
Autism spectrum and neurodivergence	• Engage in nature experiences that promote somatic awareness, especially of the arms and legs, to enhance grounding and embodiment
Body image and eating disorders	• Access nature to decrease dissociation and reduce dysmorphia by combining sensory pleasures with body appreciation activities
Digestive disorders	• Eat dirt! Dirt has good bacteria (Mycobacterium vaccae) that enhance probiotic health, so get your hands in dirt in the garden and don't obsess about it if it gets under the fingernails. Research shows it improves immune health and digestive function (Callahan, 2003; Roslund et al., 2020).

Client Worksheet

ECOTHERAPY: AN INVENTORY

PURPOSE

This worksheet will help you explore specific ecotherapy activities and decide which of them can be incorporated into your life.

BACKGROUND

Ecotherapy is based on the foundational knowledge that people and nature coexist in an interdependent relationship that is meant to be mutually beneficial. An umbrella term, *ecotherapy* (sometimes called nature therapy) refers to any therapeutic outdoor activity in which people connect with nature to enhance their well-being. Ecotherapy improves mental health by decreasing anxiety, depression, and stress, and by increasing our ability to build relationships. It is also found to help with ADHD, chronic pain, recovery from medical procedures, mood, self-esteem, memory, fatigue, and trauma.

Immersing ourselves in the natural world also creates opportunities to experience awe, which is a powerful emotion in healing, learning, and exploring spirituality and meaning-making. Experiencing awe can ease our physical, mental, and emotional suffering. It can enhance trauma recovery, help us endure depression and chronic illness, motivate us to practice self-care, and inspire a "can-do" attitude to reach our goals.

INSTRUCTIONS

Part 1: Complete an Ecotherapy Inventory

Review the following list of ecotherapy activities and:

1. Draw a box around any activities that you are currently participating in.

2. Circle any activities that you have participated in before.

3. Star any activities that you are interested in participating in or wish to further explore.

ACTIVITY	NOTES
Stargazing	You can use the SkyView app to identify stars in the night sky
Bird-watching	A pocket guide or app can help you identify unfamiliar feathered friends
Green exercise	Go walking, running, or cycling in nature
Hiking	Find trails in your area and consider going with a friend or group
Rock climbing or bouldering	Connect with other climbers through a group or gym so you can belay each other
Camping	Keep things low-tech to really appreciate your surroundings
Community gardening	Find out whether there are community gardens in your area
Home gardening	You can start small, regardless of whether you have a yard, with container gardening
Outdoor meditation	Search for a labyrinth or create one in your yard
Outdoor yoga or Tai Chi	Find a group movement class in a park
Forest bathing	Spend meditative time in a natural setting while engaging your senses
Wilderness adventures	Find out whether there are groups in your area
Horseback riding	Also consider equine-assisted therapy
Arts and crafts	While outside, use natural materials to create art or use nature as inspiration
Conservation activities	Go to a beach cleanup or volunteer at a nature preserve
Visiting a park or botanical garden	Identify resources near your home and when you travel
Mushroom foraging	Find and collect edible mushrooms (but only with an expert guide!)
Whitewater rafting	Explore a one-day trip on an easy river; consider a multiday trip
Canoeing, kayaking, or paddleboarding	Look for equipment rentals in your area
Fly-fishing	Search for groups in your area; prepare by reading about fishing and meditation or tying fishing lures to relax or reduce PTSD symptoms
Swimming	Identify a local beach or lakeshore where you can swim in nature

Part 2: Do an Ecotherapy Reflection

Use the space below to write about an outdoor place that brings or has brought you happiness. If you are more artistically inclined, feel free to draw that place instead.

Consider: What brings you joy about this place? Is it quiet? What sounds can you hear? Are there animals around? Does this place inspire awe?

When you are finished, highlight the most important characteristics of the space in your description or drawing. You can use these characteristics to guide you in deciding what kinds of ecotherapy you want to focus on next.

GROUNDING, BAREFOOT WALKING, AND FOREST BATHING

Client Exercise

PURPOSE

Variations on the advice to "get outdoors" have long been offered as a solution for mental discomfort. In this activity, you'll explore the many ways you can engage with the earth, trees, and sky to feel better.

BACKGROUND

Grounding, barefoot walking, and forest bathing are activities that people have done for millennia to facilitate their well-being. **Grounding** refers to making physical contact with the ground—by standing on it with bare feet or by sleeping on the ground—and absorbing the earth's electrons. **Barefoot walking** is a form of grounding in which the soles of your feet are the grounding points, soaking up the dewy, ionized moisture of the morning. **Forest bathing** is the English translation of the Japanese term *shinrin-yoku*. Shinrin-yoku emerged in the 1980s as part of Japan's approach to preventive medicine. It is the practice of spending meditative time in a natural setting, using the five senses to enrich your connection with that setting.

Grounding reduces inflammation, pain, and stress, and it improves blood flow, energy, and sleep (Menigoz et al., 2020). It also improves the overall modulation of the vagal response (Sokal & Sokal, 2011), an important pathway of self-regulation. You can ground yourself simply by walking barefoot in the morning dew, whether that's on a sandy beach, on the forest floor, or in your backyard. Finding a few minutes every day to touch the ground can have powerful therapeutic effects.

INSTRUCTIONS

Identify an outdoor space near to where you live or work where it is safe to do grounding in the early morning for three to five minutes every day. Part of the exercise involves sitting or lying down, so bring a cloth blanket if needed but avoid rubber yoga mats.

Make sure it is safe to take off your shoes and socks—check for broken glass or anything else that could harm you. Then stand with your feet flat on the earth, hip-width apart. Lean back gently so your heels press into the earth. Then lean forward slightly so the balls of your feet press into the earth. Lift, then lower, your toes. Experiment with scrunching the earth with your toes as you focus on whole-body sensations. How does the earth feel beneath your feet?

Then walk a short distance in your green space with your shoes still off. When you are satisfied, brush off your feet and put your shoes and socks back on. Sit or lie down on the earth with your closed eyes. Can you feel the earth, including the dirt, leaves, or sticks on the ground? Feel the energy of the ground and where your body is contacting the earth.

Breathe in and out. If you are lying down, allow your belly to rise and fall with the energy of the earth. Allow yourself to become one with the earth. What can you hear? Can you listen to what is above you? To the sides of you? Can you hear anything beneath you that is on, in, or under the ground?

When you are ready to open your eyes, what do you see above you? What appears in your entire visual field? Can you integrate the discoveries of sight and sound? Can you find the chirping bird, the crashing wave, the tree branch blowing in the wind, the rapids interrupting the stream?

Take a deep inhale through your nose. In the short time since you have arrived, how has your sensory awareness expanded? What has changed about your mental clarity? Your mood?

ALTERNATE ACTIVITIES

The previous grounding exercise may not work well for everyone—maybe you're surrounded by concrete. Or maybe you'd like to add variety to your usual grounding routine. Here are some additional ideas to consider:

- Plan a trip to a nearby park, or perhaps even a day away in the country or at a cabin.

- Plan a trip to an ocean, lake, or stream and dip your feet in.

- Gather sand from the beach (where allowed) to use for a healing sand bath:

    o Fill an old pillowcase with 2–3 pounds of sand from the beach or lakeshore. The sand should not have been sterilized or sold commercially.

    o Pour the sand onto a cookie sheet and place in the oven at 325 degrees for 15 minutes. Then pour it back into the pillowcase.

    o Apply topical arnica salve to any body part that is injured, tense, or sore. (If you have it available, a 1:1 ratio of CBD to THC cannabis salve works well too). Then apply the sand bag by resting it on the body part. It should be hot, but not hot enough to burn. The sand heals by its warmth, leading to improved lymphatic flow and relaxation.

THE BLUE-GREEN WORLD

Client Exercise

PURPOSE

Regular exposure to nature's blue-green light spectrum will soothe your brain. This activity will help you get started.

BACKGROUND

Nature's colors help regulate melatonin levels in the brain. The green, blue, and blue-green wavelengths are essential for brain function, including circadian rhythm. The absence of these colors in our everyday environment correlates with chronic stress. One study found that surgical patients who could see a cluster of trees from their hospital room window were discharged sooner and required less pain medication than patients whose rooms looked out on a brick wall (Ulrich, 1984). During the acute lockdown period of the 2020 COVID-19 pandemic, exposure to nature's blue-green space served as a stress buffer and helped people cope with the lockdown (Pouso et al., 2021).

INSTRUCTIONS

First, identify a green space that you can easily access. The more natural this place feels to you, the better, but any green space will do. If you are fortunate enough to live somewhere with ample green space, you can switch up where you do this exercise. If not, you can think of your single green space as your special place for this ritual.

Bring a hat, some drinking water, a towel or blanket, and a journal or other paper for writing down your thoughts. Silence your phone to prevent distractions. You might like to bring a friend and take turns guiding each other through this process.

Once you are in your green space:

- Find a place to sit or lie down.

- Close your eyes and feel the sensation of the air wafting over and around you.

- Listen for the sounds—what are they?

- Open your eyes and look around.

- What colors do you see, and what gives you the greatest pleasure?

- Feel free to write down in your journal how you feel the colors and other sensations are affecting you.

TERPENES

PURPOSE

Many of nature's fragrances emanate from plant chemicals called terpenes. You can integrate terpenes into your life to enhance mood and well-being.

BACKGROUND

Terpenes are the class of phytochemicals primarily responsible for the piney scents of the forest. They are released into the air by coniferous trees (pines, firs, spruce) along with rosemary, eucalyptus, and other plants. Terpenes have well-established anti-inflammatory effects when inhaled, making them useful for addressing pain, asthma, dermatitis, arthritis, and traumatic brain injury (Kim et al., 2020).

The following are all terpenes; you will likely recognize many of them.

NAME	DESCRIPTION	HEALING PROPERTIES
Bisabolol	Gives chamomile its soothing smell	Has anti-inflammatory, analgesic, and antimicrobial properties
Borneol	Is found in many plants, including cannabis, sunflower, and teak tree; its odor is a mixture of mint and damp earth	Has anti-inflammatory and analgesic properties
Camphene	Largely responsible for the earthy, musky smell most people associate with cannabis	Has antioxidant and antibacterial properties
Caryophyllene	Gives cloves and black pepper their warm, spicy scent and flavor	Has anti-inflammatory, antifungal, and antibacterial properties; good for digestion
Delta 3 carene	Derived from cannabis; its scent is sweet and woodsy	Has anti-inflammatory properties
Eucalyptol	Derived from eucalyptus oil	Has antibacterial and antifungal properties; the oil is often used in bronchial steams
Geraniol	Found in many flowering species, like citronella, rose, and geranium	May act as an antioxidant; may be a neuroprotective agent

NAME	DESCRIPTION	HEALING PROPERTIES
Humulene	Gives hops their spicy, bitter taste and smell	Has antibacterial, anti-inflammatory, antinociceptive, and anti-tumorigenic properties
Limonene	Particularly abundant in cannabis strains; also found in many fruit peels and peppermint	Has mood-boosting effects, aids digestion, and may soothe heartburn
Linalool	Responsible for lavender's famously relaxing properties	Has antianxiety, antipsychotic, antiepileptic, and analgesic properties
Myrcene	Found in mangoes, lemongrass, and thyme	Has anti-inflammatory, muscle-relaxing, and even sedating effects
Pinene	Named for the pine species to which it lends its intense aroma; also found in aromatic kitchen herbs	Aids memory; contributes to alert well-being
Phytol	Provides the famously nostalgic scent of freshly cut grass; also found in green tea	Has anti-insomnia, antioxidant, and immunosuppressant properties
Terpinolene	This herbaceous scent is in tea tree oil, rosemary, and sage	Is a mood booster with antibacterial, antifungal, anti-insomnia, and antiseptic properties
Trans-nerolidol	Its sweet, spicy scent is what makes jasmine flowers so enjoyable	Is an antioxidant, antiparasitic, antimicrobial, and anticancer agent
Valencene	Named for its source, Valencia oranges	Is a very effective repellent against mosquitoes, ticks, and fleas; has antiallergic and anti-inflammatory properties

INSTRUCTIONS

Plan to visit a green space that is accessible to you—the more natural, the better. You might visit a park, nature preserve, or campground where you can immerse yourself in the outdoors. If you don't have access to this type of space, simply find the greenest spot you can, or you can bring nature to you by purchasing terpenes (in the form of plants, foods, or essential oils) to use in this exercise.

Once you are in your green space, find a spot where you will have some privacy. Now explore your environment:

- Use a plant identifier app, such as PictureThis or LeafSnap, to identify some of the trees, bushes, grasses, flowers, and other plants in the area.

- With your eyes closed or open, inhale deeply through the nose. What do you smell?

- Inhale again. Can you identify which smells come from which plants?

- Can you name a terpene you are smelling?

- If there is a body of water in this area, are any smells coming from it?

- Can you smell the wind?

- Can you smell the dirt?

- Continue to explore this green space. Familiarize yourself with the flora and fauna, including learning about toxic plants or venomous insects, so you know what to stay clear of as well as what you can touch, sniff, and taste (if allowed).

- If you have access to conifers, rosemary bushes, or eucalyptus trees, try crunching a handful of their needles and inhaling the scent. How does it make you feel?

- Stay in your green space for as long as you can. Play in this space, exploring the natural world in new ways.

REFLECTION

While in your green space, or after you return home, take a few minutes to reflect on your experience.

How did you feel before your time in nature? During the exercise? How do you feel now?

_____

_____

_____

_____

_____

_____

Jot down your reactions, emotions, and sensations.

_____

_____

_____

_____

_____

_____

_____

When will you visit your green space again?

_____

_____

_____

Where would you like to go next?

_____

_____

_____

6

HUMAN-ANIMAL RELATIONSHIPS

ANIMAL-ASSISTED METHODS OF SELF-REGULATION

Our relationships with other beings have the potential to be profoundly healing. Deep experiences of love, care, and co-regulation occur both among humans and between humans and different animal species. Dogs, cats, birds, horses, cows, elephants, dolphins, and more can experience interspecies connections.

We know that with dogs and horses in particular, healing can be bidirectional when a caring relationship is present. Family dogs synchronize their behavior to both adults and children in the family (Wanser et al., 2021), which strengthens affiliative connections. Both dogs and horses can work effectively with individuals with PTSD (Fisher et al., 2021) and others with disrupted capacities for attachment. Some programs involve humans with PTSD helping animals with PTSD to heal, suggesting the power of a mutually healing relationship (Schlote, 2018).

There are many avenues for introducing and supporting the human-animal bond in therapy or at home. For instance, walking a dog may be just the reason a sedentary client needs to get up and out, while a client's fear of touch based on prior traumatic experiences can be the subject of dog-assisted interventions in the therapeutic setting (Korn, 2013/2022). While the interventions may differ across species, the principles of human-animal connection remain universal and are bound only by our creativity and the limits of verbal and nonverbal communication across the species involved.

In addition to verbal and nonverbal communication, which facilitates deep connections, we use a subtle form of communication called intuition, tuning in with nonverbal communication. When we connect profoundly with another breathing, pulsating, oscillating being, our rhythms entrain and synchronize: We tune in, our brain wave energy synchronizes with each other, we may breathe in unison, and we share emotional alignment—hence the phrase "feeling in sync." This heightened cognitive flexibility allows for a more profound connection, empathy, and attachment with humans and other animals (Grahn et al., 2021; He et al., 2016; McCraty & Zayas, 2014). Animals are naturally intuitive and our rhythms often entrain; they tune in to our needs and respond at these subtle levels (Birke & Thompson, 2019).

Dogs are easily trained to respond to our many needs, which explains why many cultures view them as guardians of the night, guides to the underworld, and healers who lick the wounds of the infirm. In Celtic mythology, dogs were believed to heal merely by their presence. Today, the science (and our experience!) show that dogs do indeed heal us in many ways. They get us out of bed for a walk when we are depressed, get us to the dog park to socialize with others, and provide nonjudgmental love and care.

Dogs can also be trained to perform services to aid in activities of daily living, to "sniff" out elevated blood sugar or cancer, and to warn of effects of dysautonomia. For an individual experiencing traumatic stress and fitful sleep, a trained service dog can help by recognizing when the human is experiencing a nightmare, a night terror, sleepwalking, or even obstructive sleep apnea, and then responding by waking the human. To be effective, the dog can either sleep in the bed or nearby, based on the specific needs of their companion (Scotland-Coogan, 2019).

Joe's Story

Joe was a retired service member who had TBI and PTSD following three tours in Afghanistan. On his final tour, he was near an IED when it blew up and killed two of his friends. Joe suffered nightmares that made sleeping for more than a few hours a night nearly impossible. He could not tolerate sleep medications. He told me, "I can't bear falling asleep because of my dreams. I wake up in a sweat, screaming, and my wife now sleeps in another room. I have scared my three-year-old with the noise I make. The problem is I can't seem to wake up, but I stay in the dream screaming."

I consulted with a service dog trainer, who confirmed that we could train a service dog to wake Joe up at the initial sign of distressed noise, indicating that Joe was moving into a nightmare state. Joe and his wife agreed that they would like to work with a service dog for his nightmares and for some additional concerns, including his fear when going into crowded public spaces. After working with a trainer, Joe and his wife welcomed Randy, a Labrador retriever, into their home. Whenever Joe began to show the signs of distressed sleep, Randy would gently nudge him awake.

After several successful weeks, Joe's wife rejoined him for bedtime, and their three-year-old began to sleep soundly. Over time, we used a combination of herbal medicine, exposure therapy (using psychodrama), mindfulness, yoga, and (of course) Randy. Joe's sleep latency and duration improved, and his nightmares decreased in both intensity and frequency, allowing him to awaken feeling restored. Randy became an integral part of the family, serving as a healer that united them more deeply than ever.

In this chapter, I'll explore the various healing roles of animals—particularly dogs, but also including horses and cats—and their service to people with mental or physical health challenges. You'll see how animals can offer a wonderful nonpharmaceutical option for self-regulation, attachment, dissociation, phobias, and even suicidality. If your client isn't interested or ready for animal-assisted methods, that's okay—it won't be for everyone. As always, you will be integrating and adapting methods for the needs of each client. The tools in this chapter will help you and your client explore whether and how to incorporate a human-animal bond into their healing process.

Human-Animal Relationships at a Glance

WELLNESS TARGET	RECOMMENDATIONS
Depression	• People with lethargy and lack of movement or exercise may benefit from walking a dog or having an animal to take care of
Anxiety and panic	• A service dog can be trained to identify anxiety or panic attacks just before their onset and can provide caring relief or a reminder to access self-care strategies, including taking glycine
OCD	• Service dogs can be trained to decrease intrusive thoughts by applying deep pressure with their paws or interrupting obsessive behaviors
Bipolar disorder	• Service dogs can be trained to help someone go to bed at a regular time, get sunlight, and take nutrients or medication at the same time daily
Insomnia	• Dogs can provide friendship when the client is awake in the evening or remind them to eat a snack before bed for blood sugar handling
Stress, trauma, and PTSD	• Emotional support or service animals can promote secure attachment, provide safe touch and unconditional love, and enhance interpersonal/interspecies communication
ADHD	• Emotional support, companion, or service dogs can help children and adults focus, reduce anxiety, and provide a willing friend to stroke when the client is feeling upset
Chronic pain	• Animals can provide opportunities for gentle movement, including slow walks and flexing of painful hands and arms • Touching and stroking enhances endorphins, which reduces pain • Holding a warm animal on one's lap can provide warmth and ease pain
Substance use disorder	• Focusing on the care of another being can instill hope and meaning to counter depression and isolation • A service animal can be trained in relapse prevention

WELLNESS TARGET	RECOMMENDATIONS
Cognition and memory	• Engaging with an animal can counter cognitive decline by promoting exercise and communication • Animals are especially useful during late stages of dementia when only nonverbal communication is possible • Animals can reduce the agitation associated with cognitive impairment
Autism spectrum and neurodivergence	• Animals can enhance communication and touch experiences • Taking care of an animal brings the client's awareness to their hands and improves focus • Interaction with an animal also reduces stress and enhances empathy
Body image and eating disorders	• Animals can listen to clients' concerns without judgment and help them engage in movement • Caring for a differently abled animal can help clients build inner compassion for their own body
Digestive disorders	• Stroking animals before eating induces a parasympathetic response, which aids the digestive response

EXPLORING OUR BONDS WITH ANIMALS

Clinician Exercise

PURPOSE

In this exercise, you will inquire into your client's experiences with animals to better ascertain whether and how they may benefit from animal-assisted therapy.

BACKGROUND

Most clients you see have had some form of contact, past or present, with live animals. Many have spent time with their family's or their friends' pets. Some might have encountered city-dwelling or wild animals in their habitats. Others may have cared for an animal in the past or would like to do so now. Gently investigating their history with the animal world can lead to clarity about whether and how they might benefit from an animal companion.

INSTRUCTIONS

Ask your client to answer these questions:

- Do you have any experiences you'd like to share with me about pets or domesticated animals you've spent time with (whether your own, a friend's, or even an animal you met in passing)?

- Do you have any experiences with birds or other city-dwelling animals? With farm animals? With wild animals?

After listening to their stories, use your judgment to broach other potential questions:

- Is there an animal whose qualities or symbolism you felt drawn to as a child?

- Is there an animal whose qualities you have felt drawn to more recently?

- Have animals appeared to you in dreams that you've felt were significant?

For some clients, you may want to reflect back to them their experience of a connection to the animal world or encourage them to do journaling or other reflections on the animals they spoke about, whether actual or symbolic.

For clients who have positive feelings toward animals and who would benefit from a relationship with one, the following worksheets can guide your continuing work.

Clinician Handout

PURPOSE

There are times when you will be asked to evaluate a client, make a referral, or write a letter for animal support. There are several types of animal assistants; understanding the differences between these classifications will allow you to educate clients and make appropriate referrals.

BACKGROUND

So much mental distress occurs in isolation and disconnection, which is why helping clients build relationships—both with humans and with animals—is essential. Especially for clients who are depressed, immobilized, or in pain, it can be helpful to have an animal to care for. There are subtle biological and physiological exchanges that can occur with animals that help to regulate the nervous system. Enhancing clients' social connection and relationship to animals increases the love hormone (oxytocin), among other benefits.

DID YOU KNOW?

Oxytocin is called "the love hormone" because it is released in response to birthing and lactation. It stimulates contractions, aids in mother-child bonding, and drives a neurohormone response to attachment behaviors. Petting animals, hugging, cuddling, rocking someone, having sex, and consuming vitamins C and D or dietary fats are all precursors to oxytocin.

Given the power of this hormone, there are emerging clinical applications of intranasal oxytocin (Quintana et al., 2021) for many mental and physical health concerns—including schizophrenia, autism spectrum disorder, and PTSD—but the methods and utility are still in the nascent stage.

TYPES OF ANIMAL ASSISTANTS

Many types of animals assist our well-being, including horses, cats, pigs, birds, and reptiles. Dogs are the most common animal assistants, and the following paragraphs will explain the different categories of canine assistants: therapy, emotional support, service, psychiatric assistance, and companion animals. Understanding the differences between them will help you determine whether and how a client may benefit from a particular type of animal assistant.

Therapy Animals

Therapy animals accompany their owners in a variety of settings to provide comfort, affection, and support.

Therapy dogs must meet the following requirements:

- Must be at least 1 year of age

- Must be well-socialized

- Can be trained by the owner or a trainer

- Must pass the Canine Good Citizen test for obedience

- Other tests may be required

- Must be certified and registered with a reputable national organization

Therapy dogs can help children and adults alike restore healthy touch through stroking or patting behaviors, particularly for trauma associated with physical or sexual abuse, or suicidality and self-harming. Being able to reclaim the power of healing touch with animals is a first step to recovery.

Emotional Support Animals

An emotional support animal is any animal that provides comfort to a person to help relieve symptoms or effects of mental illness.

These are the requirements for emotional support animals:

- Should be well-behaved

- No formal training is necessary

- Clients require a letter from a mental health practitioner (see the **Sample Letter for an Emotional Support Animal**, p. 111)

DID YOU KNOW?

The Fair Housing Act (FHA) states that people with mental or physical disabilities cannot be refused to house along with their service animal or assistant animal, even when homes have strict "no pets allowed" policies. However, there are a few exceptions to the law:

- If the animal is too large for the house or accommodation (e.g., a horse), the property owner does not have to accept it.

- If the building has four or fewer units and the owner occupies one of them, they do not have to accept service animals or assistant animals.

- If the home is a single-family house that is rented without the help of a real estate agent, the owner has the right to refuse service animals and assistant animals.

Service Animals

Service animals are specially trained to perform specific tasks for a person who has a disability.

Service dogs must meet the following requirements:

- Have been individually trained to do work or perform tasks for a person with a disability

- Great socialization and public skills

- There is no official certification or licensing requirement in place for service dogs

- Requires written documentation from a health care provider about the need for a service animal

Psychiatric Assistance Animals

This is a subcategory of service animals. Psychiatric assistance animals are specially trained to perform specific tasks for a person who has a psychiatric disorder.

These are the requirements for psychiatric assistance dogs:

- Need 1–2 years of specialized training

- Clients can adopt from a service dog organization, self-train, or work with a professional dog trainer

- Often required to show certification that the dog is trained to perform specific tasks in line with the handler's needs

- Must pass the General Public Access Test

DID YOU KNOW?

Service dogs and psychiatric assistance dogs are legally protected under the Americans with Disabilities Act. They are always allowed to accompany their handler. People cannot ask about the handler's disability; require medical documentation, a special identification card, or training documentation for the dog; or ask that the dog demonstrate its ability to perform the work or task. They *can* ask:

- Is the dog a service animal?

- What work or task has the dog been trained to perform?

However, if a service animal is out of control and the handler does not take effective action to control it, or if the animal is not housebroken, that animal may be excluded from access or entry.

Companion Animals

This term refers to the everyday animals in our lives who provide us with company, amusement, love, and happiness. There is no special training required for a companion animal, just lots of love!

SAMPLE LETTER FOR AN EMOTIONAL SUPPORT ANIMAL

Clinician Worksheet

PURPOSE

You can use this template when writing a letter for a client in need of verification for an emotional support animal.

BACKGROUND

Individuals who qualify for an emotional support animal may require a letter in order to have that animal in a housing unit that normally prohibits animals. You will need to conduct an assessment and diagnose a DSM-5 category that meets the definition of a disability.

TEMPLATE

[*Clinician name
Practice name
Address
Phone/fax
Email*]

To Whom It May Concern [*or name of property manager or housing authority*]:

[*Client name*] is currently under my professional care for treatment for a mental illness defined by DSM-5. [*Client name*] meets the definition of disability under the Americans with Disabilities Act, the Fair Housing Act, and the Rehabilitation Act of 1973.

[*Client name*]'s mental impairment substantially limits more than one major life activity. I have prescribed one emotional support animal ([*type of animal—e.g., canine*]) *as part of the treatment program developed for* [*client name*]. The presence of this emotional support animal is necessary for [*client name*]'s mental health. I am a licensed mental health counselor, licensed in the state of [*state*] *by the [name of licensing board] since [date]. My license number is [number]; it is current and expires on [date].*

I am familiar with the clinical research literature about the benefits of an assistance animal for people with mental health disorders and would be happy to share these citations with you or discuss this further at your request.

Please allow [*client name*] to be accompanied by their emotional support animal in their place of dwelling and in other public places as required. If you have any questions or require phone verification, please do not hesitate to call me at [*phone*].

Sincerely,
[*Clinician name and credentials*]

ARE YOU READY FOR AN ANIMAL ASSISTANT?

PURPOSE

This activity will help you determine whether you are ready to bring an animal assistant into your life.

BACKGROUND

Human-animal relationships have the potential to be profoundly healing. Depending on your physical and mental health conditions, you may qualify for a service animal (which are specially trained to perform certain tasks for their handlers) or an emotional support animal (which are permitted in some contexts where animals usually are not). And of course, there are companion animals, also known as pets—they may not have specialized training, but they are still supportive and loving companions!

INSTRUCTIONS

Take some time to answer the following questions, then share your responses with your mental health professional. They can help you assess whether your current circumstances are well-suited to bringing an animal into your life, and whether you might qualify for a service or emotional support animal. (If you decide that you are not ready for an animal of your own, that's okay! See the **Ways to Connect with Animals** handout, p. 115, for other ways to spend time with animals.)

What kind of animal (e.g., dog, cat) would you like to adopt? _____

Are there any restrictions on or fees for animals where you live? _____

_____

Do you have enough space inside and outside your home for the type of animal you'd like to adopt? (For a large dog, you'll need a fenced yard or access to space for walking and running.)

_____

_____

Does your schedule allow you enough time to spend with the animal, so they are not alone for long hours?

_____

Do you have enough financial resources for food, veterinary bills, toys, and other necessities? (For an estimate of the cost of owning a dog or cat, see https://www.aspca.org/pet-care/general-pet-care/cutting-pet-care-costs.)

_____

_____

Are you able to care for the animal by yourself, including walking or playing with the animal for exercise, or will someone else help with their care?

_____

_____

Are you allergic to any animals, or is a member of your household?

_____

_____

Will you have enough time and resources to train the animal?

_____

_____

Do you prefer a puppy or kitten—with the extra training and cost this entails—or an older animal?

_____

_____

Do you have patience for letting out a dog or keeping cat litter cleaned?

_____

_____

Have you explored the meaning of the history you have with animals, both positive and negative? How might this affect your experience and your choices?

_____

_____

IS ANIMAL-ASSISTED THERAPY RIGHT FOR MY CLINICAL PRACTICE?

PURPOSE

This worksheet will help you explore the option of integrating an animal assistant into your therapy practice.

BACKGROUND

Integrating a therapy animal into your clinical practice can help children and adults alike, particularly those who are survivors of physical or sexual abuse, or who struggle with suicidality and self-harm. A therapy animal can help restore the enjoyment of healthy touch as clients practice stroking or petting behaviors. Being able to reclaim the power of healing touch with animals is a first step to recovery.

SHOULD I HAVE AN ANIMAL ASSISTANT?

There are many factors to consider when deciding whether and how to integrate an animal into your therapy practice. If you are considering adopting an animal, you should ask yourself the questions from the **Are You Ready for an Animal Assistant?** client worksheet (p. 112). And of course, there are additional considerations for a therapy animal specifically:

- Will you be training an animal that is already in your life, or adopting a new animal?

- If you have a particular animal in mind, are they well-socialized and otherwise well-suited to becoming a therapy animal? Consider temperament, habits, and past experiences, including any trauma and triggers. You may also want to hire a certified trainer to conduct a temperament test with your animal.

- What type of animal are you considering? (For example, you may love snakes, but clients may not want to pet and cuddle with one as much as they might a golden retriever.)

- What are your reasons for wanting to include an animal assistant in your practice, and how well would the animal you're considering fulfill those expectations?

- In what settings and situations would you like to integrate the therapy animal?

    ○ In your home office?

    ○ In an office outside your home? If so, are animals allowed? Is there sufficient indoor and outdoor space for the animal?

    ○ Visiting hospitals or other public areas to support people?

- Does your animal assistant meet the requirements for a registered therapy animal, if needed? (See the **Animal Assistants: Types and Benefits** handout, p. 108, for more information.)

WAYS TO CONNECT WITH ANIMALS

Client Handout

PURPOSE

There are many ways to connect with animals that can be beneficial to your mental health. This worksheet provides some options for you to explore. Especially if you do not have an animal companion of your own, these are great ways to spend more time with friends from other species.

BACKGROUND

Many people who have experienced trauma have difficulty feeling compassion for themselves. Animals offer a mirror for love and can catalyze compassion. When you have been hurt by humans, oftentimes connecting with another species offers you an opportunity to tune in to and express the love that persists within in spite of the hurt. Caring for animals, and advocating for their welfare, can also help you to take your mind off your problems and to find purpose and meaning in life.

ACTIVITIES

Here are some ways that you can connect with animals:

- Volunteer at a shelter or rescue.

- Offer to pet-sit or dog-walk for others.

- Spend time with the animal companion of a friend, relative, or neighbor.

- Visit a cat café (a combination café and cat rescue).

- Join a session of animal yoga (e.g., goat yoga) or cow hugging.

- Visit a bird sanctuary (a safe place for wild birds to recover from injuries).

- Engage in activism on behalf of animals. Here are some movements to consider:

    o Empty the Tanks: https://emptythetanks.org/

    o Nonhuman Rights Project: https://www.nonhumanrights.org/

    o Global Federation of Animal Sanctuaries: https://www.sanctuaryfederation.org/

- View photos or videos of young mammals (e.g., puppies, kittens). Simply looking at these young animals can evoke compassion—both toward them and toward yourself.

7

DIGESTION

In the 40-plus years that I have been practicing integrative mental health, I have seen that where there is mental distress, there is always a problem with digestion somewhere along the gastrointestinal (GI) tract. Also called the digestive tract, this is the hollow tube that begins in the mouth and ends at the anus. Digestion can go wrong anywhere along the tube, leading to cascading effects down the tubal road. Not chewing food well enough, gastroesophageal reflux disease (GERD), poor liver function, gallstones, small intestinal bacterial overgrowth (SIBO), intestinal permeability, food allergies, gas, diarrhea, constipation, irritable bowel syndrome (IBS), inflammatory bowel disease (IBD), hemorrhoids, and more—somewhere you will find that your client who arrives for mental health also has a digestive problem, or more than one.

Many of these clients will be taking medications for digestive problems, but these pharmaceuticals typically are suppressing their symptoms, not addressing the root cause itself. Further, some of these medications, when used for prolonged periods, are associated with nutrient deficits (Mumtaz et al., 2022) or, worse, cognitive decline (Kumar et al., 2020). The integrative approach I outline here allows you to identify and treat the cause, improving both physical and mental health.

Fortunately, you do not need to be an expert in this area to help your clients. Find some compatible functional nutrition and medicine clinicians to collaborate with; even GI specialists know how important mental health is to digestion for their clients (they often just don't have the time to spend with them). Digestion problems are not always complex, especially when identified early, and they can often be alleviated with simple changes. The use of foods, herbs, and nutrients like digestive enzymes, along with relaxation and mindfulness, can restore digestive function and support mental health.

For instance, GERD is very common, especially among people with PTSD and anxiety (Choi et al., 2018). It is triggered by the chronic stress response of sympathetic nervous system activation and the excessive use of acidic and stimulant foods like coffee, tea, alcohol, sugar, and refined flour. Conventional treatment using medications can lead to secondary health problems, as prolonged use of the proton pump inhibitors has a risk profile for cognitive decline. Simple changes like switching to cold-brewed coffee (which reduces the acid; Rao & Fuller, 2018), using deglycyrrhizinated licorice (DGL) to soothe the mucosa, and practicing mindful eating can make a difference in your clients' GERD symptoms.

DID YOU KNOW?
Digestion and sleep are closely connected. Poor sleep is a factor that may reveal digestive disturbances. People with digestive problems sleep fewer hours and have less restorative sleep. Eating too quickly, skipping meals, eating large meals, irregular mealtimes, stimulant foods, alcohol, spicy foods, and food intolerances and allergies can all contribute to poor-quality sleep.

> If poor digestion contributes to poor mental health, then the converse is also true: Improving digestion leads to improved mental health. If someone cannot digest food, absorb it, utilize it, and move it via the vast circulatory network to nourish the brain and body, then they are likely to sputter, just like a car without fuel. Therefore, identifying "digestion distress" is key in integrative mental health.

DIGESTIVE DISSOCIATION

I use the term *digestive dissociation* to refer to the fact that most people are dissociated or disconnected from their digestion. For some, it's just because the digestive process is controlled by the autonomic nervous system, so they eat and hardly think about it—until an organ complains, of course. But it can also result from negative experiences or traumas, such as toilet training, forced enemas, unwanted anal penetration, or medical trauma, such as surgeries or the trauma of chronic illness like Crohn's or celiac disease, where people often suffer for years before diagnosis and treatment. I find that people also "stuff" their feelings away in the "garbage disposal" of the GI tract, which eventually transports it to the toilet! Some people are squeamish about their own bodily processes or the end products.

Decreasing digestive dissociation is a key goal of the interventions in this chapter. This is also where mindfulness merges with improving digestion: Anytime you enhance awareness of a body's functions, and make conscious what is often unconscious or beneath the surface of active awareness, you enhance health. The contrary can also occur, though I see it much more rarely in clinical practice. This involves hyperawareness of each digestion sensory experience: fear about gas; the sense of food staying in the stomach, or its transit time being too fast or too slow; or a hyperfocus on the process of fecal elimination.

THE SECOND BRAIN

One of the most critical areas of research that has illuminated the importance of proper digestive functioning is the discovery of the "second brain"—the enteric nervous system of the gut—and how it communicates with the first brain housed in the skull (Gershon, 1998). The enteric nervous system functions as a highly complex, bidirectional highway between the brain and the gut. The gut sends signals to the brain via afferent pathways, and it receives sympathetic and parasympathetic input in return (Gershon & Margolis, 2021).

The gut is also part of a larger system called the microbiome, which you can think of as a community of neighbors living in and on your body. Some neighbors you get along with—they are helpful and enhance your life. But there are others you'd prefer to kick out of the neighborhood because they cause problems, like toxic bacteria. Each person's microbiome is unique, based on their DNA and the interaction with the environment.

While you can't change DNA, you *can* change the environmental exposures that can trigger illness. This is central to the use of nutrition for mental health. For example, prebiotics (derived from fiber in foods) and probiotics (found in fermented foods) feed the microbiome neighborhood, keeping everything in balance. Therefore, increasing fiber intake from fruits and vegetables—and eating fermented foods like sauerkraut, kimchee, and freshly made fermented dairy like kefir, labneh, and yogurt—can feed the microbiome and keep it working properly. There may still be a few toxic neighbors around, but they are kept at bay and are not heavy "influencers."

The complex interrelationships between nutrition and the brain, mind, and body are evident in clients with anxiety disorders. Anxiety worsens inflammatory bowel disorders, but once we enhance gut function with nutrition—such as with glutamine, curcumin, butyric acid, prebiotics, and probiotics—eliminate allergens, and reduce gut permeability, the gut is much happier, and so are the brain and mind.

Juanita's Story

Juanita had a history of anxiety and panic attacks along with diagnosed colitis. Several practitioners had prescribed medications, none of which had been helpful. Juanita had then seen nutritionists and functional medicine doctors, who had put her on numerous supplements and herbs, which she had problems taking and digesting, and which also had not helped. In our intake, I obtained a comprehensive history of her digestive symptoms, which began in childhood, and I compared this to the timeline she provided when she shared her history of trauma. I then allowed her to make the connections among the different forms of distress she had experienced.

Juanita and I created a plan to move ahead in post-trauma therapy and to focus on one simple smoothie a day that would contain foods soothing to her gut as well as glutamine, which would help her to heal. I suggested that later, when she felt better, we would add another nutritional product. By making the connections between her gut and her traumas evident—and by not overwhelming her with too many treatments at once—we were able to slowly make progress on both trauma and gut recovery.

CLINICAL PEARL

Because the gut is so critical to mental health, bariatric surgery is ill-advised unless there are no other options. With bariatric surgery, the capacity to absorb and utilize nutrients is diminished. Postsurgical exacerbation or development of addictive behaviors and even suicidality are serious potential side effects (Castaneda et al., 2019). Careful screening is required, and people with histories of complex trauma and eating disorders would generally be excluded due to lack of long-term efficacy.

Given the importance of the gut to mental health, the exercises in this chapter will help your clients connect the dots between their stress levels, food habits, mental well-being, and digestion. As they learn how to work with it all, they will find various ways to improve their health so they can navigate life with greater ease. For some clients, the methods I've included in this book may not be sufficient to identify their digestive issues. In these cases, a comprehensive fecal analysis can provide further insight into digestion, absorption, and the fecal microbiome. Testing is advised for potential culprits including low levels of digestive enzymes, bacterial yeast, or parasitic infections. Test for fecal calprotectin to differentiate between IBD and IBS. I often combine initial salivary testing for common allergens like gluten and casein along with a stool sample.

Digestion at a Glance

WELLNESS TARGET	RECOMMENDATIONS
Depression	• Encourage gardening to promote exposure to good bacteria in the dirt • Assess for GERD, hypoactive elimination • People who take antidepressants have a higher risk of Clostridium difficile infection; get a fecal test
Anxiety and panic	• Eat fermented foods, which support gut function and GABA production • Reduce anxiety with biofeedback (reduces stress hormones, which exacerbate digestive function) • Steroids for colitis increase anxiety—find alternatives
OCD	• A disrupted microbiome influences OCD behaviors; evaluate for intestinal permeability and consider glutamine support • Ensure prebiotics and probiotics are especially focused on mood
Bipolar disorder	• High rates of digestive disorders in people with bipolar suggest a disrupted microbiome, so apply bioindividual approaches to restoring gut flora via diet and supplementation
Insomnia	• Evaluate for GERD, IBD, and colitis as co-occurring in insomnia
Stress, trauma, and PTSD	• Decrease dissociation and enhance mindful eating to ease digestion • Transform self-medication behaviors that involve alcohol, sugar, or harmful drugs
ADHD	• Assess for digestive dysfunction, gas bloating, pain, diarrhea • Evaluate for food allergies or sensitivities, which are common • Often reactive to refined flours, sugars, and junk foods—limit their consumption • No synthetic sweeteners, which can disrupt mood
Chronic pain	• Emphasize analgesic foods and spices • Eat easy-to-digest foods, which heal gut permeability and reduce inflammatory process • Chronic NSAID disrupts digestion—find alternatives

WELLNESS TARGET	RECOMMENDATIONS
Substance use disorder	• During recovery, provide easily digested low-glycemic protein and fat-rich meals • Add bitter greens to aid liver and gallbladder function • Focus on hydration and decrease dissociation with self-massage • Begin culinary education and link to self-care • Educate about the nutritional basis for substance use disorders
Cognition and memory	• Ensure B-12-rich foods (animal proteins), as the aging reduces intrinsic factors required for B-12 uptake • Slow glucose uptake with fiber; improve EFAs emulsion with bitter greens; address gut function with prebiotics and probiotics • Reduce inflammation, if there is a history of TBI; balance abnormal release of neurotransmitters; address intestinal permeability
Autism spectrum and neurodivergence	• Ensure adequate fiber intake • Assess for adequate cholesterol levels • Enhance digestion with proteolytic enzymes to avoid putrefaction associated with a disrupted microbiome • Address food textures and flavors to ensure optimal digestion and elimination • May benefit from belly massages for sensory processing and peristalsis
Body image and eating disorders	• Educate about digestive processes and the nutritional needs of the body and mind • Explain the neurochemical basis of eating disorders to reduce shame • Encourage macro- and micromineral-rich foods, including zinc
Digestive disorders	• Encourage small meals to enhance digestion • Chew mouthfuls of food into liquid 100 times before swallowing; chew mindfully • Combine small amounts of raw fruits and vegetables for enzymatic action

DIGESTIVE ORGANS COLORING ACTIVITY

PURPOSE

Learning the locations of your digestive organs will help you better understand how your gut functions and will enhance your ability to take care of it (and you). This activity prepares you for the **Digestive Organs Matching Game** (p. 133), where you will explore the functions of these organs.

BACKGROUND

Your mental health is deeply interconnected with your digestive health. If your digestion is not working well, you cannot absorb the nutrients that nourish the brain, mind, and body. When you enhance digestion, you improve gut function and the availability of chemicals that enhance mood, focus, and cognition. The first step in improving your digestion is to learn the location (and next, the function) of each organ in the digestive system. This knowledge enables you to identify symptoms better and to palpate your organs when you feel discomfort.

INSTRUCTIONS

Color in the following diagram of the digestive system. It will be most helpful to start at the mouth, where the digestive process begins with food entering the body, and continue coloring each organ along the way until you reach the end of the digestive system and process, where leftover waste exits the body.

Digestive Organs Diagram

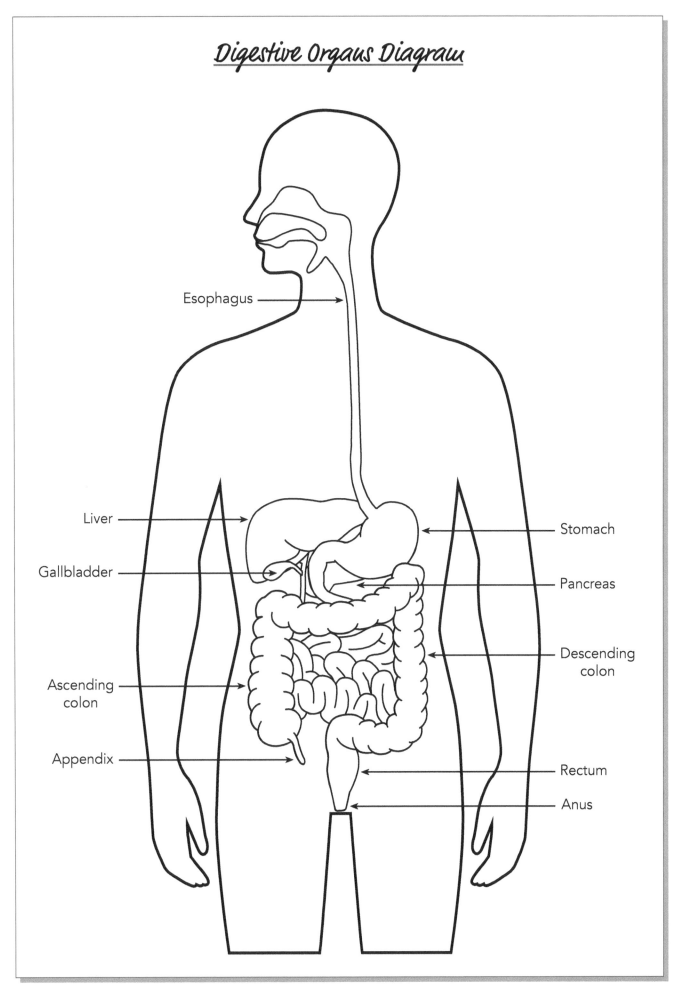

MINDFULNESS EXERCISES FOR DIGESTION

Client Exercise

PURPOSE

These simple mindfulness exercises guide you in tuning in to the experience of eating and your digestive process. This will help you better understand, appreciate, and enhance how your body turns food into nourishment for your physical and mental health.

BACKGROUND

Your mental health is deeply interconnected with your digestive health. Enhancing your digestion allows you to absorb the nutrients that improve your mood, focus, and cognition. It works in reverse too: Practicing mindful awareness and mindful eating promotes relaxation and optimal digestion.

Try the following mindfulness exercises. The first focuses on the sensory experience of eating, the second teaches the importance of thoroughly chewing your food, and the third increases your awareness of your digestive organs and processes.

CHEWING THE RAISIN*

- Hold a raisin and observe it as though you are the first person to ever touch a raisin and you are investigating for the first time. See the raisin in all its detail; observe every part of it—the wrinkles, the way the light shines on it.

- Touch the raisin and explore the texture and sensation.

- Smell the raisin and inhale its aroma. Take note of how this fragrance may stimulate your stomach or mouth.

- Gently and slowly place the raisin in your mouth and, before chewing, take time to consider how it feels on your tongue and any other sensations you notice. Slowly position the raisin for chewing.

- Chew the raisin a couple of times and notice what happens when you do, really tasting it in all of its subtle complexities. Before swallowing, notice how the texture of the raisin changes as you chew it. When you are ready, think about swallowing the raisin and experience the intention of swallowing. Then swallow the raisin.

- Afterward, see if you can feel the raisin as it moves to your stomach. Observe how you feel after this exercise in mindful eating.

---

* Adapted from Korn, L. E. (2016b). *Nutrition essentials for mental health: A complete guide to the food-mood connection.* W.W. Norton & Company.

ONE HUNDRED TIMES

- Prepare a small plate with a variety of healthy foods. For example, you might include a gluten-free cracker, a dried fig, an orange slice, and a piece of raw broccoli.

- As you enjoy your snack, chew each bite of food 100 times, or until it is liquid, before swallowing. Bring your awareness to the experience of chewing; notice the different tastes and textures of each bite.

- After you have finished, reflect on this experience. Did some types of food require more chewing before they liquefied? How many times do you usually chew each bite of food? How did your experience of eating change when you chewed 100 times?

ENHANCING DIGESTION BODY SCAN

This script will guide you through a body scan that combines all the senses: visualization, taste, smell, and touch through palpation. Your therapist can read it out loud to you, or you can record it to use in the future. Before recording, you may wish to skim through the script and look up the pronunciation of any unfamiliar terms (since the scientific names for different parts of the digestive system are used). While recording, practice the visualization to ensure you go slowly enough to follow later. The exercise will take about 60 minutes to complete.

- To begin, find a comfortable position, either sitting upright with the soles of your feet stable on the ground beneath you or lying down with your arms and legs extended.

- Take a couple of deep breaths in through your nose and out through your mouth—air filling your lungs, your chest rising and then falling again.

- Feel your body relaxing with each breath that leaves your body. Maybe you want to close your eyes. If not, that is also perfectly fine—whatever works best for you. Slowly breathe in and out.

- Let out a deep sigh, just letting the air flow out of your body and all the tension and stress with it. Feel your body become heavy, settling deeper and deeper into your position.

- Are you noticing some parts of your body more than others? Are there feelings of tension, maybe even pain? Whatever the sensation, note it, make room for it, and feel it changing with every breath. And then slowly—with each new breath—return your attention to your whole body.

- Feel the muscles in your chest and stomach release all the built-up tension of the day. Continue breathing in and breathing out.

- Feel the muscles in your back releasing, getting more comfortable with every breath. Breathing in and breathing out.

- Feel your arms and legs become heavy with every breath. Breathing in and breathing out.

- Feel your shoulders and neck softening, allowing the stress to float away with every breath. Breathing in and breathing out.

- Feel the tension in your face, in your forehead, in your jaw. With every out-breath let it leave your body, just slowly drifting away. Breathing in and breathing out.

- Slowly let your breathing return to its normal rhythm. There is no need for control; let your body guide you. Breathing in and breathing out.

- Give yourself a moment to notice the sensations around you. Are there any smells in your immediate surroundings that are drawing your attention? Whatever there may be, allow yourself to witness it without focusing too much on anything specific. Just make a mental note of whatever you are observing, accept it as a part of your experience, and then slowly direct your attention. Breathing in and breathing out.

- Now with your next in-breath, tune into the air flowing through your nose. As you inhale, pay attention to the sensation at the tip of your nostrils, as the air rises, gently touching your delicate nose tissue. As you inhale and exhale, marvel in this moment-to-moment awareness with every breath you take.

- Now turn your focus to how your mouth feels. Feel free to wiggle your tongue a little. Is your tongue heavy? Do you feel tension in your jaw? Open and close your jaw a little, feeling the hinge called the temporomandibular joint or TMJ. Loosen, open, loosen, and release. Explore that feeling. Using your first two to three fingers, gently massage the TMJ, releasing the tension you are holding. Let it leave your body with every breath.

- Is there something else that you are noticing? Whatever your sensation may be, take note of it and then, ever so gently, direct your attention back to your mouth.

- Now imagine that you have a few raisins in your hand. Or you can use actual raisins if you would like to. Lift them toward your mouth and nose and smell them, allowing the aroma to fill your nostrils. Take a few inhalations and notice how the smell stimulates the flow of saliva in your mouth.

- Place the raisins in your mouth and begin slowly chewing. Pay attention to the texture. Feel the movement of your tongue and teeth as they break down the food into smaller particles. Observe how this affects your mood. Feel the creation of saliva that might be collecting in your mouth as you chew and break down the foods, textures, and flavors that rise and fall on different parts of the tongue. Feel the saliva mixing with the food, moistening and dissolving the food and beginning the chemical process of breaking down carbohydrates.

- Savor the taste as it stimulates your taste buds. What subtle variations in flavor do you notice as the food begins to mix with your saliva and break down while you chew? Take your time chewing until it is liquid in your mouth. This softened, moist mass of chewed food, or bolus, is now ready to begin its journey toward digestion and nourishment.

126

- Thank your tongue for facilitating the movement of your food, for allowing you to taste it and also for enabling you to speak. Thank your salivary glands for producing saliva, which helps you digest your carbohydrates and maintain a healthy mouth microbiome.

- Now take a moment to gently swallow a few times. Notice the movement of the tongue as it pushes the food to the back of the mouth into the pharynx, the part of the alimentary canal immediately behind the mouth. How does it feel as the food contacts the pharynx? Are you noticing any tension? Give yourself a moment to fully witness the act of swallowing.

- Take note of any sensations, accept them as a part of your experience, and then gently release any tension you are holding. Let the tension leave your body with every breath as you continue to relax.

- As you swallow, imagine (or experience) the well-chewed food as it moves through the pharynx and is then pushed down into the esophagus. How does this transition feel? As the food passes down, can you sense the opening and closing of the upper esophageal sphincter? This is a bundle of muscles that acts like a gateway to keep air out of the esophagus as it allows food to pass through. Feel the liquid mix of well-chewed raisins and saliva travel all the way down your esophagus, a muscular tube about eight inches long, extending from your throat to your stomach.

- As it travels down, let your awareness travel with it as the esophagus propels the food downward, lubricating it as it goes. While chewing your food and swallowing was a voluntary action, the movement through the esophagus is an involuntary motion. This is called peristalsis, where muscles contract and relax, pushing the food along to its destination. Can you tune into this alternating wave?

- Imagine the smooth pink mucosa lining the walls of the esophagus. Visualize the location of the esophagus descending between the spinal column and the trachea, also called the windpipe.

- Now you have arrived at the end of your esophagus, where you have the lower esophageal sphincter. This is another little gate that meets the stomach. It opens to let food into the stomach and closes to keep stomach acid from backing up. Thank your esophagus for transporting the food down to your stomach. This gate or sphincter should be closed most of the time and open as the food reaches it, allowing the partially digested mass of saliva and raisins to enter the stomach.

- If you have digestive problems like acid reflux, also called heartburn, let your sphincter know how much you care for it and ask your sphincter now to close and protect you from acid rising up. Let your sphincter know you will take good care of your digestion to help it do its job even better. Visualize this change with your breath. Breathing in and breathing out. Placing an ice pack over this area 15 minutes before eating will help close the sphincter and reduce the rise of acid. Do you want to grab an ice pack now and feel the cool, soothing effect it brings?

- Imagine the bolus now entering the stomach, a muscular bag located at the top left part of your abdominal cavity, just under the ribs. Here the powerful stomach muscles mechanically churn the food around, further helping to break it down while mixing it with gastric juices. Imagine this process unfolding as the stomach acid, produced by digestive glands in the stomach lining, breaks down the proteins in the food and transforms it into an acidic soupy liquid, called chyme, as it readies to travel to the next stage of digestion.

- Now as you breathe, tune into your stomach. How is it feeling? Place both hands on your upper abdomen and gently palpate this area under the ribs on the left side. Can you name your sensations? Would you describe them as positive, neutral, or negative? Do you have gas, bloating, or burning?

- Let your stomach relax and hang out. All too often we are told to suck it in, but now just let it relax and be. Feel your breath flow in and out of your stomach.

- Visualize your stomach resting underneath your palms. Thank your stomach for holding the food while it gets mixed with the enzymes and acids that allow the breakdown process.

- Imagine this well-mixed chyme in the stomach, now ready to move on. Feel the waves of muscle contractions in the stomach as they propel the chyme through a valve at the lower end of the stomach, called the pyloric sphincter. This little valve releases just a little bit of chyme at a time, about an eighth of an ounce, leaving the rest in the stomach to be mixed further. The pylorus propels the chyme into the first part of the small intestine, the duodenum.

- Visualize the duodenum extending from the end of the stomach, curling around in a C-shaped tube. Here, the chyme is joined by gastric secretions from the liver, gallbladder, and pancreas, which further digest the food.

- Continue your palpation, moving from the stomach on the left toward the center of the upper abdomen and slightly down, feeling for any tension or sensitivity. Breathe into this area and invite any tension to release.

- Tune into your liver, a large organ located just under the right rib. Gently place your hand here. Do you feel any tension here? Visualize your liver. If you want, you can give it a gentle massage by feeling a bit underneath the rib cage. Let yourself explore the feelings under the ribs—you can even contact the diaphragm and palpate this whole area below the ribs. It may feel full or even tender. Note how as you breathe in it's a bit tighter and as you exhale you can feel more deeply underneath.

- Note any sensations, accept them as a part of your experience, and then gently release any tension you are holding. Your body is wise. Let any tension release with every breath as you continue to relax.

- Imagine the liver as it produces bile salts that in turn emulsify the fats you eat. Just like dish soap breaks up the grease on your plate, this is what the liver does.

- Now move your hands just to the left and below the liver and tune into your gallbladder, a small, pear-shaped sack about four inches long. The gallbladder stores the bile from the liver and releases it through the bile ducts into the duodenum, where it is mixed with the chyme. Can you tune into this squeezing action of the gallbladder and of the bile ducts?

- Gently palpate the liver and the area just below it, giving a gentle massage to the gallbladder.

- Imagine this bile mixing with the chyme in the duodenum, helping to make fat-soluble vitamins and minerals more available to the bloodstream. As this process continues, the gallbladder will release all of its stored bile and deflate like a balloon, waiting to be filled up again.

- As you breathe, take a moment to trace a diagonal path with your left hand, from your belly button to the middle of your lowest left rib. You will go back toward your stomach area but just below and to the left. About three-fourths of the way up from the belly button and your rib you can sense your powerful pancreas. Let your hand and your mind's eye rest gently there.

- Here you will sense your pancreas, a long, slender, spongy, fish-shaped organ located behind the stomach. The pancreas helps you produce digestive enzymes and bicarbonate, also helping to break down fats, proteins, and carbohydrates in the small intestine. These pancreatic juices are released through a system of ducts, culminating in the main pancreatic duct, which connects with the common bile duct from the gallbladder. Together the pancreatic juices and bile are transported into the duodenum, where they mix with the chyme. Remember to breathe and relax because the pancreas responds to relaxation and freezes up under stress.

- Take note of any sensations, accept them as a part of your experience, and then gently release any tension you are holding. Let it leave your body with every breath as you continue to relax.

- Thank your pancreas for creating all the enzymes that break down the sugars, fats, and starches you consume, and for secreting the hormones that balance your blood sugar levels.

- Thank your liver and gallbladder for their fine work digesting fats, breaking down toxins, and processing the nutrients of your foods.

- Now tune into your small intestine, where your bile and pancreatic juices are mixing with other digestive secretions from the walls of your intestines. As digestion continues, the former raisins are propelled by peristalsis into the second portion of your small intestine, the jejunum. This C-shaped tube curves down along the left side of your abdomen, below the stomach.

- Let your hands follow this path, starting just below the stomach on the left side, where the jejunum curves down and back in toward the center of the abdomen. Breathe and continue to relax, gently palpating this area. It's not necessary to know each exact location as much as how your belly actually feels letting the warmth of your hands soften any tension.

- The walls of the jejunum absorb most of the proteins, fats, carbohydrates, sugars, minerals, and vitamins you eat and digest. At the same time, glands in the mucosal lining secrete digestive enzymes and lubricating mucus. Then the muscles in the intestinal walls churn food back and forth, mixing with the digestive juices, while the wave of peristalsis moves the food along.

- Imagine the food moving into the next and longest part of the small intestines, the ileum. Nearly all of the remaining nutrients are absorbed here into the walls lining the ileum. This is the longest part of the small intestines, a winding reddish-pink tube with many folds and projections. Here the intestinal walls become thinner, the channel narrows, and peristalsis slows down.

- When you are ready, let your hand find your belly button. Gently place your flat hand on and covering all around your belly button. Let your hand draw a box about two inches around your belly button in every direction as you gently feel your small intestine—pressing slightly, exploring, feeling, inviting breathing into this area as you travel the pathway through your small intestine. Visualize the liquid mass of food that was once raisins moving through this maze that does amazing work.

- Are you noticing any tension, restriction, or tightness on your way? Take note of any sensations, accept them as a part of your experience, and then gently release any tension you are holding. Let it leave your body with every breath as you continue to relax.

- Thank your small intestine for digesting and absorbing into the bloodstream almost all of the nutrients from the foods you eat. Thank your intestines for creating the enzymes that make this possible and for helping your inner garden grow lots of chemicals that lift your spirits and soothe your stress. Let your intestines know you seek balance and to create changes that will support health. Once all of the nutrients are absorbed into the lining of the small intestine, what remains is a combination of water, electrolytes, and waste products.

- Now let your hands travel again and find the spot where your small intestine meets your large intestine. To locate this, trace a diagonal from your belly button to the middle of your right hip bone, then place your hand halfway between and feel for a touch of tension.

- This is the ileocecal valve. It often feels a little tender. That's okay. It works hard! This is the valve or gate that opens to let food pass through to the large intestine but stays closed to keep it from going backward, in the wrong direction. As you breathe, let this valve know it is in balance, thank it for doing a good job for your health, and release any tension or pain. Give it a gentle massage and gently release any tension you are holding. Let it leave your body with every breath as you continue to relax.

- Now leave the ileocecal valve and let your fingers and visualization travel up the ascending colon. You can follow along with your hand by gently moving from the ileocecal valve upward on the right side of your body until you arrive at your ribs.

- Visualize traveling up your ascending colon as the waste products make their way along, propelled by the contraction and relaxation of smooth muscle.

- Take note of any feelings of tension or constriction, or any gas. Accept these feelings as part of your experience and then gently release any tension you are holding. Let it leave your body with every breath as you continue to relax.

- Now let your mind's eye move through the transverse colon across the width of your abdomen, making sure to check for any sensations of tension. Breathing in and breathing out. Move your hands along the upper part of your abdomen, palpating as you go.

- Continue traveling down the descending colon, with your hands and with your awareness, breathing in and breathing out.

- You may come across a sense of tension or fullness, perhaps a pocket of gas. Whatever it may be, just keep breathing and releasing, allowing your sensations to come and go without holding on to them. Know your hands are healing hands filled with energy and warmth.

- Thank your large intestine for absorbing water and salts from food matter and getting rid of the waste materials.

- As you come down the descending colon, you reach the final section, called the sigmoid, which then leads into the rectum. Gently massage this area just above the left groin. What do you feel? At the end of the sigmoid, just above and behind the pubic bone, is the rectum, the area where we store waste until it is released. Check in and let yourself feel any congestion. Remind yourself that you will respond to any sensations to release waste when needed. Thank your rectum for receiving the matter to be discarded, for notifying you when there are feces to be evacuated, and for holding them until this happens.

- Finally, check in with your anus. This is another sphincter that can get tight when we feel stressed. Wiggle your anus, say hello, and let your anus know to relax if it's feeling contracted. Notice if you are clenching and allow it to relax. Breathing in and breathing out. Thank your anus for allowing the body waste to be discarded and for keeping you continent while sleeping or until you are able to release its contents.

- Having arrived at the end of your digestion journey, give yourself another moment to check in with your breath and revisit any areas where you felt tension. Remind yourself that caring for your gut means caring for your thoughts and feelings, noticing sensations as messages from your deepest self to your conscious self. The gut is called the second brain for this reason.

- When you feel ready, slowly open yourself up to your surroundings, taking in the different sensations. If you had your eyes closed, feel free to open them now.

- Remind yourself that you can return to any of these areas at any time.

- Following this exercise, give yourself some time to process your experience. Perhaps write down some notes about the sensations, images, and feelings you experienced.

DIGESTIVE ORGANS MATCHING GAME

PURPOSE

Learning the functions of your digestive organs will enhance your understanding and self-care.

BACKGROUND

Your mental health is deeply interconnected with your digestive health. If your digestion is not working well, you cannot absorb the nutrients that nourish the brain, mind, and body. When you enhance digestion, you improve gut function and the availability of chemicals that enhance mood, focus, and cognition. Understanding the function of each organ in your digestive system enables you to identify symptoms better and to palpate your organs when you feel discomfort.

INSTRUCTIONS

See if you can match each digestive organ with its description. If you completed the previous **Digestive Organs Coloring Activity** (p. 122), you can use that as a visual aid. An answer key is provided at the end of the exercise.

Anus	A. Receives the indigestible portion of food from the small intestine. Absorbs the last traces of water, essential vitamins, and minerals from this portion, to turn it into stool.
Appendix	B. Synthesizes and secretes insulin, the chemical that allows your cells to take in the glucose you eat and use it as energy.
Ascending colon	C. Digested foods, drinks, and other substances make their way here after entering the bloodstream via the small intestine. Nutrients, sugars, fats, toxins, and waste are filtered out of the blood to be broken down, stored, or excreted in the urine and stool.
Descending colon	D. The final stop for ingested food at the end of the large intestine. Extremely pliable, it can expand and contract to hold various amounts of waste before expulsion.
Esophagus	E. Not simply a container for ingested food, the muscular tissue in the walls of this organ churns the food to break it down further. Enzymes and hydrochloric acid are secreted to digest food.
Gallbladder	F. The opening that connects the end of the digestive tract to the outside world. It contains a ring of muscle called a sphincter that tightens to hold stool in and relaxes to release it.
Liver	G. Serves as a reservoir for beneficial gut bacteria and plays a role in maintaining the intestinal immune system.
Pancreas	H. A pipe with a valve at either end that connects the mouth to the stomach. Food moves down this channel via peristalsis.
Rectum	I. Holds indigestible waste, now in the form of feces, on its way to the rectum.
Stomach	J. Stores bile produced by the liver. Releases bile into the small intestine to help break down dietary fats.

ANSWER KEY

1. F   2. G

3. A   4. I

5. H   6. J

7. C   8. B

9. D   10. E

DISCOVERING YOUR DIGESTION WITH TOUCH

Client Exercise

PURPOSE

This activity will teach you how to give yourself a belly massage, which has many health benefits.

BACKGROUND

Healing self-touch, and specifically a belly massage, has many benefits: It relaxes you, helps you get "in touch," decreases digestive dissociation, and empowers you to heal and soothe yourself. You can also identify specific areas and sensations of discomfort to focus on. The first few times you do this exercise, you may want to have a diagram of the digestive organs to reference (such as the one from the **Digestive Organs Coloring Activity**).

INSTRUCTIONS

There is no right or wrong way to massage; the most important factor is being gentle, open, and intuitive.

- Find a quiet place where you can lie down on a comfortable surface.

- Begin by placing your hand just under the tip of the xiphoid process, which is the soft tissue at the end of the breastbone. This is where the esophagus enters the stomach. Using the soft pads of your fingertips, move clockwise to gently apply light pressure to your belly, moving along the outermost margins of the belly.

- As you come down the lower left side, you may feel your large intestine, called the sigmoid area, and come along the margin just above your pubic bone and up the outer side of the right abdomen. After completing this circle, continue making smaller circles, moving closer in until you are massaging close to the umbilicus (belly button).

- As you proceed in your touch, move slowly and explore different levels of pressure. Some areas may be more sensitive than others, and other areas will require more pressure to feel much. Along the way, you may feel pockets of gas or constriction or even emotional responses. You may decide to stop and just apply the warm healing touch of your fingers and hands to an area of discomfort.

- Make note of all of your sensations and emotions. You may want to make copies of your digestive system diagram, and with each belly massage mark an X on the areas of discomfort. As you continue these massages, you will notice that those X's reduce in number.

DAN TIEN: THE ELIXIR OF LIFE

Client Exercise

PURPOSE

This simple exercise can ease fatigue, nausea, GI problems, and other discomfort.

BACKGROUND

Chinese medicine identifies three dan tien points in the body. *Dan tien* can be roughly translated as "the elixir of life," suggesting the importance of these points to your health and well-being. The lower dan tien, *jing*, is also often called "*the* dan tien," as it is the original source of energy and center of power for the body. This point aids digestion, balance, and vitality. It is used in pressure point therapy, acupuncture, and when doing tai chi and chi gong. Contacting this point with your hands can rebalance you when you are fatigued, nauseous, having GI problems, or simply not feeling comfortable in your body. It's also a great way to end a belly massage.

INSTRUCTIONS

- Find the lower dan tien point by placing your first three fingers just below the navel. Place your index finger on the actual belly button. Where the third finger lies is where you will apply pressure.

- As you apply pressure, find a gentle rhythm of breathing. Allow the energy to flow and focus on your breathing.

- You should feel the nausea or upset start to dissipate. Feel the energy increase as you breathe.

- Do this for 1–2 minutes.

- If you feel nauseated, sip a cup of ginger tea during this exercise.

THE SCOOP ON POOP: CONNECTING THE DOTS BETWEEN DIET AND DIGESTION

Client Worksheet

PURPOSE

Evaluating your stool will help you improve your diet and alleviate digestive issues.

BACKGROUND

The Bristol Stool Form Scale **is a** widely used research tool that describes the different types of stool. You can use it to review your stool and identify any potential issues, then adjust your diet accordingly.

INSTRUCTIONS

First, consider your "regular stool"—what your bowel movements look like on a typical day (in contrast to a response to an unusual food, food poisoning, exceptional stress, etc.). Use the Bristol Stool Form Scale to classify your stool.

BRISTOL STOOL FORM SCALE		
TYPE	**DESCRIPTION**	**EXAMPLE**
1	Separate hard lumps, like nuts; difficult to pass; can be black	
2	Sausage-shaped, but lumpy	
3	Like a sausage but with cracks on the surface; can be black	
4	Like a sausage or snake; smooth and soft	
5	Soft blobs with clear-cut edges; easy to pass	
6	Fluffy pieces with ragged edges; mushy	
7	Watery with no solid pieces—entirely liquid	

What does your stool type mean?

- **Types 1 and 2** indicate constipation.

- **Types 3 and 4** are the ideal stools.

- **Type 5** indicates a lack of dietary fiber.

- **Types 6 and 7** indicate diarrhea.

To better identify any digestive issues, observe your stool for seven days. This is especially helpful if your stool type tends to vary a lot. Use the chart that follows to record the date, time, Bristol stool type, and any other observations for each bowel movement.

This exercise is best done in conjunction with the **Food-Mood Diary** (p. 68). Tracking your diet, mood, and stool simultaneously will allow you to see the connections between what you eat and how it affects you, both physically and emotionally.

DATE	TIME	TYPE OF STOOL	OTHER OBSERVATIONS (bloating, pain, undigested food, etc.)
		1 2 3 4 5 6 7	
		1 2 3 4 5 6 7	
		1 2 3 4 5 6 7	
		1 2 3 4 5 6 7	
		1 2 3 4 5 6 7	
		1 2 3 4 5 6 7	
		1 2 3 4 5 6 7	

ADDRESSING INFLAMMATION, PAIN, AND DEPRESSION

Client Handout

PURPOSE

This handout will help you better understand what inflammation is and how to address it.

BACKGROUND

It is important to be able to differentiate between an inflammation process that is normal, localized, and even beneficial, and chronic inflammation, which underlies numerous disease processes, including depression. Improving digestion by eating anti-inflammatory foods is a vitally important method for reducing inflammatory diseases.

ACUTE VS. CHRONIC INFLAMMATION

Also called localized inflammation, this describes the symptoms of an activated immune system. It may occur from a paper cut, a broken arm, a cold, a stubbed toe—any sudden body damage. Symptoms include puffiness, redness, soreness, heat, pain, stiffness, congestion, and itching. These symptoms indicate a well-functioning immune system, where the white blood cells rush to the scene of injury and infection to repair damaged skin barrier and kill any pathogenic invaders.

Chronic inflammation, in contrast, is a low-grade inflammatory response that persists for months to years. As the immune system works overtime, inflammation slowly damages the body. This inflammation may result from continued exposure to relatively low levels of an allergen or toxins like mold in the home. Food additives, processed and packaged foods, refined sugars, and carbohydrates—which are staples of the standard American diet (SAD)—all contribute to inflammation. The body reacts to this influx of not-so-good substances by sending chemicals to the skin, the sinuses, the gut, and the brain. Over time, these chemicals break down healthy cells and tissues.

Did you know that depression reflects a chronic inflammation process? Histamine is one of the chemicals that immune cells release when the body is chronically inflamed. A recent study showed that histamine inhibits the release of serotonin, the "happy" chemical in the brain (Hersey et al., 2021). Selective serotonin reuptake inhibitors (SSRIs) have long been the go-to pharmaceutical treatment for depression. Treating the inflammation by reducing exposure to histamine-triggering substances can help to treat the depression symptoms as well.

A simple way to help alleviate pain and depression is to incorporate turmeric into your diet. Turmeric, which can be purchased in both root and powdered form, contains curcumin, which is a potent antidepressant and anti-inflammatory. Turmeric is the main ingredient in curry and works well in a variety of recipes—just be sure to combine it with freshly ground black pepper, which is necessary for the absorption of the curcumin. Drinking a turmeric latte daily is a delicious way to ease pain and lift your mood.

SAD

Standard American Diet

Food additives, processed and packaged foods, refined sugars, refined carbohydrates, vegetable oils and fake fats

HAPPY

Food That Elevates Mood

Proteins (animal, plant, legume), healthy fats (olive oil, butter, fresh lard, coconut), vegetables, fruits, raw seeds and nuts, whole grains (for some people)

TURMERIC LATTE

Client Recipe

This traditional Ayurvedic beverage can be drunk either hot or cold.

Ingredients

- 1.5 cups fresh almond, hemp, or coconut milk
- 1 tsp. coconut oil (optional)
- 2 tsp. turmeric powder or fresh ground turmeric root
- ¼ tsp. cardamom powder
- ½ tsp. ground cinnamon
- ½ tsp. fresh chopped ginger or powder
- ¼ tsp. fresh ground black peppercorns
- 3 drops vanilla extract

Directions

For a hot latte, add all ingredients to a saucepan and simmer for 5 minutes, then whisk to blend. To drink cold, add all ingredients to a blender and mix until smooth. Sweeten with a few drops of stevia or a little raw honey, if desired.

INFLAMMATION AND NIGHTSHADE FOODS

PURPOSE

This exercise will help you determine whether you are sensitive to nightshade foods.

BACKGROUND

Many people are sensitive to nightshade foods. The symptoms include bloating, joint stiffness, and pain, which may be mistaken for osteoarthritis (Childers & Margoles, 1993). Common nightshades include potatoes, eggplant, peppers, and tomatoes.

INSTRUCTIONS

Using the log that follows, identify the level of pain or stiffness you feel in your joints on a scale of 1–10 (1 = little to none, 10 = the most intense pain). Some joints may have different levels of pain or stiffness; assign a number to each joint that bothers you. There are 360 joints in the human body, but if you have sensitivity to nightshades, you will most likely feel pain in your elbows, hands, fingers, knees, ankles, neck, or back.

Now identify all the nightshade foods you currently eat by circling them in the list below:

Ashwagandha	Eggplant	Naranjilla	Pimentos	Tobacco
Bush tomatoes	Garden huckleberries	Pepinos	Potatoes**	Tomatillos
Cape gooseberries	Goji berries	Peppers*	Tamarillos	Tomatoes
Cocona	Ground cherries			

*Excluding peppercorns, all types of peppers are nightshades. This includes all varieties of bell peppers, chili peppers, and so on. Peppers are found in many spices, seasonings, condiments, and sauces, so check the ingredients list.

**Excluding sweet potatoes, all types of potatoes are nightshades.

Eliminate all nightshade foods from your diet for four weeks. Each week, rate your joint pain or stiffness in the chart. At week 4, compare your ratings to those from week 1. Note any differences and the degrees of difference. If you feel much better, then continue with a nightshade-free diet. If you do not notice any difference, it is unlikely that nightshades are the culprit.

You may choose to have an occasional nightshade food, even if you are sensitive to them. On these occasions, pull out your chart, and notice how you feel within 48 hours after eating the food. It may be that you can tolerate a tomato here or some eggplant there. You will find, though, that there is a certain threshold for what you can eat before symptoms kick in. Do your best to determine whether an occasional treat can be tolerated or whether the consequences are severe enough that you should avoid nightshades altogether.

Inflammation and Nightshade Food Log

DATE	JOINT(S) WITH PAIN/STIFFNESS	INTENSITY (1–10)	NIGHTSHADES EATEN (PAST 48 HOURS)

Client Recipe

Purpose

These recipes provide tasty alternatives to nightshade foods.

Background

If you are sensitive to nightshades, you will experience symptoms like bloating, joint stiffness, and pain after consuming these foods, making it necessary to eliminate them from your diet. However, there is no reason you can't enjoy your favorite dishes when you give up nightshades. The following recipes use tasty substitutions (pineapple for tomatoes and jicama for potatoes). Give them a try!

Pineapple-Onion-Papaya Barbecue Sauce

This sublime sauce satisfies the sweet, sour, and tart taste buds all at once. It can be added to almost any food, including rice, fish, meat, poultry, tofu, raw apples, or crackers and cheese.

Ingredients

- 2 tbsp. virgin olive oil
- 2 cups yellow onion, minced
- 1 cup crushed fresh pineapple
- 2 garlic cloves, minced
- 2 cups crushed ripe papaya
- ¾ cup pineapple juice
- ½ cup apple cider vinegar

- ¼ cup dark unsulfured molasses
- 2 tbsp. dry mustard
- 1 tbsp. ground cumin
- 2 tsp. freshly ground black pepper
- ¼ cup Worcestershire sauce
- 1 bay leaf

Directions

Heat the oil in a heavy, non-aluminum saucepan until hot. Add the onions, pineapple, and garlic and cook over medium heat, stirring often, until the onions are soft. Add all remaining ingredients and stir well. Let the mixture heat through slowly. Simmer over very low heat for 1 hour. Remove the bay leaf. Adjust the seasonings to taste; you may also add cayenne.

Jicama Fries

For healthy fries, try substituting jicama. Jicama is a root vegetable that is low in fat and high in soluble fiber, the oligofructose inulin. This type of fiber is prebiotic; it has a low glycemic index and is rich in minerals and vitamins. Jicama can also be eaten raw.

Ingredients

- 1 medium jicama, peeled and cut into thin slices about ¼ inch thick (about 4–5 cups)

- 1 tbsp. coconut oil

- ½ tsp. turmeric powder

- ½ tsp. garlic powder

- ½ tsp. onion powder

- ½ tsp. sea salt

- ¼ tsp. black pepper

Directions

Preheat the oven to 400°F. Bring a pot of water to boil, add the jicama slices, and simmer for 8–10 minutes. Drain the water and pat the fries dry with a towel. In a large bowl, combine the remaining ingredients, then add the fries and toss to coat evenly. Spread the fries onto a baking stone or a baking sheet lined with parchment paper, making sure the fries are well-spaced (or they will steam and get soft rather than crispy). Bake for 30 minutes, flip the fries over, then bake for another 20–30 minutes or until the fries are crispy and slightly brown. Serve with homemade guacamole if desired.

GLUTEN SENSITIVITY

Client Handout

PURPOSE

Removing gluten from the diet can be helpful, and even essential, to some people's health. This information sheet will help you explore whether you might be sensitive to gluten.

BACKGROUND

Gluten is a protein found in wheat, barley, and rye. Studies find that more than half of people with mental health problems—especially psychosis, depression, and autism spectrum disorder—have celiac disease or gluten sensitivity (Jackson et al., 2012; Woodford, 2021).

Celiac disease is a genetically based autoimmune disease in which eating gluten triggers an immune response in the small intestine that damages the lining of the intestine and prevents it from absorbing nutrients. This can lead to serious complications. There is no cure for celiac disease, but most people can manage the symptoms by following a strict gluten-free diet.

Non-celiac gluten sensitivity (NCGS), often called gluten sensitivity or gluten intolerance, can involve similar symptoms to celiac disease—such as depression, intestinal upset, brain fog, and fatigue—but not always. NCGS results from changes in intestinal mucosa and GI barrier disruption. However, gluten sensitivity can also be associated with or mistaken for fermentable oligosaccharides, disaccharides, monosaccharides, and polyols (FODMAPs), which are short-chain sugars that are not easily digested. Additional concerns include exposure to gliadomorphin, an opiate protein that occurs as gluten is digested, leading to intestinal dysfunction and mental distress. Some people with gluten sensitivity can tolerate a very small amount of gluten without becoming ill.

It is also important to distinguish both celiac disease and gluten sensitivity from a wheat allergy, which is a food allergy that can range in severity from mild discomfort to life-threatening anaphylaxis.

SYMPTOMS

Celiac Disease and Gluten Sensitivity

- Diarrhea
- Constipation
- Abdominal pain/ cramps
- Bloating

- Gas
- Nausea
- Vomiting
- Weight loss

- Fatigue
- Brain fog
- Headaches
- Joint pain

- Mouth ulcers
- Itchy, blistery skin rash
- Balance problems
- Cognitive impairment
- Numbness/tingling in the feet and hands
- Depression, psychotic disorder

Wheat Allergy

- Diarrhea
- Abdominal pain/ cramps
- Nausea
- Vomiting
- Headache
- Nasal congestion
- Hives, itchy rash, or swelling of the skin
- Swelling, itching, or irritation of the mouth or throat
- Difficulty breathing
- Anaphylaxis

If there is overlap between your symptoms and those listed, you should consider being tested.

TESTING

Celiac disease can be diagnosed through serum testing, genetic testing, or endoscopy. A wheat allergy can be confirmed through a skin test or blood test. Gluten sensitivity may be diagnosed based on symptoms and a negative test for the other two conditions. Testing options include Cyrex Labs, which tests for all the elements of gluten/gliadin proteins, and DiagnosTechs, which has a test for salivary antibodies for gluten sensitivity.

Eliminating gluten from your diet for 90 days will also allow you to assess if you feel better without gluten. However, you should *not* do this yet if you are planning to be tested! Reducing the amount of gluten in your diet will affect the results of some of these tests, and you could get a false negative (a result that indicates you do not have the condition when you actually do).

DID YOU KNOW?

Going 100 percent gluten-free is more complicated than many people realize. For example, many foods that would be naturally gluten-free are cross-contaminated with sources of gluten during the growing, harvesting, processing, or preparation phase—and this won't always be declared on the food label or menu. A dietitian can help you get started if you will be navigating the gluten-free world.

HISTAMINES AND MAST CELL ACTIVATION SYNDROME

Clinician Handout

PURPOSE

This clinician handout provides important context for the client worksheet that follows, **Identifying Histamine Foods**.

BACKGROUND

Brain fog, anxiety, depression, and insomnia are among the most common symptoms of histamine intolerance and mast cell activation syndrome. Yet these immune syndromes are virtually unknown in the mental health field. The information here will help you better understand these syndromes, and the worksheet that follows will help clients explore whether histamines may be causing or exacerbating their symptoms.

HISTAMINE INTOLERANCE

Histamine is the substance found in the body when experiencing a mild, moderate, or severe reaction to a known allergen. Higher levels of histamine in the body correspond with more severe allergic reactions (like anaphylaxis).

Approximately 1 percent of the population has histamine intolerance (Maintz & Novak, 2007). This may well be an underestimate; the symptoms of this condition are so wide-ranging that it often goes undiagnosed. These symptoms include nasal congestion, headache, stomach distress, wheezing, flushing, low blood pressure, and even abnormal heart rhythm.

MAST CELL ACTIVATION SYNDROME

This syndrome, commonly abbreviated as MCAS, is a more severe form of histamine dysfunction. It refers to a condition in which a person suffers episodes of severe adverse allergic symptoms, such as anaphylaxis, hives, swelling, and severe diarrhea. These symptoms result from the release of high levels of bioactive compounds from mast cells.

When a person's immune system is dysregulated and hyperaroused, the mast cells can become overreactive. Mast cells are involved in brain injuries, neuropsychiatric disorders, stress, neuroinflammation, and neurodegeneration. The effects of chronic anxiety, PTSD, and MCAS are bidirectional, with each potentially exacerbating the other symptomatically (Kempuraj et al., 2017).

If your client has a history of allergies, food intolerances, and unexplained diverse symptoms, it may be valuable to do an assessment for histamine intolerance or mast cell activation syndrome.

Symptoms Caused by Histamines

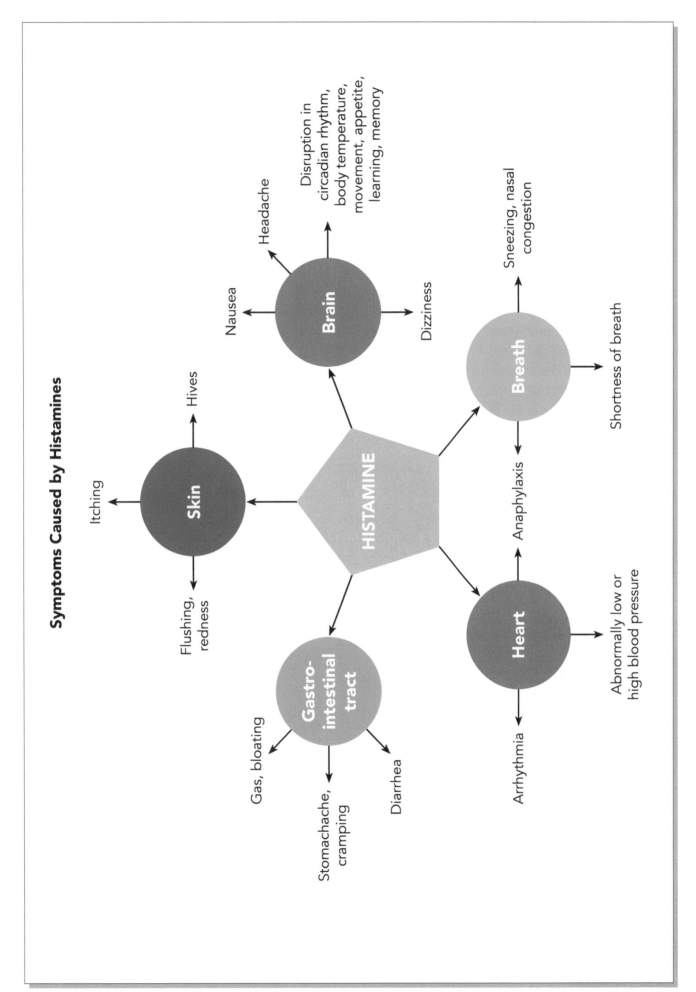

Client Worksheet

IDENTIFYING HISTAMINE FOODS

PURPOSE

This worksheet will help you test your tolerance or intolerance for histamine foods.

BACKGROUND

Histamine is the substance found in the body when experiencing an allergic reaction. It is also found in foods—some foods are rich in histamine, others are low in histamine, and there are even antihistamine foods. For example, fermented foods, such as aged cheeses, sauerkraut, and red wine, are full of histamine, while citrus fruits have a unique capacity to release histamine already stored in the body's tissues. People with histamine intolerance cannot properly digest the histamine in foods, so the histamine accumulates in their bodies. These individuals may benefit from a low-histamine diet.

Here are some common foods, organized by histamine status. Use this as a reference as you complete the activities that follow.

Histamine Foods

- Aged cheeses
- Alcohol
- Canned fish
- Cherries
- Chili powder
- Cinnamon

- Citrus fruits
- Cloves
- Eggplant
- Eggs
- Kimchi

- MSG (monosodium glutamate)
- Nuts
- Pickles
- Processed meats

Protein foods containing the amino acid histidine

- Sauerkraut
- Smoked fish
- Soy

- Spinach
- Strawberries
- Tomatoes

- Vinegar
- Yogurt

Antihistamine Foods, Herbs, and Supplements

- Apples
- Basil

- Brazil nuts
- Chamomile tea

- Dietary fiber
- Diindolylmethane (DIM)

- Galangal
- Luteolin
- Moringa
- Nettle tea

- Onions
- Peaches
- Quercetin
- Turmeric

- Vitamin C
- Watercress

Nonhistamine Foods

- Minimally processed foods, aside from those on the previous list (processing includes peeling vegetables and fruits)

SELF-TEST FOR IDENTIFYING FOOD REACTIVITY

Any food can cause an allergic or intolerant immune response. You can test your responses to different foods using a simple exercise known as the Coca pulse test. Dr. Arthur Coca was an immunologist who suggested that an offending food would cause a reaction in the immune system by raising the heart rate. This is the basis of the pulse test, an adaptation of which is presented here.

Instructions

- Before getting started, make sure you have these material ready: a clock or timer, filtered water, and the foods you want to test.

- To test yourself for food reactivity, take a small piece of the food that you want to check. Record the type of food in the **Histamine Food Log** that follows.

- Sit down and relax for a few minutes to allow your heart rate to drop.

- Check your pulse at your wrist for 60 seconds (time it with a clock or stopwatch). Count your heartbeats for this full minute. This is your resting heart rate; write it down at the top of the chart.

- Place the piece of food on your tongue and keep it there for 30 seconds.

- At 30 seconds, keep the food on your tongue and recheck your pulse for a full minute. Record your current heart rate in the chart.

- Spit out the food and rinse your mouth with filtered water.

- Compare the new heart rate to your resting heart rate. If there was a change, write down the difference (e.g., +4) in the last column of the chart.

- Let your pulse return to your resting rate before testing a different food.

- Any food that caused your heart rate to rise by six or more beats per minute indicates a stress reaction. You may want to pursue additional testing to confirm these intolerances, and you should consider eliminating these foods from your diet.

If you have found that you react to certain foods, or to histamine-rich foods in general, you should consider eliminating those foods from your diet. During this elimination period, it will be helpful to track your progress in a food journal. Each day, write down your observations about the experience. Use the following questions to guide your reflection:

- Have you experienced a reduction of uncomfortable symptoms? A change in your energy? Your sleep or mood?

- What foods are you eating in place of the offending foods? How do you like these substitute foods? Are you missing any of the offending foods in particular? Are there better substitutes you can come up with for those foods?

DID YOU KNOW?

Antihistamine drugs (such as Benadryl, Zyrtec, Claritin, and Xyzal) are sedating and suppress the neurotransmitter acetylcholine. They are associated with mild cognitive impairment and other learning difficulties in children and dementia in older adults (Andre et al., 2019; Reinold et al., 2021). Do you use these medications? If so, you might talk to your doctor about exploring other options.

Histamine Food Log

Date: _____

Resting heart rate: _____

FOOD	HEART RATE FOR THIS FOOD	CHANGE IN HEART RATE

8
CULINARY MEDICINE

Culinary medicine is focused on helping people make personal decisions about how to access and eat high-quality meals that help prevent and treat disease and restore well-being (La Puma, 2016). Culinary medicine for mental health can be as simple as gathering and preparing fresh, tasty, and satisfying foods, and as complex as addressing DSM-5 criteria for eating disorders using innovative, personalized culinary strategies.

Self-nourishment in all its forms—especially with food and nutrition—is the foundation of integrative medicine and the key to improving mental health. Diet is just as much a contributing factor to poor mental health as it is a method for improving it. For example, it has been well-established that eating a gluten-free diet can lead to improvements in people with psychotic disorders (Levinta et al., 2018), and that a diet high in processed foods and sugar is a significant risk factor for depression (Pagliai et al., 2021). Conversely, seafood, organ meats, and plants are among the most antidepressant foods in the world, as they contain antidepressant nutrients like folate, iron, long-chain omega-3 fatty acids (EPA and DHA), magnesium, potassium, selenium, thiamine, vitamin A, vitamin B6, vitamin B12, vitamin C, and zinc (LaChance & Ramsey, 2018).

In this chapter, I will explore a variety of ways to work with food as medicine—let the kitchen be your pharmacy! Since the taste of a good meal can bring people joy, it's easy to engage clients of all ages in the shared learning that includes gathering and preparing food, as well as enjoying the ritual of a meal together. Clients also find it empowering to learn how they can improve their mental health by making relatively simple changes to their diet.

Of course, just because a change is straightforward doesn't mean that it's necessarily easy for a client to make and maintain. A variety of factors can impact a client's ability to change their diet, including past and present family dynamics around food, how easily they can access healthy foods given their location and finances, and food allergies and sensitivities. Any discussion of nutrition and mental health must also address two issues that people tend to avoid acknowledging: eating disorders and body size stigmatization.

EATING DISORDERS AND CULINARY MEDICINE

One of the most common imbalances that you will see when exploring culinary medicine with clients is the variety of eating disorders that clients may present with. Eating disorders in general may be understood as a response to trauma, cultural oppression, or nutrient deficiencies that affect eating behaviors, including cravings, binging, purging, restrictions, and orthorexia. As you explore culinary medicine with your clients, it is important to keep in mind the spectrum of attitudes about foods and culinary practices, as well as the latest fads and changing science. Your goal is to reduce your clients' suffering and to help them define and engage empowered choices that enhance their well-being.

Understanding the biology of eating disorders—and integrating specific foods, nutrients, and herbs based on this knowledge—enhances treatment and reduces relapse. For example, there is no question that certain foods, such as highly refined carbs (particularly those laden with gluten and fat), are triggers for binge eating. Therefore, any analysis and treatment of disordered eating has to address the complexity of the effects of these highly refined sugary foods, which have been identified by some researchers as an addictive "poison" (Lustig, 2020). Additional pieces of the puzzle that you must address include testing for food allergies or sensitivities—which can drive craving or restriction, digestive distress, and self-medication behaviors (eating foods that create a biochemical response that leads to alterations in consciousness, including affect and cognitive function)—and exploring harmful cultural beliefs and attitudes about body size.

CLINICAL PEARL

People experience a lot of shame around their food choices, for a variety of reasons. When you talk about food with clients, you want to emphasize that it isn't about an ideology or a belief system, but simply about fueling their bodies.

ADDRESSING BODY SIZE STIGMATIZATION

Conversations about food, diet, and body weight can be triggering for clients, especially for those with body dysmorphia or disordered eating, or who hope to gain or lose weight. If a client is struggling with body image, it may be important to discuss the relationship between eating for their health and the social mores, beliefs, and judgments about body size, fat levels, and what a healthy body "should" look like (including the dreaded and specious measure called the body mass index, or BMI, which is not a reliable indicator of health).

Explain to your client that there is no one "right" body size for everyone. Drawing on the concept of bioindividuality may be helpful here. It is also important to clarify that the work you will be doing together in culinary medicine is not about changing their weight or their body size, but nourishing their body, mind, and spirit. I usually give the following explanation to the client within the first few minutes of our discussion:

> Culinary medicine and nutrition for mental health isn't about losing weight, gaining weight, or working out to change your body shape. It's about connecting with your deepest needs and finding the foods that nourish you, energize you, and help you feel good in your mind, body, and spirit. That's our work, and my goal is to support you feeling your best. This is about letting go of preconceived ideas or what anyone has ever said to you—professionals, family, or otherwise—and to discover for yourself the joy and wellness that is your right.

WHERE TO BEGIN?

When beginning to explore culinary medicine and mental health with a client, it is important to refer to their intake form. Review their description of their early life experiences eating meals in their family of origin and what they have identified as their goals and obstacles. Many people have experiences rooted in stress or trauma; perhaps there was food insecurity, or no one made meals for the children, or there was bickering at the table. Or there may have been nutritional issues and even medical trauma, such as meals that were heavily processed, leading to stomachaches or hyperactivity, resulting in medications that had lingering effects on the gut-brain axis.

Your role is to understand any obstacles the client has and to help them identify creative options for working around their blockages while also addressing the root cause. Whatever a client brings "to the table," be sure to explore the underlying experiences that will shape their engagement in culinary health activities.

Beth's Story

Beth had been traumatized in the kitchen as a child. Her parents were demeaning and often threw pots and pans. As a result, Beth did not want to spend time in a kitchen. This left her partner, who was stuck with all the food preparation, upset. I asked the couple if they would be interested in preparing food outside of the kitchen. They were enthusiastic about this option, so we developed a plan to create a smoothie bar with a blender, juicer, small fridge, and cutting counter in a room in their house that was near a bathroom (for rinsing appliances and dishes). Then they made plans to purchase a gas grill and create a cooking space on their patio for use during the summer months. In this way, Beth deconditioned from her early life trauma, restored her enjoyment for food preparation, and shared "not-kitchen" duty with her partner.

The resources in this chapter will help you guide your clients in exploring their past and present family dynamics around food, the financial dimensions to eating well, the possibility of food allergies and sensitivities, and other fundamentals in establishing a diet that is good for their physical and mental health. As we know, mood follows food!

Culinary Medicine at a Glance

WELLNESS TARGET	RECOMMENDATIONS
Depression	<ul><li>Eat green papaya salad, chocolate, raw butter, raw soaked almonds, fermented foods, spinach, saffron rice, figs</li><li>Test for histamine and gluten intolerance</li></ul>
Anxiety and panic	<ul><li>Incorporate more vinegars, meats, bone broths, oatmeal, celery</li><li>Reduce dietary stressors, including caffeine and sugar</li><li>Eat more acidic foods, including animal proteins and red meat, for overbreathing</li></ul>
OCD	<ul><li>Consume plenty of healthy fats</li><li>Address whether purine foods can be useful</li><li>Redirect obsessive-compulsive behaviors to preparing complex, healthy meals by following detailed recipes</li></ul>
Bipolar disorder	<ul><li>Align food intake with circadian rhythm: larger meals in the morning and midday, and a smaller, carbohydrate-rich meal in the evening</li><li>Snack before bed (no later than midnight)</li></ul>
Insomnia	<ul><li>Eat grains and starchy carbs in the evening (e.g., oatmeal)</li><li>Eliminate stimulants</li><li>To reduce hypoglycemia-induced middle night awakening, eat 4 ounces total of a combination of protein, fat, and starchy carbs 1 hour before bed</li><li>Eliminate sleep medications</li><li>SSRIs can have stimulating effects, so talk to a prescriber about reducing or eliminating</li></ul>
Stress, trauma, and PTSD	<ul><li>Consume protein, sea salt, Brainbow foods, bone and chicken broths, collagen broths, anti-inflammatory spices, algae</li><li>For vegetarians, consume plenty of essential fatty acids</li></ul>

WELLNESS TARGET	RECOMMENDATIONS
ADHD	• Emphasize protein and healthy fat in the morning, carbs in the afternoon • Eliminate cow's milk • Always pair protein, fat, and carbs in a meal—never carbs alone • Send young clients to school with an apple and raw nuts, or an animal protein snack
Chronic pain	• Encourage an anti-inflammatory diet • Eat a diet rich in polyphenols and antioxidants • Test for nightshade sensitivity
Substance use disorder	• Eliminate refined sugar in the case of alcohol abuse • Use easily assimilated proteins, broths, collagens, and vegetable juices during the recovery period; include nutrient-dense fats (e.g., coconut and fish oils) for brain function
Cognition and memory	• Eat a diet higher in protein, fats, and complex carbs (e.g., organic eggs, spinach, green tea powder, chocolate, coffee, coconut turmeric rice)
Autism spectrum and neurodivergence	• Follows the GAPS diet; eliminate gluten and casein; increase cholesterol and glucoraphanin • Add powdered greens in smoothies
Body image and eating disorders	• Use collagen as a nutrient-dense protein • Eliminate all glutenous grains in the case of bulimia • Add nutrient-dense smoothies with whey and vitamins/minerals in the case of anorexia
Digestive disorders	• Eliminate refined carbohydrates and sugar • Reduce acidic and tannin foods (e.g., make cold-pressed coffee) • Drink plenty of water to aid digestion and reduce GERD • Eat fermented foods and probiotics to support the intestinal garden • Drink simple, freshly made bone broths, add collagen to smoothies, or make gelatin molds to heal leaky gut

Clinician Handout

PURPOSE

When educating clients about the health benefits of various foods, it's helpful to use colors instead of complex vitamin and chemical names. This handout presents what I call the Brainbow foods—a colorful way to nourish the brain, mind, and body.

BACKGROUND

The colors in foods signify their chemicals and the benefits they have for physical and mental health. The following chart shows the Brainbow foods and their effects. Explore the different colors to determine which foods you would like to eat more of. You may need to do more research to identify which vitamins and constituents survive or benefit from cooking—for example, apples and blueberries are best eaten raw, while tomatoes provide good nourishment for the eyes and prostate when cooked.

THE BRAINBOW FOODS

COLOR	GENERAL QUALITIES	SPECIFIC QUALITIES AND FOODS
Red	Improves memory, digestion, and heart health; lowers blood pressure; is anti-inflammatory	Lycopene (tomatoes, watermelon, pink grapefruit); anthocyanins (strawberries, raspberries, red grapes); antioxidants (cherries, cranberries); vitamin C (red bell peppers, beets, strawberries, tomatoes); vitamin A (beets, tomatoes)
Orange	Improves digestion; boosts immunity; prevents cellular damage; promotes healthy mucous membranes	Antioxidants (sweet potatoes); beta-carotene (sweet potatoes, pumpkins, carrots); vitamin A (peaches, sweet potatoes); folate (oranges); vitamin C (peaches, sweet potatoes, oranges)
Yellow	Improves brain function and digestion; boosts immunity	Antioxidants (bananas); beta-carotene (carrots); vitamin A (bell peppers, sweet potatoes); folate (oranges); vitamin C (peaches, bananas, oranges)
Green	Boosts detoxification; promotes oxidative stress reduction; improves brain, heart, and liver function	Antioxidants (dark leafy greens); vitamin A (kale, spinach); vitamin K (bok choy, broccoli); magnesium (edamame, avocado); calcium (kale, okra, spinach); nitrates for the heart and mood (celery, lettuce, spinach); lutein (asparagus, green peas, zucchini); folate (broccoli, spinach)
Blue	Reduces blood pressure; boosts immunity, cellular protection and recovery, new cell growth, circulation, and detoxification; lowers blood sugar	Anthocyanin (blueberries); antioxidants (blue quandong); fiber and flavonoids (lactarius indigo); vitamin B (elderberries); vitamin C (blueberries); vitamin E (blueberries, blue quandong); vitamin K (blackberries, blue quandong); calcium and phosphorus (blue corn)
Purple	Reduces blood pressure; boosts immunity, cellular protection and recovery, new cell growth, circulation, and detoxification; lowers blood sugar	Anthocyanin (hibiscus, blackberries); antioxidants (blackberries); fiber and flavonoids (purple cabbage); vitamin B (plums, blackberries); vitamin C (purple onion, eggplant); vitamin E (purple carrot); vitamin K (purple cabbage, plums); calcium and phosphorus (eggplant)
White	Reduces blood pressure; boosts immunity, cellular protection and recovery, new cell growth, circulation, and detoxification; lowers blood sugar	Vitamin B (chickpeas, cauliflower); quercetin (cauliflower, onion, white potato); potassium (white beans, mushrooms); selenium (garlic, cereals, white grains); sulfur (chickpeas, oats); diindolylmethane (DIM) for detox of estrogen (cauliflower)

FAMILY FOOD PREFERENCES

PURPOSE

This worksheet will help you, your family—defined broadly as those you live with or prepare and share food with—and your therapist work together to navigate nutrition needs and food choices.

BACKGROUND

Each of us has unique thoughts, feelings, and needs when it comes to food and nutrition. Often, the members of a household want to eat at different times. Some may want to eat different types of food—for example, one person may be a vegetarian, or be gluten sensitive, or be trying to gain weight, while another is not. Families tend to feel pressure to get everybody on the same schedule and eating the same foods. Yet we know, based on bioindividuality, that each person's body has its own needs for specific "fuel." How, then, do we decide when it's more important to set a shared expectation for the whole family, and when it's more important to be flexible so individual needs are met?

INSTRUCTIONS

Each of your family members will be filling out a copy of the following survey in advance of your next family session. Your therapist will then help you explore both the points of unity and the areas of disagreement within your family. This will allow you to identify ways that you might change your family's habits around food and nutrition to best meet everyone's needs.

Family Food Survey

Name: _____ Age: _____

Describe the types of foods you want to eat (e.g., vegetables, animal proteins, fast foods, tacos, Asian cuisines). Give details!

_____

_____

_____

_____

How important is what you eat to you? Give it a rating from 1 to 5 by filling in that many stars.

1: Not important ☆ ☆ ☆ ☆ ☆ 5: Very important

Are there certain foods that you believe are "good" or "bad"? List these foods and explain why you would describe them as good/bad.

_____

_____

_____

_____

_____

List some foods that you...

HATE	DISLIKE	LIKE	LOVE	CAN'T GIVE UP

List any food allergies or sensitivities that you have. Include any foods that cause problems for you (e.g., stomachaches, gas, bloating, bad breath, itching/tingling in your mouth, acne, hives/rash).

_____

_____

_____

_____

Write down the time of day (e.g., 7:30 a.m.) that you prefer to eat each meal:

BREAKFAST	LUNCH	DINNER	SNACKS

Will you help shop for food? If so, in what way? If not, why not?

_____

_____

_____

List any special recipes or foods you would like to try.

_____

_____

_____

_____

Do you want to help prepare food?

_____

_____

Will you help clean up?

_____

_____

FOOD ACCESSIBILITY

Client Worksheet

PURPOSE

This worksheet will help you consider the costs of lower- and higher-quality foods—both in terms of money and health—and identify ways to access healthier foods.

BACKGROUND

People often think that eating natural and healthier food is more expensive, but this isn't always the case. Some considerations also include the cost of poor health that can result from the use of cheaper foods. One study showed that eating healthier foods—like fruits, vegetables, fish, and nuts—cost only $1.50 more a day than unhealthy, processed foods such as refined grains (Rao et al., 2013).

INSTRUCTIONS

Here are some ways that you can reduce the cost or time involved in choosing healthier foods. Review this list and put a check mark by all the actions you would like to try. Then put a star by one action that you can accomplish in the next week. This is your first step toward healthier eating!

- ❑ Purchase frozen fruits and vegetables, which are more affordable than fresh produce but just as healthy.

- ❑ Locate second-day food bins at grocers in your area and make use of them.

- ❑ Incorporate more root vegetables into your diet—they are affordable and nutrient dense.

- ❑ Less expensive cuts of beef, chicken, and fish are often the most nutritious.

- ❑ Ask your local fishmonger for fish heads and bones to make soups.

- ❑ Join or start a buying cooperative.

- ❑ Volunteer at a local CSA (community-supported agriculture).

- ❑ Create a garden in your yard, or join or start a community garden.

- ❑ Harvest fruits and vegetables in the summer and freeze or can them for the winter.

- ❑ Grow sprouts in the kitchen from seeds (alfalfa, clover, fenugreek, etc.).

- ❑ Make fresh tepache, sauerkraut, or kimchi for affordable probiotics.

❑   Connect with local farmers or gardeners—you may be able to trade goods or services for their produce.

❑   See if a local college or university offers free education or collaborative agricultural resources.

❑   Consider purchasing tools that will make meal preparation easier and faster (slow cooker, pressure cooker, blender, bread maker, etc.). The benefits over time may well offset the initial cost.

❑   Keep ready-to-eat fruits, vegetables, and proteins on hand. You don't need to have a complicated recipe in mind—just put them together on a platter! A combination like sliced bell peppers, grapes, almonds, goat cheese, sliced turkey, and crackers makes for a nutritious snack or meal.

DID YOU KNOW?

If you can, it's ideal to choose organically raised foods. Whole foods from local, small-scale farming operations (free-range eggs, grass-fed meats and dairy, etc.) are better for you and for the earth.

THE MOST IMPORTANT FOODS TO SPEND MONEY ON

Client Worksheet

PURPOSE

This activity will help you identify what your food costs are and where you may wish to make changes.

BACKGROUND

Cooking healthy meals at home is no more expensive than grabbing takeout, fast food, or snacks on the go; in fact, it's usually cheaper. Although it may feel like your weekly load of groceries costs more than the food you get from coffee shops, restaurants, or vending machines, if you calculate the cost per serving of meals cooked from scratch, you will find that you save money by purchasing healthy ingredients and preparing meals and snacks at home.

INSTRUCTIONS

Answer the following questions, which will guide you in evaluating your current food habits—and reveal options for both cheaper and healthier foods.

Make a list of your favorite foods and menu items.

_____

_____

_____

_____

_____

Make a list of takeout or fast foods that you eat and what you spend on them.

_____

_____

_____

_____

_____

List high-quality, low-cost foods you have been eager to explore (hint: think of unprocessed, whole foods).

_____

_____

_____

_____

List your digestive problems (and those of family members):

- ❑ Gas
- ❑ Bloating
- ❑ Acid reflux

- ❑ Constipation
- ❑ Diarrhea
- ❑ Inflammatory bowel syndrome

- ❑ Fatty liver
- ❑ Hemorrhoids
- ❑ Other: _____

List the medicines you take for these problems (OTC and prescription) and how much you spend on them.

_____

_____

_____

_____

Are the foods you eat contributing to these symptoms? You may need to do a little research.

_____

_____

_____

_____

_____

In the following chart, list current foods that you would like to change and their healthier alternatives. How much money might you save (on food or medications) each year by making these changes?

ORIGINAL FOOD	HEALTHIER SWAP	MONEY SAVED

Who could support you in making these changes (your family, friends, etc.)?

_____

_____

_____

Consider making these changes and seeing what happens for a period of three months. Then evaluate your experience, noting any changes in your symptoms or your spending.

CALCULATE YOUR NEED FOR PROTEIN

Clinician Handout

PURPOSE

This handout will help you consider your client's protein intake so you can make adjustments as necessary.

BACKGROUND

Protein contains amino acids, which are the building blocks for brain chemicals, muscles, and connective tissue. There is a lot of controversy about protein—whether it should be derived from plants or animals and how much is needed at what stages in the life cycle. Many people, especially the food insecure and elders, do not get enough protein. Animal protein is the most expensive type of food, so when clients are on a tight budget, recommend using bones, fish heads, and cheaper cuts of small amounts of animal protein. Raw nuts and seeds are also good protein sources. Protein is essential for a good mood, so evaluate protein levels when clients are depressed or anxious.

INSTRUCTIONS

To determine a client's recommended intake per day, you can use this calculator: https://www.nal.usda.gov/human-nutrition-and-food-safety/dri-calculator. (The protein result will appear in the macronutrients section.)

Then, using the **Food-Mood Diary** (p. 68) yourself or with your client, add in the amounts of protein being eaten and calculate whether it is enough or too much. Brainstorm how to adjust protein levels in order to optimize brain and body function.

TICKLING YOUR TASTEBUDS WITH FOOD

PURPOSE

This activity will help you recondition your ability to taste subtle flavors.

BACKGROUND

Junk food is addictive. The flavors are so potent, especially the sweet and salty, that it is like a drug to your taste buds, the most direct route to the brain. Detoxing from junk food and practicing mindful eating will allow you to rediscover the wonderful range of flavors in healthy foods.

INSTRUCTIONS

Try the following activities.

Prepare a small plate of healthy foods, making sure to include a wide variety of flavors and textures. One by one, put the different foods in your mouth and experience their unique qualities. Notice how each food tastes, recognize its texture, and identify what you do or don't like about this food. Record your observations here.

_____

_____

_____

_____

_____

Stop using salt for one week and record any changes that you notice. At the end of the week, chew on a piece of celery. Do you experience the saltiness it naturally has? How does it taste, compared to before you did this experiment?

_____

_____

_____

_____

Eliminate or taper your sugar consumption for one week. At the end of the week, eat some grapes or a banana, which are high in fructose, a natural sugar. Did you notice how sweet these foods were before? Do they seem sweeter now, since you stopped eating refined sugar? Record any changes you experience.

_____

_____

_____

_____

_____

THE FIFTH TASTE: UMAMI

Client Exercise

PURPOSE

This worksheet explains the chemical origins of umami, the "fifth taste," and guides you in exploring the umami taste centers.

BACKGROUND

There are five basic tastes: sweet, sour, salty, bitter, and umami. Also known as the "fifth taste," umami is the taste of savory food. It was identified in 1908 by Japanese researcher Kikunae Ikeda. The presence of the umami taste signals that the food you are eating is safe, nutritious, ripe, and rich in protein. In contrast, bitter and sour tastes may signal toxic, spoiled, or unripe foods, which is why some people, especially young children, may dislike cruciferous vegetables.

Umami is the only taste that is sensed evenly across the whole tongue. It is a mild, subtle taste that lingers on the tongue longer than bitter, sour, or salty tastes. Adding umami ingredients to your dishes deepens their flavor, and it can be a substitute for excess fat and salt. Umami-rich ingredients activate the salivary response, which aids digestion and can even reverse taste impairment in the elderly (Sasano et al., 2014). Umami also offers mental health benefits, as it can satiate and calm the mind.

UMAMI FOODS

The following is a list of umami-rich foods.

Glutamate Foods

Glutamate is an amino acid found in proteins, especially cheeses, fish, meats, and veggies. Avoid monosodium glutamate (MSG), which is an added flavor enhancer.

- Asparagus
- Beets
- Broccoli
- Cheeses (especially aged cheeses like parmesan)
- Mushrooms
- Onions
- Peas
- Seaweed (especially kombu kelp)
- Tomatoes

Inosinate Foods

Inosinate is found naturally in meat and fish, but do avoid it when used as an additive in packaged foods like ramen.

- Beef
- Dried bonito
- Pork
- Poultry
- Sardines

Guanylate Foods

Guanylate naturally occurs in mushrooms, but it is also an additive to packaged foods and often hidden as a "natural flavor"; avoid the additive form.

- Dried porcini, shiitake, and morel mushrooms

Other Umami-Rich Ingredients and Foods

- Caviar
- Fish sauces and other traditional fermented seafood products
- Ketchup
- Marmite and Vegemite
- Miso
- Nutritional yeast
- Soy sauce
- Traditional fermented grain or fermented legume products
- Worcestershire sauce

DID YOU KNOW?

To avoid hidden additives—or to avoid needing to read labels at all—shop for fresh, unpackaged foods. Prepare your own foods, sauces, and spice mixes. This reduces your exposure to food additives that can trigger physical or emotional reactivity.

INSTRUCTIONS

To begin exploring umami, choose one or more umami-rich foods from the list to taste. Be aware that it's possible to react or be intolerant to many of these foods. You can use the Coca pulse test (described in the **Identifying Histamine Foods** worksheet, p. 150) when experimenting with these foods to detect an adverse reaction. Once you've identified a food to work with, go through the following mindful eating activity:

- Start by finding a pleasant place to sit down. It should be somewhere you can focus, ideally seated with your feet flat on the ground and a table in front of you.

- Place a very small piece of your umami food, no bigger than your fingertip, under your tongue. Without chewing, what sensation does this placement give you?

- Now shift the piece of food to the top of your tongue, again without chewing. What sensation do you get here?

- Begin to chew your piece of food. How does the taste sensation change as you break it down? Is there a certain part of your tongue or mouth where you taste the flavor of the food most intensely? Do different components of the flavor come through on different parts of your tongue or mouth?

- Keep chewing! Umami is generally the last taste to emerge, and it comes from well-chewed food.

Client Recipe

Purpose

Discover a recipe that supports the experience of feeling grounded.

Background

In Ayurvedic medicine, roots are connected to the root chakra, our pelvis. Roots remind us that we, too, come from the earth, even as we reach for the stars. When you want to feel grounded emotionally, go for the roots. When you crave something sweet and don't want sugar, bake a root vegetable instead. The roots in this recipe are warming and nourishing, and may remind you of simple pleasures.

Ingredients

- 3 lb. parsnips, peeled and sliced

- 2 potatoes, peeled and sliced

- 2 apples or pears, peeled, cored, and sliced

- 6 tbsp. butter

- ½ cup water

- Salt and pepper, to taste

Directions

Put the parsnips, potatoes, apples or pears, butter, water, and salt and pepper into a medium, heavy-bottomed pot. Cover and cook the mixture over medium heat, stirring from time to time, until everything is very soft, about 4 minutes. Mash or purée the vegetables (do not drain them) to the consistency you like. Drizzle a little melted butter on top.

MANGO BLUEBERRY GINGER SALAD

Client Recipe

Purpose

Try this recipe to experience the many benefits of mangoes. When paired with the antioxidant benefits of blueberries and the zing of anti-inflammatory ginger, you have a wonderful side dish that balances a simple protein meal or serves as dessert.

Background

Mangoes are sacred in India, where they originate, and they are considered the queen of fruits—and with good reason! Aside from their heavenly flavor, mangoes are rich in vitamins and minerals. They are high in fiber, which will help your body reduce cholesterol. They are also rich in antioxidants, which help your eyes filter the harmful blue light that dampens the brain and eyesight. Mangoes have digestive benefits as well: They lower the risk of gastrointestinal cancer, are effective, gentle laxatives, and are anti-inflammatory. In this recipe you will enjoy the complementary tastes of three ingredients that bring out the best in each other.

Prepare this salad just 30 minutes ahead of your meal, or let it sit overnight, covered, in the fridge.

Ingredients

- 2 large ripe mangoes
- 1 cup fresh or frozen blueberries
- 3 tsp. candied ginger (dust or rinse off the sugar)

Directions

Peel and cube the mango. Toss in the blueberries. Chop the ginger into tiny pieces and mix in for a sensational treat.

CHECK YOUR SOURCES: SUGAR AND HEALTHY SUBSTITUTES

PURPOSE

This activity will help you identify your current sources of sugar and healthier substitutes.

BACKGROUND

Consuming refined sugar contributes to depression, anxiety, PTSD, ADHD, PMS, digestive issues, and more. Reducing the sugar in your diet will not only improve your mental and physical health—it will also allow you to fully appreciate the natural sweetness of healthier substitutes, since you will no longer be desensitized by the extreme sweetness of refined sugar.

INSTRUCTIONS

Review the left-hand column and place a check mark by any sources of sugar in your diet. For each row that you checked, read the right-hand column for healthier alternatives you could incorporate into your diet.

SUGAR SOURCES	HEALTHY SUBSTITUTES
❑ Pastries or muffins	Smoothie sweetened with stevia, sweet potatoes and raw butter, or homemade baked goods made with natural sugar substitutes, such as applesauce
❑ Cereals	Granola, muesli, quinoa, or oatmeal with fresh fruit
❑ Flavored yogurts	Goat, coconut, rice, almond, hemp, or Greek yogurt topped with fresh fruit
❑ Soft drinks	Mineral water flavored with frozen fruit and stevia
❑ Sports drinks	Coconut water, electrolyte-infused water, aloe water, or watermelon juice
❑ Granola or energy bars	Raw nut/seed mix (e.g., pumpkin seeds, sunflower seeds, sesame seeds, chia seeds, walnuts, pecans, pistachios, hazelnuts, cashews)
❑ Caffeinated drinks (teas, coffees, energy drinks)	Green tea, matcha, chai, organic decaf coffee, yerba mate, roasted dandelion root, rhodiola tea, or Ramón nut coffee (café de capomo)
❑ Commercial salad dressings	Extra virgin olive oil, balsamic vinaigrette, sesame and ginger dressing, avocado and lime dressing, or tahini

TAMING YOUR SWEET TOOTH WITH POPPED AMARANTH

Purpose

Popped amaranth is similar to popcorn, and it can be made into a sweet dessert that will help you reduce the refined sugar in your diet.

Background

Many people are sensitive to corn—but you can still enjoy a popping dessert! Try using amaranth instead. It is a superfood, gluten-free, and rich in vitamins and minerals like manganese, which protects brain function. It is also rich in fiber and easy to digest. Besides popping it, you can also make amaranth porridge and add a little raw honey and hemp milk.

Ingredients

- ½ cup amaranth seeds

Directions

Preheat a high pot over medium-high heat. Spread about one tablespoon of the seeds, as evenly as possible, on the bottom of the hot pot. Wait for the seeds to pop. This should be immediate. If they don't pop right away, the pot isn't hot enough; discard that batch and start over.

Once the popping starts, shake the pot to ensure all the seeds pop and the popped seeds don't burn. Once the puffing ceases, remove the popped amaranth and put it into a sieve to shake out the unpuffed seeds. Then transfer the popped amaranth to a bowl and repeat the same process until all the seeds are popped. For each tablespoon of raw amaranth, you'll get about two tablespoons of popped amaranth.

Variation:

Alegrías

Alegría means "happiness." This is a variation of popped amaranth that is perfect for dessert. The Indigenous peoples of Mexico traditionally made offerings to the gods with alegrías or amaranth cakes sweetened with honey.

Ingredients

- 2 cups almonds, pepita seeds, or other nuts
- ½ cup dried fruit of your choice (I recommend apple and raisins)
- 3 tbsp. raw honey
- ½ tsp. cinnamon
- 2 cups popped amaranth
- Cocoa powder or ground chili, to taste (optional)

Directions

Chop the almonds and toast them in a pan without oil until golden brown. Cut the dried fruit into tiny pieces if necessary. In a bowl, thoroughly mix the almonds and dried fruit with the popped amaranth. Put a pan on low heat and add the honey and cinnamon. Heat carefully until the honey is liquefied, but don't let it boil. Pour the liquid over the amaranth mixture and mix well. Line a baking sheet with parchment paper and spread the amaranth and honey mixture evenly onto it. Press the mix a bit so that the honey can glue the amaranth grains together. If desired, sprinkle with cocoa powder or ground chili. Let the mixture sit in a cool, dry place for several hours. Once it has hardened, cut it into bars or squares and enjoy!

12-WEEK FOOD-MOOD PSYCHOCULINARY GROUP FORMAT

Clinician Handout

PURPOSE

This handout provides the basic structure for a 12-week psychoculinary group.

BACKGROUND

One of the best ways to introduce culinary medicine into your practice is to do a group or a workshop. The outline that follows provides a jumping-off point for a psychoculinary group. You can integrate any counseling method you prefer with the experiential techniques described in this book. You might include mindful eating, breathing exercises, movement, education about digestion, self-care methods focused on food and mood, or recipe sharing.

You can also adapt this outline for a public-style workshop series, where you can present these ideas and practices to your community on a weekend morning or afternoon. In this case, you would focus more on education and shared culinary experiences, linking mindfulness and cooking with healthy recipes that improve mood, reduce anxiety and hyperactivity, and aid sleep.

INSTRUCTIONS

First, you will need to create your vision for the group or groups you want to provide. I recommend defining each group by a specific age and population (e.g., kids, teens, perimenopausal women, elders, caregivers of people with dementia) and a specific mental health focus (e.g., depression, insomnia, eating disorders, chronic illness, substance use prevention).

You will tailor your methods and areas of focus to best serve that specific group. For example, I have been successful in the past by using lots of arts and movement when working with children, focusing on body image and yoga with teens, addressing self-care and time management with adults, and facilitating connections and meditation when working with elders. I have also developed programs in different languages and adapted the foods to address specific cultural values and joys. Reflect on what *your* group needs and will connect with.

As you plan your group, you may find that you need additional support. This might include securing funding to purchase foods, forming nonprofit and public partnerships, designing a group that insurance will cover, or engaging volunteers. You might co-lead the group with a registered dietitian, nutritionist, or yoga instructor. In my experience, people want opportunities to contribute when the work helps others.

When you are ready to enroll participants, I recommend limiting each group to 6–8 people for 90–120 minutes per session. Hold the sessions in a setting that has a kitchen, if possible, so the group can learn to make and share a healthy snack toward the end of each session.

Each participant makes a commitment for the group duration. Provide each individual with a notebook or handouts with plenty of room to keep a journal each week. After the 12-week series is over, renew participation options and, if desired, develop a level 2 version of the group.

BASIC GROUP STRUCTURE

Week 1

- Ask the group members to introduce themselves and begin compassionate goal-setting: Have each member name one goal they have, one obstacle they experience to achieving that goal, and one way the group can help them achieve their goal.

- Introduce the concept of mindfulness. You will open each group meeting with a mindfulness exercise and provide a handout so participants can practice at home.

Week 2

- Guide participants through the *Enhancing Digestion Body Scan* from the **Mindfulness Exercises for Digestion** handout (p. 124). Facilitate discussion of what people observed. Ask them to make a few notes in their journal, as they will repeat the body scan later and compare their experience.

- Introduce the **Food-Mood Diary** (p. 68).

- Continue reflection on goals and obstacles.

- Teach a breathing exercise to enhance sleep, such as **Ultradian Rhythm Exercises: "Hello, Brain"** (p. 82).

- Discuss plans for a final potluck (week 12).

Week 3

- Ask the participants to share about the meaning of food and their relationship with food, including one positive and one challenging aspect of their relationship to food.

- Guide participants in *Chewing the Raisin* from the **Mindfulness Exercises for Digestion** handout (p. 124).

Week 4

- Discuss foods in the participants' family of origin and their current family: What was early life mealtime like? How has it influenced you as an adult? Your digestion? Your food choices, purchasing process, and preparation?

- Guide participants in the *One Hundred Times* exercise from the **Mindfulness Exercises for Digestion** handout (p. 124).

Week 5

- Review the link between food and addictions: How do we use food to self-medicate? What are the healthy alternatives to sugar and refined foods? Review the principle of substitutions.

- Do a **Food-Mood Diary** review as a group, or divide the group into dyads who discuss their diaries and then return as a group to share their observations. Ensure that this is a shame-free discussion.

- Bring, or demonstrate how to prepare, a healthy sweet snack (such as vanilla chia seed pudding or dates stuffed with pecans).

Week 6

- Discuss food and body image: How do we make decisions about what we eat? What foods do we like, what foods don't we like, what do we crave, and what foods are interesting to us but we have not yet explored? What are the messages we receive—from our family members, our society, and others—about our bodies?

- Introduce kinesthetic, core, or balancing exercises (such as the **Kinesthetic Body Exercise**, p. 251, or the **Drumstick Exercises**, p. 254).

Week 7

- Review the role of "the second brain" in food and digestion: How do we feel when we eat? How do we follow our gut (intuition)?

- Explore which foods and nutrients enhance digestion.

- Provide psychoeducation on digestion using the **Digestive Organs Coloring Activity** (p. 122) and **Digestive Organs Matching Game** (p. 133).

- Do a guided visualization and teach belly self-massage for relaxed digestion (**Discovering Your Digestion with Touch**, p. 135, and **Dan Tien: The Elixir of Life**, p. 136).

- Snack on a fermented food like sauerkraut, kimchi, or a yogurt-based smoothie.

Week 8

- Explore fats and fear: What have we been taught about fats?

- Discuss fats, good and bad.

- Explain how adding muscle through exercise increases energy.

- Guide the participants in another belly self-massage.

- Serve, or demonstrate how to prepare, a coconut-based snack and discuss the benefits of coconut.

Week 9

- Explore how to prepare healthy foods: Discuss what makes foods healthy or unhealthy.

- Identify alternatives to unhealthy fats and sugars or deep frying (with the final potluck in mind) and write these ideas down in a food substitutions list.

- Share ideas for recipes for mental health.

- Practice forced-nostril breathing and *uddiyana bandha* (**Breathing for Anxiety and Eating Disorders**, p. 295).

Week 10

- Discuss adherence and how to overcome obstacles.

- Make a list for a support team.

Week 11

- Conduct the *Enhancing Digestion Body Scan* again. Ask the participants to share whether and how their experience has changed since week 2.

- Each person takes a turn identifying their strengths, resilience, and the next two steps they are going to take in their culinary self-care program.

- Prepare for the potluck: Each person identifies what they would like to bring, including the recipe. Ensure there is a balance of foods (not eight salads, for example). People may choose to prepare something together as well.

- Invite the group members to share their self-care exercises.

Week 12

- Final potluck celebration—each person brings a healthy dish with a copy of the recipe and speaks for a few minutes about its benefits for mental well-being.

- Provide a brief overview of the group process, emphasizing one area of positive growth or contribution for each individual.

- Discuss new learning and experiences, next steps, and goals.

9

NUTRITIONAL SUPPLEMENTS

TARGETED SUPPLEMENTATION PROTOCOLS

Diet is essential, but it is not sufficient. While improving diet is the best place to start nutritional change, supplementation is often required to address long-term nutrient deficits or imbalances. In these cases, supplements can restore lost nutrient levels, such as CoQ10 when using statins, or B12 with metformin or a vegan or vegetarian diet. There is also growing evidence that targeted nutritional supplements can support brain biochemistry and provide an alternative to psychotropic medications (Korn, 2016b; Rucklidge et al., 2021). Some nutrients can even synergize the benefits of medication. For example, when vitamin B6 is added to an SSRI, it acts like a coenzyme that enhances serotonin synthesis.

Nutritional supplementation may include the use of natural or synthetic vitamins, minerals, special nutrients like CoQ10, probiotics (now also called psychobiotics because of their action on the brain-mind), fungi, and animal glandulars.

The famed physician and pharmacologist Carl Pfeiffer once said, "For every drug that benefits a patient, there is a natural substance that can achieve the same effect." The Brainbow Blueprint is founded on this belief. When you want to affect brain chemicals like neurotransmitters, there are many nutritional supplements (along with foods and herbs) that do so. These include vitamins C and D, the B vitamins, omega-3 fatty acids, and minerals like magnesium, all of which are simple to use and are beneficial for almost everyone. These may be self-prescribed without side effects.

However, people have different genetic needs for vitamins and minerals, so appropriate nutrient supplementation is as complex as any intervention and must be tailored to the needs of the individual. There is an art and a science to using all supplements. While the wrong choices rarely cause harm, an inexact approach will hamper benefits, so consider pursuing further training and education, as well as collaboration with trained professionals. In addition, always keep in mind that supplements, like foods, range in quality. Natural, additive-free vitamins provide better quality and therefore efficacy.

When pursuing additional training, you may choose to learn about nutritional supplementation at a basic level, where you become competent enough to make recommendations or collaborate with a nutritional expert, or you might consider getting credentialed. As a starting point, I suggest that you become familiar with the scientific and lay literature on supplementation (Korn, 2016b; Rucklidge & Kaplan, 2016) and choose up to three supplements you want to learn about that have broad applications. Be sure you understand the benefits, side effects, and dosing. Among the broadly applied supplements, also known as nutraceuticals, are omega fatty acids, folate (B9), N-acetyl cysteine (NAC), and probiotics (Marx et al., 2017).

Your goal is to build enough trust and rapport with your clients that they will ask you questions and share their ideas with you. For example, a client may be experimenting with two herbal and nutrient antidepressants in addition to their prescription SSRI. With some fundamental knowledge of psychopharmacology, you will know whether to sound the alarm, because combining these SSRIs can lead to serotonin syndrome and the SSRI dose may need to be lowered to prevent that from occurring.

CLINICAL PEARL
The most important contribution you can make to your clients' nutritional health is knowing the potential for foods and supplements to effect change, whether that advice comes from you or a collaborating professional.

WHEN MULTIPLE HEALTH PRACTITIONERS ARE INVOLVED

Some clients who are taking supplements are already see a nutritional therapist. Still others self-prescribe or have several "cooks in the kitchen"—meaning they are taking advice from a combination of nutritionists, friends, the internet, their primary care provider, or others. This can become problematic, either because the supplementation fails to achieve the intended goals or because the dose is too high, potentially contributing to gas, diarrhea, or even serotonin syndrome. It is not uncommon for clients to have several health advisers from different disciplines recommending many things, which often conflict.

Therefore, when working to develop a targeted supplementation protocol, ask your clients about the supplements they are using during the intake, including whether they are self-prescribed or prescribed through another provider. This serves several purposes: It lets your clients know that you recognize the value of nutritional supplementation; it gives you an opportunity to educate clients on the efficacy of certain supplements (and any potential drug-nutrient interactions); and it enhances collaboration with other health care professionals who are supporting your clients' overall well-being.

If your client is seeing other providers, it is essential to explore who these providers are and what roles they play. Gently advise the client that if other providers are providing them with nutritional recommendations, it is in their best interest to coordinate with all providers and not triangulate, as often happens, due to distrust or lack of information. I explain to my clients that while I understand they may have concerns about trust or confidence or are just "hedging their bets," a disjointed approach only leads to confusion and failure.

Rachel's Story

I had been working with Rachel for two years and was helping her to taper from several psychotropics, including benzodiazepines. She was on an amino acid and B-vitamin-rich protocol to help traverse her detoxification, and she was having great success, as she was in the process of tapering the last 50 mg of an SSRI. Then, needing advice about a yeast infection, Rachel sought care from a nurse practitioner, who asked her to begin a very rigid anti-candida diet and to take a series of nutrients. This was counter to some of the work Rachel and I had been doing together, which involved decreasing rigid thinking and behaviors and doing more intuitive eating. Rachel called me one night in despair, feeling like she was backsliding and unable to cope. She told me of the new diet and protocol, and I offered to talk with the nurse practitioner to explain our program and to find an accommodation so we could address Rachel's health goals by working in unison. It turned out that the nurse practitioner was unaware of Rachel's current diet and protocol, and she was happy to coordinate care.

ENSURING SUCCESS WITH SUPPLEMENTS

In my experience, clients want to adhere to their supplement plans. They want to feel better and be successful. But there are obstacles to systematic self-care. For example, people who experience depression or PTSD may have challenges rooted in learned helplessness, and people with attentional difficulties may find it hard to create and maintain a self-care schedule. Addressing individual client needs enhances the capacity for supplement plan adherence.

This chapter will provide you with the tools you need to set your clients up for supplementation success. First, I introduce the common supplements that are essential for mental health. I will address how to select high-quality supplements, check for drug-supplement-herb interactions, and ensure adherence to supplement regimens. As you review the suggestions in the following table and throughout the chapter, keep in mind that these are just recommendations based on clinical literature. The specific dose combination and priority of use should be assessed based on the individual client needs.

Nutritional Supplements at a Glance

WELLNESS TARGET	RECOMMENDATIONS
Depression	• Amino acids, support adrenal function with adaptogens, magnesium, zinc picolinate, vitamin D, 5-HTP
Anxiety and panic	• GABA support: lactium B-complex vitamins, psyllium, magnesium, lithium orotate, glycine, niacinamide
OCD	• Inositol, choline, borage oil, N-acetyl cysteine, niacin, vitamin B12
Bipolar disorder	• Lithium orotate, phosphatidylserine, methylfolate
Insomnia	• N-acetyl cysteine, milk biopeptides
Stress, trauma, and PTSD	• Glandulars (liver, brain, and hypothalamus): B-complex, taurine, lithium orotate
ADHD	• Plant digestive enzymes, magnesium threonate, free amino acids
Chronic pain	• Natural COX2 inhibitors, natural KAPPA-B inhibitors, DL-phenylalanine, vitamin D, proteolytic enzymes, CoQ10, fish oil
Substance use disorder	• Niacinamide, B vitamins, B6, multiminerals, chromium, vitamin C, acetyl-L-carnitine, CoQ10, fish oil, borage oil
Cognition and memory	• NAC, fish oil/krill/GLA, lithium orotate, taurine, lutein (enhances memory), B12 (methylcobalamin), vitamin D, choline
Autism spectrum and neurodivergence	• Fish oil; EPA; DHA; L-carnitine; vitamins A, B2, B5, B6, folate (B-9) and B12; vitamins C, E, and CoQ10
Body image and eating disorders	• Free amino acids, glycine, tryptophan, zinc, B vitamins, milk biopeptides
Digestive disorders	• Gastrazyme (vitamin U and chlorophyll), zinc-carnosine, HCL acid, glutamine, plant digestive enzymes

THE FOUR MOST IMPORTANT SUPPLEMENTS

Clinician Handout

PURPOSE

This handout outlines the most important supplements, why they are used, and associated tests.

BACKGROUND

These are the four most important evidence-based nutritional supplements for mental health:

- Vitamin D
- Vitamin B-complex with minerals
- Omega-3 essential fatty acids
- Magnesium

I recommend testing clients' levels of these four nutrients annually. If you are making nutritional changes, you may choose to test every six months. The testing frequency will also be determined according to the symptoms, imbalances, interventions, and time required to see change. An annual review of each client's levels is important, as the body changes and may heal or develop other issues over time, requiring changes in supplementation.

With all supplements, quality is essential. For example, a client is better off having one high-quality omega-3 fatty acid than three poor-quality, additive-filled capsules. Also remember to recognize the limitations of your own knowledge—there is an art and science to nutritional supplementation, and it's always wise to work with a professional.

Vitamin D

Vitamin D has two forms: D2 and the active form, D3, which is the preferred type of supplement to use. Vitamin D is technically a neurohormone that supports calcium metabolism, improves immune function, reduces inflammation and depression, and supports cognitive function (Anjum et al., 2018; Groves et al., 2014; Weir et al., 2020). It is wise to suspect a vitamin D deficiency in almost everyone who is not actively supplementing, especially if living above the 37th parallel. Vitamin D levels can be assessed through a blood test annually.

DID YOU KNOW?

Many laboratory test values define a range that is normal, not optimal. For example, the normal range for vitamin D is usually lower than the established optimal levels for pain and depression (50–80 ng/mL). Keep this in mind when interpreting clients' lab results.

Vitamin B-Complex

If your client is an elder or a vegetarian, vitamin B12 (methylcobalamin or adenosylcobalamin) is essential and should be contained within the B-complex. Contrary to myth, one cannot get B12 from any food other than animal protein. You may also decide to use only active B-complex vitamins, such as methylfolate. However, methylfolate is not for everyone. It can lead to side effects in those without an MTHFR variation, it can enhance the effects of antidepressants, and it can trigger mania in people with bipolar disorder. Aside from methylfolate, you might consider (with the guidance of a professional) phosphorylated B-complex vitamins, B2 and B6, and methylated B12.

Magnesium

Most people are deficient in magnesium; signs include fatigue, depression, anxiety, asthma, menstrual cramps, arrhythmias, and muscle spasms. Magnesium is involved in over 300 biochemical actions in the body, including balancing glucose levels, protein synthesis, and mitochondrial function. We obtain—or should obtain—magnesium in dark leafy greens, but poor soil quality leads to low levels, along with prescription medicine use, poor gut function, and metabolic syndrome.

There are different forms of magnesium, which each serve different functions. For example, magnesium citrate can serve as a laxative in a pinch. (However, it is not to be depended upon—the root cause of the constipation should be identified.) I often recommend magnesium threonate during the evening for sleep and deep relaxation, or for individuals with migraines, anxiety, panic, or seizure disorders. Magnesium glycinate is ideal during the day for all other bodily functions.

Magnesium levels should be measured by a magnesium red blood cell test; serum levels will not provide an accurate picture.

Omega-3 Fatty Acids

The three ways to access healthy omega-3 fatty acids are by eating fish, krill, or algae; consuming plant/seed fats; and supplementation. Fish oil is the most common supplement. It usually features two types of omega-3 fatty acids: DHA and EPA. In supplement form, these omega-3s come as triglycerides or are refined into ethyl esters. Triglycerides are absorbed better than the more heavily processed ethyl esters.

Look for the terms FFA (free fatty acids), TG (triglycerides), or rTG (re-esterified triglycerides) on the label. Research suggests that people with the APOE4 allele do better with the phospholipid form of DHA, which is found in fish or special phospholipid supplements. However, one of the main problems with fish oil is toxicity with heavy metals. The manufacturing process must eliminate heavy metals.

DID YOU KNOW?
There is well-established evidence that a combination of dietary changes emphasizing fish, olive oil, and fresh fruits and vegetables (called the Mediterranean diet), when combined with supplemental fish oil, improves mental health in people with depression (Parletta et al., 2019).

A vegetarian alternative to fish oil is algae-derived omega-3. Chia, hemp, and flax seeds (and their oil) also contain omega-3 fatty acids. The seeds can be added to smoothies or granola, and the pressed oil can be used in salad dressings.

Omega Quant (https://omegaquant.com) provides a detailed analysis of omega fatty acid levels.

Blood spot levels can be tested as needed. DHA is essential for healthy brain development in infants and supports neurological development in children, so ensure that clients who are breastfeeding have sufficient omega-3s in their diet and that children are receiving supplementation if needed.

HOW TO READ A NUTRITIONAL SUPPLEMENT LABEL

Client Handout

PURPOSE

This handout explains how to read supplement labels and assess their quality.

BACKGROUND

The quality of nutritional supplements is as important as the quality of food we eat. Low-quality supplements contain additives or cheap, synthetic chemicals that diminish their benefits. However, it can be challenging to determine the quality of a given supplement. The following guidelines will teach you what to look for on the supplement's label so you can replace any low-quality supplements you may be taking with effective, high-quality alternatives.

INSTRUCTIONS

Use the following questions to evaluate each supplement that you are currently taking or that you intend to purchase.

1. Is the supplement natural or synthetic?

    o   Just because a label says "natural" does not mean it is—it only needs to have 10 percent natural vitamin content to qualify for that label.

    o   The "DL" form of any vitamin is synthetic.

    o   Here are more examples of the natural and synthetic forms of nutrients:

NATURAL FORM	SYNTHETIC FORM
Folate	Folic acid
Methylcobalamin, adenosylcobalamin	B12 (cyanocobalamin)
Choline	Choline chloride, bitartrate
Triglyceride EPA, triglyceride DHA	Ethyl ester EPA, ethyl ester
D-alpha-tocopherol	DL-alpha-tocopherol

2. How are the supplements created?

   o Research the company. Look for current good manufacturing practices (cGMPs) that exceed FDA guidelines for dietary supplements. Look for standards that ensure ingredients are pure and free of contaminants, heavy metals, solvent residues, pathogens, GMOs, and gluten.

3. What order are the ingredients listed in?

   o Supplement ingredients are listed in order of amount present, with more predominant ingredients coming first.

4. Does the supplement contain fillers and additives?

   o Some fillers and additives are neutral, but others—like dyes, colors, and certain preservatives—should be avoided.

   o Here are some common supplement additives and their attributes:

ADDITIVE	DESCRIPTION	VERDICT
Cellulose	A structural carbohydrate derived from plants, cellulose is commonly used as a binding, bulking, and coating agent in supplement pills. That is, cellulose takes up excess space in the pill capsule while holding active and inactive ingredients together.	Neutral
Citric acid	Citric acid may be added to liquid supplements to discourage fungal and bacterial growth and to enhance taste. Citric acid is regarded as safe for human consumption when derived from citrus fruits. However, forms derived from *Aspergillus niger* (black mold), are an allergen and inflammatory agent and should be avoided.	Avoid
Gelatin	Gelatin is a binding and coating agent. It binds active and inactive ingredients in a pill capsule together and makes the pill easier to swallow. Gelatin is rendered from animal bones, usually pig and cow bones and hooves. It is safe for human consumption. It is also high in collagen, an essential structural protein.	Neutral, but avoid if you are vegan or vegetarian
Magnesium stearate	Magnesium stearate is a flow enhancer added to tablets and capsules to distribute their active ingredients evenly. It also acts as a binding agent. Consumption of magnesium stearate has no confirmed adverse effects on human health.	Neutral
Maltodextrin	Maltodextrin acts as a filler in supplement capsules, tablets, and liquids. In general, it is a safe, inert carrier for other ingredients. However, maltodextrin is relatively energy-dense (4kcal/g) with a low nutritional value.	Neutral, but better to avoid

ADDITIVE	DESCRIPTION	VERDICT
Potassium sorbate	As an acidifier, potassium sorbate acts as a preservative in liquid supplements by lowering the pH value of the formulation. This discourages fungal and bacterial growth, increasing shelf life. Potassium sorbate is associated with toxicity to DNA and negative effects on immunity.	Avoid
Silicon dioxide	Silicon dioxide has anti-caking, flow-enhancing properties due to its ability to absorb moisture. It is added to supplements to keep active ingredients evenly distributed during production. It is generally considered safe for human consumption. However, a few studies suggest it may inhibit nutrient absorption in the gut and contribute to inflammation.	Unclear; avoid when possible
Sorbitol	Sorbitol is added to supplements as a sweetening agent. It can cause gastrointestinal distress, which can inhibit nutrient absorption. It is deadly to dogs.	Avoid, especially if FODMAP sensitive
Soy lecithin	Soy lecithin acts as an emulsifier in supplements and foods. It is a nontoxic, well-tolerated excipient (a medium for delivering nutriceuticals). It is a source of choline and inositol, and it protects active ingredients like vitamins A and E from oxidation.	Neutral, even positive
Soybean oil	Soybean oil acts as a filler when added to supplements. It is high in omega-6 fatty acids, and it is associated with inflammatory properties.	Avoid
Stearic acid	Stearic acid is a saturated fatty acid found in many foods. It is added to supplements for its lubricating properties, which are useful both during manufacturing and as the supplement moves through your digestive system. Stearic acid is inert and biocompatible, meaning it is safe for human consumption. Some studies suggest it may be beneficial to cardiovascular health.	Neutral, even potentially positive
Titanium dioxide	Titanium dioxide is a whitening agent added to supplements for cosmetic effects. It is not considered safe due to its potential as a carcinogen, and it reduces nutrient absorption in the small intestine.	Avoid

NUTRITIONAL SUPPLEMENTS: TIPS FOR SUCCESS

Client Worksheet

PURPOSE

Nutritional supplements only work if you take them regularly. This worksheet will help you plan how you will take your supplements to best fit your needs and schedule.

BACKGROUND

If we had better access to nutrient-dense foods grown on pesticide-free earth, instead of junk food preserved with chemicals in plastic—and if we were free to follow our natural rhythms, rather than being stuck in the grind of long, stressful hours at work or other responsibilities—then we might not need nutritional supplements. But this is not the nature of modern life for many of us. Supplementation can help address the missing nutrients in our diet and even treat illnesses.

INSTRUCTIONS

Reflect on the following questions, which will help you identify any obstacles you may face when trying to maintain a supplement routine—and how you can overcome these obstacles. For more ideas and support, discuss your answers with your mental health professional and review the tips that follow this questionnaire.

What are your feelings about taking supplements like vitamins or minerals?

_____

_____

_____

_____

If you currently take supplements or medications, do you have trouble adhering to your schedule for taking them?

_____

_____

_____

Do you think you will be able to stick to a daily routine for taking supplements? Why or why not?

_____

_____

_____

_____

What would make it easier for you to stick to your supplement routine?

_____

_____

_____

_____

What is your preference for the form of the supplements? Check all that apply:

❑ Capsule   ❑ Powder

❑ Pill   ❑ Liquid

❑ Add to food or a smoothie (see the **Create Your Supplement Smoothie** recipe, p. 197)

❑ Other: _____

DID YOU KNOW?

Some supplements should not be taken at the same time as certain other supplements, medications, or foods, while others are more effective when taken with other nutrients (for example, vitamin C helps your body absorb iron). Before you start your supplement schedule, read the labels on all your supplements and medications, and consult your nutritionist.

TIPS FOR SUPPLEMENT SUCCESS

To increase your chance of success, take your supplements at the same times each day. You might want to set daily reminders, such as an alarm on your phone with fun music. I recommend keeping a supply of your supplements in your car (be sure that they don't get too hot), in your desk or locker at work, or in your bag so you always have them on hand. You might also find it helpful to use a pill organizer, especially if you tend to forget whether you've taken your supplements. Finally, find a supplement accountability buddy if you need someone to keep you on track!

CREATE YOUR SUPPLEMENT SMOOTHIE

Client Recipe

Purpose

This handout will help you brainstorm how to add your supplements to a smoothie so they're easier (and delicious) to take.

Background

Adding liquid fats and powdered vitamins, minerals, and nutrients into a smoothie is a delicious way to take your supplements. Make smoothies in the morning and divide them up to drink throughout the day. You can query family members for their favorite ingredients and share recipes with friends. Use the information below to help you experiment with different supplement smoothie recipes.

Instructions

Choose ingredients from each of the following categories to design your own supplement smoothie:

- **Liquid base:** Include at least 4–6 oz. of your favorite milk.

    o   Non-dairy: Almond, oat, hemp, cashew, goat, or raw milk

    o   If you're trying to gain weight, add a few tablespoons of organic full-fat cream

- **1–2 compatible fruits or vegetables:** If you have digestive problems, keep it simple— use 1–2 fruits (like a banana and berries) or 1–2 vegetables (like kale and spinach) at a time. Avoid mixing fruits and veggies in the same smoothie.

    o   Fruits: Bananas, berries, mangoes, peaches, cherries, kiwi (fresh or frozen)

    o   Vegetables: Clover sprouts, leafy greens, raw or lightly steamed spinach, kale

- **Fats:** When using fat-soluble vitamins (A, D, E, and K), include some fat to enhance absorption.

    o   Oils: Hemp, coconut, fish, borage, flax (hemp and flax have a touch of bitterness, so add a teaspoon only)

    o   Foods: Raw unsalted nut butter, avocado, raw flax, chia, raw sunflower, or pumpkin seeds

- **Supplements:** You can open capsules, grind pills, or buy powders, liquid fats, oils, or seeds.

- **Tasty and healthy additions:**

  - Sweeteners: Raw honey, yacón syrup, grade B maple syrup, stevia

  - Proteins: Raw hemp protein powder, greens powder, almond or cashew butter

  - Mood boosters: Green tea/matcha powder, a little coffee, chocolate, rhodiola

  - Digestion aid: Greens powder, powdered enzymes, probiotics

  - Constipation or glucose control: ½ tsp. psyllium, chia, fresh or dried nopal cactus

  - Circulation: Cayenne pepper

  - Thyroid: Powdered kelp

- **Bonus tip:** Consider the time of day you will be drinking your smoothie.

  - Morning mood ingredients: Coconut, coffee, matcha powder, chocolate, rhodiola, yerba mate

  - Evening mood ingredients: Oatmeal, coconut, cream, cherries, chamomile

NUTRITIONAL SUPPLEMENTATION FOR CHILDREN

PURPOSE

This worksheet will help you explore whether your child would benefit from nutritional supplements and learn how to administer them safely. It should be completed with your clinician's guidance.

BACKGROUND

Just like adults, children can benefit from the use of nutritional supplements. Fish and plant oils and vitamins are available in gummies and liquids that are tasty for kids. You can also add liquid and powdered supplements to fun recipes, such as smoothies, popsicles, and healthy candies. Before you add supplements to your child's diet, however, it is essential that you understand your child's nutritional needs and recommended dosages, as they are different from those of an adult.

WHERE TO BEGIN?

If you are pregnant or breastfeeding, ensure a DHA-rich diet, which supports the development of a strong brain and neurological system. Supplementation with DHA fish oil is essential, especially if you are not getting DHA in your diet (for example, if you are a vegetarian). Infants may also be given small amounts of fish oil, especially if they are formula-fed rather than breastfed.

For children past infancy, start with a good quality fish oil, a multivitamin and multimineral, and vitamin D. Especially if your child experiences sensory motor challenges or texture-based food pickiness, they may not like vitamin-rich foods such as green vegetables; adding green foods powder or their other supplements to a smoothie or popsicle is a great way to ensure your child is eating—and enjoying—these nutrients.

Children who experienced adverse conditions in utero, including drug and alcohol exposure, benefit from intensive support for their brain development, including healthy fats, B vitamins, and amino acid–rich nutrients.

As children age, or when they are under stress, they need more support. For example, children with skin problems benefit from borage oil, and children who are having sleep troubles may need bioactive milk peptides and chamomile tea. Nutritional therapies, combined with culinary and herbal medicine, provide alternatives to psychotropics in children.

CLARK'S RULE: ADJUSTING ADULT DOSES TO CHILDREN

This simple formula, known as Clark's rule, is used to adjust adult doses of nutrients and herbs to children. Divide your child's weight by the average standard weight of 150 pounds (68 kilograms) and multiply by the adult dose of the drug or supplement.

child's weight (in lb.) ÷ 150 lb. × adult dose = pediatric dose

child's weight (in kg.) ÷ 68 kg. × adult dose = pediatric dose

REFLECTION

Answer the following questions, then share this information with your clinician so you can discuss together your child's specific needs.

What symptoms is your child experiencing?

_____

_____

_____

_____

_____

List all medications your child is taking for those symptoms.

_____

_____

_____

_____

_____

Many symptoms can be treated with alternatives to pharmaceuticals (such as herbs or supplements), allowing for dose reduction or elimination. Are you interested in exploring such alternatives with your clinician? Are there any possible alternatives that you've already identified?

_____

_____

_____

If your child is on more than one medication or experiences multiple symptoms, put these in priority order. Which should be addressed first, and which can wait until later?

_____

_____

_____

_____

_____

List the people, groups, or resources you trust to provide reliable support and information as you make decisions about your child's medications and supplements. (Your clinician can also help you identify these resources.)

_____

_____

_____

_____

_____

USING DRUG-NUTRIENT-HERB DATABASES FOR SAFETY

PURPOSE

This worksheet will help you assess for drug-nutrient-herb interactions to ensure your clients' safety.

BACKGROUND

Drugs, nutrients, and herbs all interact with one another. They can synergize each other's effects, inhibit the effects, or be neutral. This, combined with an individual's genetic makeup, should inform your choices and dosing.

INSTRUCTIONS

Refer to the client's intake form and begin with any pharmaceutical medications the client is taking. Use an online database (such as this one from Integrative Therapeutics: https://www.integrativepro.com/drug-nutrient-interaction-checker) to check for any potential interactions between each medication and the herbs or nutrients that your client is taking or that you'd like to recommend. Just because there is an interaction doesn't mean you can't recommend these herbs or nutrients. It is essential, however, to assess potential interactions. Under expert guidance, this is also the principle under which people reduce pharmaceutical medicine use by replacing it with alternatives.

You can use the following template to record your notes. In the first two columns, list each medication, supplement, or herb that the client is taking and their dosages. In the third column, note whether any of the other drugs, nutrients, or herbs the client is taking interact with the one in question, and make sure to indicate the type of interaction between them: positive (+), negative (–), or neutral (leave blank). Finally, determine how you will advise the client—to continue, stop, or seek further consultation for this item—and record any other notes.

Drug–Nutrient–Herb Interactions

Client name: _____

MEDICATION, SUPPLEMENT, OR HERB NAME	DOSAGE	INTERACTS WITH (NAME AND +, –, OR NEITHER)	PROCEED, STOP, OR CONSULT?	NOTES

HERBAL MEDICINE

In this chapter, I will explore the types of herbs that can be useful when addressing mental and cognitive health. Herbal medicine is one of the oldest forms of medicine, and the science behind it is well developed. Many well-known commercial pharmaceuticals are derived from herbs; indeed, allopathic medicine and pharmaceuticals evolved out of the use of herbal medicines prior to the 20th century. There are strict pharmaceutical guidelines for the compounding and production of herbs to optimize their effects. The active components in pharmaceuticals are often concentrated and synthesized, which leads to both potent effects and side effects.

HERBAL MEDICINE METHODS

When used in the context of integrative medicine and nutrition, herbal medicine can involve any of the following methods:

- **Allopathic or conventional** methods exploit natural resources for compounds that can be synthesized, concentrated, and patented as medicines.

- **Naturopathic and functional** methods are rooted in the art and science of natural medicine. Herbs, applied topically or internally, constitute an essential part of the repertoire.

- **Complementary and alternative** methods use herbal medicines to complement pharmaceutical use or to replace it to avoid side effects.

- **Traditional or cultural** practices are most often rooted in specific Indigenous cultural traditions and herbs endemic to the region. They may reflect empirical science and are often shared and available worldwide, such as Asian medicine practices and Ayurveda from India.

Regardless of the specific method involved, herbal medicine is well-suited to address both emotional and physical distress. For example, significant evidence suggests that herbal medicines can play an important role in the treatment of anxiety, depression, and insomnia (Sarris, 2018; Zhang et al., 2019). Kava is a potent antianxiety botanical (Ooi et al. 2018), while St. John's wort is effective for mild to moderate depression (Ng et al., 2017). Valerian, hops, and passionflower—what I call the three sisters of sleep (Korn, 2019)—reduce the time it takes to fall asleep and enhance sleep duration (Maroo et al., 2013). Herbs are also used for physical symptoms like blood pressure, headaches, and ulcerative colitis (Lobay, 2015; Yarnell, 2017; Hu et al., 2022). People with digestive disorders can reduce gas with dill and fennel, while slippery elm bark soothes inflammation due to acid reflux. Experimentation with herbs can also be a powerful support for clients who wish to reduce medications. In short, everyone can benefit from incorporating herbs and spices into their diet.

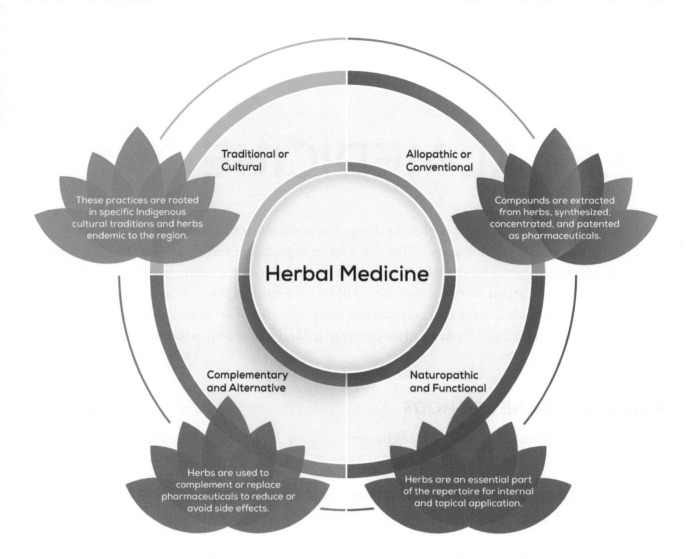

Traditional or Cultural

These practices are rooted in specific Indigenous cultural traditions and herbs endemic to the region.

Allopathic or Conventional

Compounds are extracted from herbs, synthesized, concentrated, and patented as pharmaceuticals.

Herbal Medicine

Complementary and Alternative

Herbs are used to complement or replace pharmaceuticals to reduce or avoid side effects.

Naturopathic and Functional

Herbs are an essential part of the repertoire for internal and topical application.

I encourage my clients to regard the kitchen as their pharmacy—to use foods, herbs, and spices for their nourishing, medicinal, and mood-altering qualities. Herbs can also affect mood and well-being at the sensory level through their delicious, mood-altering tastes and smells. Importantly, the nervous system responds to sensory input, especially odors and tastes; for example, umami stimulates and improves digestion (Kitamura et al., 2010). Engaging all of the senses, the mind, and the body can be the focus of psychoeducation.

The practice of herbal medicine in the United States is unregulated—anyone can practice it—but you can gain knowledge and competence through naturopathic universities, acupuncture and herbal medicine schools, and traditional schools based in local or Indigenous science and wisdom. There are also conferences, journals, reference books, and organizations devoted to the clinical application of herbs.

In addition, I believe that the best way to develop competence in herbal medicine is to learn about one herb at a time. Therefore, this chapter introduces a range of herbs by their type and function. I also provide starter recipes in the form of herbal teas, drinks, and smoothies, which is a wonderful way to introduce clients to the wide world of herbal medicine. (For more information on other types of herbal preparations—including tinctures, extracts, cordials, and poultices—see my book *Natural Woman* [2019].)

Working with herbs is an art and a science. Some herbs are simple, without any potential side effects or drug interactions, while others require more complex knowledge. Herbs, like therapy, often work best when different components are combined. The potential of using herbs to help clients is limitless, and it can become part of a client's self-care program and rituals. The following chart can provide a jumping-off point for exploring herbs with clients who have various mental wellness targets. Remember to check for drug-herb-nutrient interactions (see **Using Drug-Nutrient-Herb Databases for Safety**, p. 202) before making individual recommendations.

Herbal Medicine at a Glance

WELLNESS TARGET	RECOMMENDATIONS
Depression	• St. John's wort, rhodiola, coffee
Anxiety and panic	• Kava, valerian-hops-passionflower (VHP), skullcap, CBD oil
OCD	• Hops, cannabis (high CBD ratio), St. John's wort, licorice root, milk thistle
Bipolar disorder	• Borage seed, bilberry, St. John's wort, ashwagandha, saffron
Insomnia	• VHP, lavela, ashwagandha
Stress, trauma, and PTSD	• Astragalus, maca, licorice, citrus, kava, gotu kola
ADHD	• Lion's mane, ginkgo, maca, coffee, rhodiola
Chronic pain	• Boswellia, white willow, turmeric, black pepper, ginger, cayenne pepper (topical), green tea
Substance use disorder	• Ginseng, licorice, corydalis, valerian, saffron, dandelion
Cognition and memory	• Huperzine A, ginkgo, vinpocetine, lemon balm (Melissa officinalis), cat's claw
Autism spectrum and neurodivergence	• Red clover, alfalfa, cinnamon, dandelion
Body image and eating disorders	• Hawthorne, borage, valerian, hops, plum flower (Xiao Chai Hu Wan)
Digestive disorders	• Slippery elm bark, licorice root tea, cabbage leaf tea, dandelion

Clinician Handout

PURPOSE

This handout introduces some of the most useful herbs for mental health.

BACKGROUND

Herbs are classified by their actions on the body and mind. Some herbs do "double duty." For example, skullcap helps with anxiety and depression in addition to relieving physical pain.

The following are descriptions of key categories of herbs for you to explore as you build your knowledge of herbal medicine for mental health.

HERBS BY FUNCTION

- **Adaptogens** help us adapt to stress. They restore resilience, build endurance, and reduce fatigue. They most often support adrenal and immune function. When a client is presenting with symptoms of stress, fatigue, and depression, you might start with adaptogens to regulate the stress response. Some common adaptogens include ashwagandha, licorice root, and eleuthero (Siberian ginseng).

- **Analgesics** provide pain relief and are used orally or topically. Common analgesic herbs include arnica, corydalis, skullcap, and white willow bark.

- **Anti-inflammatory** herbs are closely linked to herbs that decrease pain, heat, and other symptoms of inflammation. Common anti-inflammatory herbs include boswellia, turmeric, and white willow bark. (Keep in mind that turmeric must be mixed with a little black pepper and fat to be assimilated.) One of the benefits of these herbs is that they can reduce or eliminate dependence on pharmaceutical NSAID use, which can negatively affect liver and stomach function over time. Some herbs are both analgesic and anti-inflammatory, most notably cannabis. The THC component is anti-inflammatory, whereas the CBD is anxiolytic and more sedative.

- **Antidepressant** herbs alleviate depression and improve mood and focus. Common herbs include lemon balm (also good for agitated or anxious depression), oats, saffron, and St. John's Wort.

- **Antidipsotropic** herbs support sobriety with alcohol. Among those are oats and kudzu.

- **Aromatic** herbs are fragrant and rich in essential oils called aromatics. They are a simple way to boost mood and they stimulate the appetite, making them useful for picky eaters, such as children or adults on the autism spectrum. Lavender, peppermint, rosemary, and sage are among the most used in foods and teas. Some, like sage, are even burned.

- **Bitter** herbs are helpful for people who have digestive problems, especially if they can't digest fats well, have gallbladder and liver issues, or experience constipation. Dandelion greens and roots are among the best known; I like to use these when they are fresh in the spring, in place of spinach (for example, in quiches or omelets).

- **Carminatives** prevent gas and bloating. Anise seed, cardamom pod, dill, and fennel seed are among the most effective. Add them to the food you are cooking or prepare a simple tea to drink just after the meal.

- **Hepatic** herbs support liver function and regeneration. They are especially helpful for clients whose livers have been affected by excessive use of drugs or alcohol, anesthesia and medications, or toxic environmental exposures. Herbs like milk thistle and schizandra, and vegetables like beetroot and bitter greens fall into this category.

- **Hypnotic** herbs promote relaxation and sleep. Similar to sedatives, hypnotics are often more potent. My favorite is kava, which can be deeply relaxing—but be careful, since kava can sometimes have a paradoxical effect and keep you awake.

- **Laxatives** help restore the natural rhythm of peristalsis, the movement of waste through the large intestine, by alleviating constipation. Bulking agents like chia, flaxseed, or psyllium husk are best for long-term use, but a pinch of cascara sagrada or senna will also help. Nonherbal laxatives include magnesium, vitamin C, or an enema. Avoid overreliance on laxatives; identifying the cause of constipation is critical. Some common causes are emotional distress, too little water or fiber in the diet, and food sensitivities.

- **Nervines** strengthen the nervous system and affect energy level. Some nervines, such as coffee and ginseng, are energizing and mood-boosting. Others promote relaxation and sleep. Relaxing nervines include peppermint, kava, lavender, St. John's Wort, oats, and passionflower. Sedating nervines include California poppy hops and valerian.

CLINICAL PEARL

People with anxiety or PTSD-based insomnia often use cannabis to help them fall and stay asleep. Cannabis appears to lengthen stage 4 of sleep and suppress REM sleep, which may result in reduced dreams (or nightmares). This makes cannabis a valuable short-term support during acute periods of nightmares, and it is a better option than a benzodiazepine.

However, since stage 4 is the deepest state of sleep (during which the brain slows down and rests deeply), consistent cannabis for sleep may cause grogginess in the morning. It is thus wise to limit cannabis use by replacing or rotating it with other methods, such as neurofeedback, or herbal sedatives like the "three sisters of sleep": valerian root, hops, and passionflower (VHP).

- **Rubefacients** can be used topically along with analgesics and anti-inflammatories. They increase circulation, which always aids healing, and they can be incorporated into daily use for fibromyalgia. Rubefacients include cayenne (available as a cream at the pharmacy), mustard, and stinging nettles.

- **Spasmolytic** herbs reduce spasms. The most effective herbs include chamomile, hops, passionflower, and skullcap.

- **Stimulants** boost mood and cognition, and they can be used for ADHD instead of pharmaceutical stimulants. They include ginger, ginkgo, coffee, gotu kola, and rosemary.

IT'S TEATIME

Client Worksheet

PURPOSE

This worksheet will help you explore the benefits of herbal teas for your physical and mental health.

BACKGROUND

Teas have powerful positive effects on health and well-being. There are countless types of teas, each with their own unique benefits. Teas can be made using loose leaf, roots, and seeds, and they can be served hot or cold. They can also be applied topically to swollen eyes or a wound.

Here are some commonly used teas, along with their physical and mental health benefits:

TYPE OF TEA	BENEFITS
Alfalfa	Aids digestion; enhances nutrition; analgesic
Barley	Promotes relaxation
Calendula	Use in a hip bath for fungal (yeast) infections or apply to skin irritations
Catnip	Calms muscle spasms
Cayenne pepper	Improves circulation and energy
Chai hu	Relieves PMS and depression
Chamomile	Aids digestion; reduces anxiety
Cinnamon	Lowers blood sugar; eases menstrual symptoms; reduces inflammation
Green tea	Antioxidant; slows glucose uptake; anti-inflammatory; gentle mood booster
Kava	Reduces anxiety and fear; muscle relaxant
Licorice root	Reduces stress; enhances adrenal function; aids digestion
Meadowsweet	Fever reducer; antidiarrheal; soothes headaches and nausea
Passionflower	Reduces stress and anxiety; aids with insomnia
Peppermint	Aids with nausea, gas, and headaches
Slippery elm bark	Soothes inflammation of mucous membranes; aids digestion
Yarrow	Increases appetite; anti-inflammatory; relieves pain

REFLECTION

Which teas would be most beneficial for your own health and well-being? Choose a few types of tea to try. List them here, and explain which effects you are interested in (e.g., "peppermint tea for my headaches"). Keep these teas on hand for when you experience symptoms. You might store them in your kitchen or office as an herbal first-aid kit.

_____

_____

_____

_____

_____

_____

Now review the list of teas again and consider your family roots (and leaves and seeds). Does your family drink any of these teas? What herbs did your ancestors use, and why? Which herbs are endemic to that region of the world? Would you like to try these herbs?

_____

_____

_____

_____

_____

_____

_____

DID YOU KNOW?

When making tea, consider its form. Steep leaves for 10 minutes in hot water, strain, and pour. Simmer roots and seeds gently for 15–20 minutes, strain, and pour.

HOT COCONUT KAVA

Client Recipe

Purpose

This recipe can be used to enhance an emotional, ritual experience.

Background

Kava is used traditionally in Hawaii and Polynesia to recognize nodal moments in life, like loss. Kava helps us experience feelings of grief without numbing the feelings. Because kava can be mildly stimulating, I suggest not drinking this beverage after 5:00 p.m. If children are participating in the ritual, make a children's version without the kava.

Ingredients

- 1–2 oz. kava root (¼–½ oz. ground powder kava root per person)

- 1 can (13.5 oz.) coconut cream or coconut milk

- 1 cup hemp milk

- 1 tsp. ground cinnamon or half a cinnamon stick

- Pinch cardamom

- 1 tbsp. ghee or raw butter

- 2 drops vanilla or a small piece of vanilla pod

- 10 drops stevia

Directions

Place all the ingredients except the ghee, vanilla, and stevia in a saucepan over medium heat. Simmer for 30 minutes. Remove from heat; strain out the kava root and cinnamon stick. Add the ghee, vanilla, and stevia. Froth to blend and serve hot.

Client Recipe

Purpose

These tea blends have many benefits, including lifting your energy level and your mood.

Background

Roots, seeds, flowers, and herbs can improve both your physical and mental well-being. Consider the particular benefits of the following tea blends, then pick one (or both) to try.

Stress-Buster Tea

One of my favorite teas is an adaptogen from Ayurvedic medicine that works as a natural antihistamine and digestive aid. It is composed of one root and three seeds: Licorice is soothing to the digestive system and enhances the ability to cope with stress; fenugreek and flax are mucilaginous and soothing to the mucous membranes; and fennel's rich aroma boosts mood and reduces intestinal gas.

(**Note:** Licorice root can cause fluid retention. Limit the use of licorice if you are taking a diuretic or high blood pressure medication.)

Ingredients

- One part licorice root (*Glycyrrhiza glabra*)

- One part fennel seed (*Foeniculum vulgare*)

- One part fenugreek seed (*Trigonella foenum-graecum*)

- Two parts flax seed (*Linum usitatissimum*)

Directions

I recommend buying 1 ounce of each dried herb, mixing them together, and storing the blend in a jar in the cupboard so you always have it on hand. To make the tea, simmer 2 cups of water, add 1 heaping teaspoon of the blend, and continue simmering for 20 minutes. Strain and drink hot or cold. I recommend drinking a cup each morning to provide energy for the day ahead.

Roselle and Saffron Tea

Roselle, also called *Jamaica*, can be found in Mexican or Caribbean food stores. It is a potent anti-inflammatory and antioxidant. Saffron has been shown to be an effective antidepressant (Siddiqui et al., 2018). Together, they make for a rich, mood-lifting tea.

Ingredients

- 2 cups water
- 12 dried roselle flowers
- 3–5 saffron threads
- Raw honey or stevia

Directions

Bring the water to a boil, add the herbs, and let infuse for 10 minutes. Strain and add a teaspoon of raw honey or 5 drops of stevia. If you want to make a cold brew, let the herbs infuse for 1 hour and strain.

Client Recipe

Purpose

These popsicles provide a healthy medicine for a sore throat, a cold, or low mood or energy.

Background

Also called "fire cider," this recipe was originally formulated and popularized by herbalist Rosemary Gladstar. Every ingredient has medicinal value. Vinegar is an excellent medium for extracting herbs and spices and is antibacterial. Beetroot aids detoxification by the liver. Ginger is warming and diaphoretic, which helps you sweat. Horseradish reduces and clears congestion. Onion and garlic are antiviral and antibacterial, and they thin mucus. Peppers and lemon are rich in vitamin C, and the peppers reduce pain and improve circulation. Even the honey is medicinal—it is soothing and antibacterial and provides energy during fasting due to illness. You can also add ground vitamins, minerals, or special nutrients to your batch.

Note that fire cider requires a month to macerate. I recommend always keeping a batch on hand so it's available whenever you need a pick-me-up, especially during cold or flu season. You can drink the liquid as daily "shots" for prevention or freeze it into popsicles (which is especially popular with children, and soothing on a sore throat). For a milder flavor, you can reduce or eliminate the peppers or horseradish and add more honey.

Ingredients

- ½ cup freshly grated ginger

- ½ cup grated fresh horseradish root or ground horseradish

- 1 medium onion, chopped

- 10 cloves garlic, chopped (optional)

- 2 jalapeño peppers, chopped

- 1 tbsp. ground beetroot

- Zest and juice of 1 lemon

- Several sprigs of fresh rosemary

- 1 tbsp. ground turmeric

- ¼ tsp. ground cayenne pepper

- 1 tsp. peppercorns

- 12 oz. apple cider vinegar or pineapple vinegar

- ½ cup raw honey

Directions

Put everything except the vinegar and honey in an amber glass quart jar (the darker glass blocks ultraviolet light, which would degrade the ingredients). Add the vinegar and fill to an inch below the top. Shake well. Store in a dark, cool place for a month and shake daily. After one month, use a cheesecloth to strain the pulp and pour the mixture into a clean jar. Squeeze as much of the liquid as you can from the pulp while straining. Add the honey. If desired, pour into popsicle molds and freeze until solid.

SMOOTH OUT SMOOTHIE

Client Recipe

Purpose

This recipe reduces anxiety and promotes relaxation and sleep.

Background

This smoothie works to curb anxiety during the day and aid in sleep at night. Oats are deeply relaxing to the nervous system; Wulingshen (*Xylaria nigripes*) fungus contains glutamic acid, gamma-aminobutyric acid (GABA), and glutamate decarboxylase, which have relaxing and antidepressant effects; cherries enhance melatonin; lecithin is a choline precursor and thus a sleep enhancer; the mushroom reishi quickens sleep onset; and theanine relaxes and reduces anxiety, as does magnesium threonate, which is a type of magnesium that cross the blood-brain barrier.

You'll notice that some ingredients have a dose range. Start with the lower doses, and if you respond well, stick with that. If you need more, increase the reishi first, then the theanine, then the Wulingshen.

Ingredients

- 8 oz. oat milk

- 250–500 mg Wulingshen (*Xylaria nigripes*)

- 4 oz. fresh or frozen cherries

- 1 tbsp. sunflower lecithin

- 0.5–1 g reishi powder

- 50–100 mg theanine

- 144 mg magnesium threonate

- Maple syrup or stevia to taste

Directions

Blend all ingredients until smooth and enjoy!

LEMON GINGER REFRESH

Purpose

This easy "cocktail" is anti-inflammatory and reduces pain.

Background

This sparkling beverage is a healthy substitution for soft drinks. The lemon or lime boosts your mood, aids liver function, and provides a good base for the bite of ginger that makes this drink good for pain and nausea. You can also make it with hot, nonsparkling water to alleviate morning sickness or to prevent carsickness or seasickness.

Ingredients

- 8 oz. sparkling mineral water

- 1 lemon or lime, squeezed

- 1 tbsp. grated raw ginger

- Dark agave, honey, or stevia to taste

- 1 ice cube

Directions

This drink can be prepared either hot or cold. For an iced drink, combine all ingredients in a glass, stir, and drink. You might like to use sparkling or mineral water in place of plain water.

To serve hot, add the ginger and plain water to a saucepan and simmer for 10 minutes. Pour into a cup and add the lemon or lime juice, then sweeten to taste. Do not boil the lemon or lime, and do not strain the ginger. You want to chew on and eat the ginger as you drink your refresher—it will be nice and sharp and will help reduce pain.

11

HYDROTHERAPY AND DETOXIFICATION

As the COVID-19 pandemic illustrated, the world's deep interconnectedness means that no one can completely seal themselves off from the pathogens and toxins that now circulate the globe. However, nature provides ways for us to ameliorate or neutralize many health challenges that evade the eye, from viruses to volatile chemicals. Detoxification treatments work to eliminate toxins within the body and brain. One of the most common types of detoxification is hydrotherapy, which will be a focus of this chapter.

HYDROTHERAPY

Hydrotherapy refers to a wide range of therapeutic techniques that involve water—whether hot, cold, frozen, or a combination of these. Examples include pools, hots tubs, steam baths, skin brushing, saunas, and aquatic massage. It is a safe and effective method that empowers clients to care for themselves. It is a gentle, mood-altering, immune-enhancing option that's easy to teach and has few contraindications.

The use of water and healing baths for mental and physical well-being goes back thousands of years and spans all cultures. Throughout the 19th and 20th centuries, hydrotherapy was used in mental health clinics because it was found to improve mood and alleviate physical pain. Following the onset of the COVID-19 pandemic, the use of hot and cold therapies, including saunas, received renewed attention due to their ability to enhance immune function via the adaptive immune system (Cohen, 2020; Evans et al., 2015).

Raising body temperature can help mitigate viral infections, as with a fever, by helping the immune system work more efficiently and preventing the virus from replicating. In fact, naturopathic medicine has considered fever as a symptom to manage and not suppress. Management of a temperature of up to 102–103 degrees is generally a safe approach to enable the body to fight infection. Combining heat with cold may also be beneficial for prevention and immune support because it stimulates blood, flow which oxygenates tissues. Research suggests that those who undertook daily hot baths followed by a brief cold bath had lower viral infection rates and mortality rates during the 1918 influenza pandemic (Ramirez, 2021). Hydrotherapy applications for COVID-19 are just now being explored, but they are posited to have similar effects (Ramirez et al., 2021; Bailly et al., 2022).

Hydrotherapy can be used both for prevention and treatment, and it may be used daily and intensively if someone falls ill. You can also incorporate herbs with hydrotherapy to further enhance its effects. For instance, ground mustard can be added to a fomentation and applied to the chest during bronchitis and pneumonia to aid breathing, or it may be added to a foot bath, serving as a rubefacient and diaphoretic, to relieve headaches.

CLINICAL PEARL
You may be wondering why these methods are not currently part of the mainstream repertoire. It is not that these methods do not work but that the health system is always in search of faster, more efficient interventions. Yet, as we have observed in this "age of psychotropics," fast doesn't always translate to effective and enduring.

DETOXIFICATION

The major goals of detoxification are twofold: (1) reduce exposure to exogenous toxins, and (2) increase the body's elimination capacity by aiding organ function. The conventional meaning of detoxification refers to how the body transforms and eliminates waste, most notably through major organs of elimination—the skin, liver, kidneys, and colon—which is also called biotransformation (Hodges & Minich, 2015).

The body undergoes a detoxification process naturally. The liver is considered the primary detoxification organ, and it goes through three phases of detoxification. Phase 1 involves the liver turning fat-soluble toxins into water-soluble ones, phase 2 then breaks down the water-soluble toxins to be excreted, and phase 3 takes the water-soluble toxins and transports them from the cells into circulation for elimination by the kidneys, and urine or excretion via the feces. Like other aspects of personalized health, the capacity to detoxify is genetically determined. Some people experience detox challenges that require the additional assistance of nutrients and herbs that support detoxification, like cruciferous vegetables and sulfur-rich foods like garlic and onions. Nutrients like the B vitamins and the amino acid N-acetyl cysteine (NAC)—used in allopathic medicine to help detoxification from acetaminophen poisoning—also aid phase 2.

Although the liver plays a primary role in eliminating toxins from the body, detoxification is not limited to the liver; the skin, lymphatics, and kidneys all play a role. Another recently discovered detoxification mechanism is the glymphatic system (a combination of two words, derived from *lymphatic* and *glial*) in the brain, which facilitates waste clearance at night during sleep.

GETTING STARTED

The first part of this chapter is devoted to exploring hydrotherapy and the second half to other forms of detoxification, with an emphasis on reducing dependence on psychotropic medications. To be successful at tapering medications is both an art and science. It requires understanding the individual client, psychotropic withdrawal syndrome, and the integrative methods best suited to aid and ease the process. You will also need to collaborate with prescribing providers. Above all, tapering requires patience.

CLINICAL PEARL
As a clinician, you may support your client's wish for medication changes in cases where the client's prescriber is not supportive of these changes. You can serve an important role, helping your client gain emotional strength to assert their needs and reducing the common power differential between prescribers and their patients. I often role-play with my clients, playing a resistant prescriber, which gives the client the opportunity to strengthen their voice and find the phrases they want to use.

Hydrotherapy and Detoxification at a Glance

WELLNESS TARGET	RECOMMENDATIONS
Depression	• Cold water immersion baths, cold lake swimming • Hot saunas/sweats followed by cold immersion
Anxiety and panic	• Warm bath with lavender • Skin brushing • Hot-water bottle on the belly at bedtime • Cold pack between the shoulder blades during the day
OCD	• Heated rice pads or weighted blankets on the chest and shoulders • Warm baths with magnesium
Bipolar disorder	• Cold if depressed • Heat if hypomanic or manic
Insomnia	• Warm magnesium sulfate bath before bed • Use a diffuser with lavender
Stress, trauma, and PTSD	• Skin brushing • Wet brushing with sea salt or baking soda scrub • Warm and cold packs for fatigue
ADHD	• Warm, moist heat packs when hyperactive • Cold packs to the upper back when feeling unfocused • Sandalwood diffuser

WELLNESS TARGET	RECOMMENDATIONS
Chronic pain	• Cold-water or ice packs reduce pain • Heat is soothing—use hot-water bottles, hydrocollators, paraffin baths, or sand (avoid heating pads due to the electromagnetic fields they create)
Substance use disorder	• Pulsed electromagnetic field therapy (PEMF) • Use heat during acute withdrawal • Alternate hot and cold elements for maintenance and relapse prevention
Cognition and memory	• Early stages of memory loss: hot and cold alternating, constitutional hydrotherapy • Later stages: hot-water bottles on chosen areas, paraffin baths for arthritic hands and feet
Autism spectrum and neurodivergence	• Whatever experience the individual wishes for and agrees to is indicated
Body image & eating disorders	• Constitutional hydrotherapy • Warm baths with selected aromas that enhance sensory awareness
Digestive disorders	• Place an ice pack over the diaphragm at the midpoint, at the base of the xiphoid process (tip of the breastbone) 15 minutes prior to a meal

HYDROTHERAPEUTIC METHODS FOR MENTAL HEALTH AT HOME

PURPOSE

In this worksheet, you will learn methods and principles to use water, hot and cold elements, and various natural aids to enhance your mood and health.

BACKGROUND

Hydrotherapy practices can be an aid for relaxing into sleep, altering mood, and decreasing pain and dissociation. Use these methods daily for self-care and more intensively during any detoxification process.

CREATE YOUR HYDROTHERAPY SPACE

Find an area of your home that can serve as your quiet space, where you will assemble your self-care items. Some useful home spa items are listed here; mark any that you will need or would like, and gather them in your space.

- ❑ Air purifier

- ❑ Apple cider vinegar (can be added to a bath for fatigue)

- ❑ Blackout or blockout curtains

- ❑ Breathing tools (like komuso)

- ❑ Chamomile tea (soothing and anti-inflammatory; the tea bags can be applied to the eyes)

- ❑ Coconut oil (to soothe and moisturize the body)

- ❑ Epsom salts

- ❑ Essential oils of choice

- ❑ Eye pad or mask

- ❑ Hot-water bottle, heatable rice bag, or body pads

- ❑ Incense or beeswax candles (paraffin or perfumed candles are often toxic)

- ❑ Jade roller (an instrument used in Chinese medicine to cool the body, enhance chi [energy], and aid relaxation; use the smaller end over smaller areas like the eyes and the larger end across the cheeks and forehead)

- ❏ Magnet pads (which use pulsed electromagnetic fields [PEMF] to balance our electromagnetic energy and are a good treatment for arthritis)

- ❏ Robe

- ❏ Scalp massager (can be used dry or wet; is energizing and grounding)

- ❏ Skin brush (also called a dry brush)

- ❏ Soft towels and washcloths

Feel free to add anything else that you find meaningful and nurturing. You might create an altar or area with unique items such as fresh flowers or plants, crystals, synchronicity tools (e.g., affirmation cards, Celtic runes, soul collage cards), or photos of loved ones.

You will also need a "wet" room, like a bathroom, where you can carry out water-based activities, or you can use plastic protective equipment in another space.

HYDROTHERAPY ACTIVITIES

The following are some hydrotherapy techniques you can do at home. When choosing which ones to use, consider these principles of hot and cold techniques:

- **Hot:** Relaxing; reduces chronic pain

- **Cold:** Stimulating; boosts mood; reduces acute pain

- **Hot and cold (alternating):** Enhances circulation and immune function; balances mood

Applying Heat

When feeling anxious or in pain, apply a hot-water bottle or a rice-filled heating pad to your belly or the painful area. (Avoid electric heating pads because of exposure to electrical currents.)

Applying Cold

When feeling tired or in a low mood, jump into a shower that is lukewarm and slowly make the water colder until it is as cold as you can tolerate. Let the water flow directly on your spine for 5 minutes.

Alternatively, add 1 cup of apple cider vinegar to a bathtub of cool water and soak in it for 20 minutes when you are feeling fatigued or anxious.

Applying Hot and Cold

Mix ½ cup coarse sea salt and ½ cup baking soda. Mix in enough water so it becomes a thick paste. Add a few drops of your favorite essential oil. Jump in the shower with your skin brush, get wet, turn the water off, and begin scrubbing, starting at your toes and working up your whole body, from front to back. Turn the water back on and rinse off with warm water. Then make the water as hot as is comfortable, and finish with a minute of cold water. Towel dry and drink 6 ounces of water.

Constitutional Hot and Cold Hydrotherapy

Soak a large cotton T-shirt or tank top in the sink so it is sopping wet; wring out excess water and place it flat in the freezer. Spread two wool blankets lengthwise on a bed, and place a cotton or flannel sheet over them.

Take a shower using water that is hot, but not burning or uncomfortable. Let the water fall all over you for 5 minutes. Immediately after the shower, dry quickly, get the cold shirt from the freezer, and put it on. Use no clothing under or above this shirt. Lie down on top of the sheet, then roll yourself tightly into the sheet and blankets, wrapping yourself up from neck to toes, mummy-style. (You may want to ask someone else to help you wrap up tightly.)

Remain wrapped until your shirt is warm to the touch. During this time, sleep, rest, or listen to calming music. Then slowly come out of your cocoon, dress, and stay warm. Relax for the rest of the day, perhaps taking a walk in the fresh air.

Epsom Salt Bath

This bath is relaxing and detoxifying. Add 2 cups of Epsom salts (magnesium sulfate) and ½ cup of baking soda to a warm (not hot) bath. You may also add some essential oil, such as lavender. Soak for 20 minutes. The magnesium and sulfate will be absorbed, relaxing your muscles and helping you sleep. The bath can be slippery, so use a mat.

Skin Brushing

Skin brushing is a simple yet powerful approach for anxiety, depression, and dissociation. When tapering off medications, use the brush as often as necessary, or if you feel the urge to self-harm, use the skin brush instead—it will bring you back into your body, reduce anxiety, and stimulate endorphins.

Using a firm, bristled brush, brush one to two times a day on dry skin before a shower or bath for 3–5 minutes. Brush in the direction of the heart. Begin at the feet, then slowly work up the front and back of the body. Brush the legs, buttocks, abdomen, back, and arms. Pay particular attention to the armpits and chest (but avoid the nipples). Continue to the neck.

At first, the brush may feel harsh; however, after a few sessions of brushing it should feel good and stimulating.

Client Worksheet

DETOX YOUR CABINETS, FRIDGE, AND FREEZER

PURPOSE

This worksheet will guide you through an exploration of your kitchen so you can identify and replace toxic ingredients.

BACKGROUND

It's important to know what is in your kitchen and how those foods and ingredients affect your health and mood. Some commonly used ingredients are toxic to your health. You will learn how to identify these items and replace them with healthier alternatives.

INSTRUCTIONS

Use the chart on the next page to guide your exploration. First, list the foods you find in your kitchen—including your cabinets, fridge, and freezer—and their ingredients.

Next, use the following information to learn which ingredients are unhealthy, even toxic. Review your kitchen inventory—do you see any of the problematic ingredients listed there? If so, circle them and write down a healthier substitution you can make in the right-most column.

| UNHEALTHY FOODS AND HEALTHY SUBSTITUTIONS ||
UNHEALTHY FOOD/INGREDIENT	HEALTHIER SUBSTITUTIONS
Vegetable and canola oils	Extra virgin olive oil, coconut, avocado, sesame, ghee, butter
White sugar, artificial sweeteners (e.g., saccharin, sucralose, aspartame)	Molasses, raw honey, monk fruit stevia
White all-purpose flour	Whole-grain, coconut, tapioca, almond meal, quinoa, buckwheat
Canned foods (these can have high tin levels)	Frozen foods
Packaged foods (the plastic in packaged foods can be detrimental to your health; toxic agents include bisphenols, polymers, epoxy resins, phthalates, perchlorates, nitrates, and nitrites)	Foods that are free of these ingredients—ideally, prepare your own foods from simple ingredients rather than buying prepackaged foods

KITCHEN INVENTORY		
FOOD	**INGREDIENTS**	**HEALTHIER SUBSTITUTION**

DID YOU KNOW?

Plastic packaging additives, plastic wraps, cooking utensils, cans, glue, and other toxic additives contribute to neurodevelopmental problems, endocrine/hormonal disruption, obesity, and immune suppression. Current oversight by the FDA is inadequate, so it is important for consumers to be vigilant (Trasande et al., 2018).

REFLECTION

Do you think the food substitutions you've identified will be easy or difficult changes to make? What obstacles do you think you might face?

_____

_____

_____

_____

_____

_____

_____

_____

What are three actions you can take that will help you overcome the obstacles to choosing healthier foods?

_____

_____

_____

_____

_____

MEDICATION ALTERNATIVES

Client Worksheet

PURPOSE

This worksheet will help you identify all the medications you are taking, explore alternatives you may prefer to use, and create a list to review with your prescriber.

BACKGROUND

We know that many medications, whether over-the-counter or prescribed, have significant side effects or may be made with dyes and sugars. As your health improves, you may find better alternatives in your own kitchen or herbal medicine cabinet.

The first step in making changes is to understand what you have decided to take and why. This worksheet will help you assess your current medications, learn about the benefits and risks of these medications and their possible alternatives, prioritize changes you want to make, and enhance your awareness of the whole picture of your health.

INSTRUCTIONS

First, make a list of the medicines found in your kitchen and medicine cabinet. What do you use them for? Are they over-the-counter or prescribed? What are their benefits or side effects? Use the following chart to record your notes.

MEDICATION	PURPOSE	OTC OR RX?	BENEFITS/ SIDE EFFECTS	POSSIBLE ALTERNATIVES

Of the medications you've listed, which ones would you like to change? Circle these in the chart. Then work with your integrative provider to identify possible alternatives for these medications (for example, turmeric has an analgesic effect and could replace aspirin or acetaminophen). Write down these alternatives in the last column of the chart.

You may decide to pursue some of these changes by discussing them with your prescribing health professional. Many people feel skittish about raising these questions with their providers, so it's helpful to write down your thoughts and questions in advance. You can use the following template for initiating the conversation with your provider.

TEMPLATE: DISCUSSING ALTERNATIVES WITH YOUR PROVIDER

Dr. _____, I am eager to make lifestyle changes and reduce or even eliminate some of the medications I am using.

Here is a list of the medications I am interested in changing, the symptoms they are currently addressing, and the substitutions or lifestyle changes I am planning to make in order to achieve my goals.

MEDICATION	PURPOSE/ SYMPTOMS ADDRESSED	PROPOSED ALTERNATIVE

Are you able to advise me about the best next steps? I understand if your area of expertise does not include the alternatives I am considering; in this case, are you able to consult with my integrative provider, _____, or refer me to another health professional?

Thank you for your time and guidance.

READINESS TO TAPER CHECKLIST

Clinician Worksheet

PURPOSE

This worksheet provides you with an interview process and readiness checklist to explore whether your client is ready to taper from psychotropic medications and what will optimize success.

BACKGROUND

In my clinical experience, people can absolutely reduce, taper, and even eliminate psychotropic medications successfully. But many clients—especially those who have been on medications for years—return to their medications when they experience discomfort or what they feel is a return of symptoms. Successful tapering requires education about the medications and discontinuation process, a robust self-care routine, support (I call this the "taper team"), and patience to tolerate going slowly. The most crucial element of successful tapering and maintenance is the pace of the taper. I recommend a pace that is much slower than what is often suggested by prescribers. Tapering is not only about brain chemistry; it is about attitude, support, and dispelling myths and negative beliefs.

INSTRUCTIONS

Explain to the client at the start that they will want to engage their prescriber in the taper plan. If the prescriber is not willing to assist, the client will want to find another prescriber. See the **Recruiting Your Taper Team** worksheet (p. 237) for guidance on having a productive conversation with a prescriber.

If their prescriber agrees, complete the following sections to assess whether your client is ready to begin the tapering process.

CLIENT INTERVIEW

Client name: _____ Date of birth: _____

Intake form attached? ❑ Yes ❑ No

How many different medications are you taking?

_____

_____

_____

For how long have you been using each medication?

_____

_____

_____

What do you think is the best order of priority for tapering? (*The final decision may require input from the prescriber.*)

_____

_____

_____

What are your current stress levels? Do you anticipate any stressors during the tapering process?

_____

_____

_____

What and who are your social supports? Are they in place to assist you in successfully carrying out the plan?

_____

_____

_____

What pace of withdrawal do you anticipate? (*Review this answer periodically.*)

_____

_____

What outcome do you hope to achieve? (*This can range from a reduction of dose to the elimination of medications.*)

_____

_____

CLINICIAN REFLECTION

What do you identify as optimal and achievable for this client's tapering process?

_____

_____

_____

_____

List the medications the client is seeking to taper, and learn about their half-life and recommended tapering process. (_It can be helpful to the client's understanding if they also do this research._)

_____

_____

_____

_____

_____

_____

Have you completed the following with the client?

- ❑   Assessed the medications' benefits (or lack thereof)

- ❑   Assessed the client's current side effects

- ❑   Assessed how have things changed over time since using the medications

- ❑   Confirmed that the client's self-care strategies are stable and consistent

- ❑   Educated the client about self-care and there being no "quick fix"

- ❑   Incorporated methods to address dissociation

- ❑   Explored the challenges (e.g., misinformation, triggers) and benefits of obtaining support from online or social media groups

- ❑   Conducted a discussion of withdrawal syndrome

CLINICAL CONSIDERATIONS

Often, people think that tapering simply involves stopping the medication and coping with the potential side effects. However, a successful taper must address not only the client's physical health, but also the long-held beliefs and fears of the client, the clinician, and others.

Clients can be hypervigilant, looking for any signs that their symptoms are returning. Some may have been using medications for years, even decades, and requiring medication is part of their identity; it takes time for them to forge a new self-concept without medication. Clients may also be influenced by prescribers, family members, or others around them who fear that the client will relapse or who believe that the client must always be on medications.

You may share some of these fears and have concerns about your client's safety. It is important to identify and address these beliefs as you work with the client to plan a safe, effective, and supportive tapering process.

Considering the information that you've gathered, identify any potential obstacles to your client's tapering goal and when they might appear during the process. Then, brainstorm possible actions that you could take with the client to overcome these obstacles.

POTENTIAL OBSTACLES	TIMELINE	ACTIONS

Once you've determined that the client is ready to begin the tapering process, ask them to complete the **Recruiting Your Taper Team** worksheet (p. 237), then work with them to develop a realistic plan using the **Taper Calendar** (p. 239).

RECRUITING YOUR TAPER TEAM

PURPOSE

This worksheet will help you identify your "taper team"—the people in your life who can support you during the process of tapering off medications.

BACKGROUND

Tapering off medications can be a stressful, taxing process. Before you begin, you must have a solid support system in place. Use your social circle to support your health and wellness. You will return the support someday, or you may have already "paid it forward."

INSTRUCTIONS

Fill in the provided roster with the names of people who could make up your support system, and identify how they might be able to support you during the tapering process.

NAME	HOW CAN THEY HELP?

Be sure to have open conversations with your taper team members about how long the tapering process might take, what they should expect, and what you might need from them. You can use the following dialogue prompts to guide these conversations.

DIALOGUE WITH FRIENDS AND FAMILY

I am working with my therapist and prescriber to taper off some/all of my medications over the next ___ months/years. Having a "taper team"—people who will support me to achieve this goal—will be important to my success. I feel you would be an important member of my team, if you're willing to help.

Specific Questions

- If I feel anxious/fearful/stressed, can I call you up once a day/week to discuss how the tapering process is going?

- If I'm having a hard day, could we meet somewhere or video call to talk face-to-face?

- Would you be able to accompany me to some of my appointments?

- Could we plan to...

  o Go for a walk together?

  o Cook a meal together?

  o Share tea or coffee?

  o Do a self-care activity together?

  o Commit to an exercise class/routine that we hold each other accountable for?

  (Decide how often you will do this activity together—for example, go for a 30-minute walk once a week—so they know what to expect.)

Remember to express your gratitude for this person's support (if they agree to join your taper team) or for their consideration and honest evaluation of their availability (if they decline).

DIALOGUE WITH A PRESCRIBER

I have been on the medication(s) _____ for ____ months/years. As you may know, I have been experiencing side effects, such as _____.

I want to reduce/eliminate medications, and my therapist and I want to engage your support so that I can be successful doing so. I have researched how to do this, and my health has already been improving as a result of therapy and my self-care program. I'd like to review my taper plan with you and obtain your feedback.

Specific Questions

- Would you be available to talk to my therapist at some point so that we are all on the same page as far as my process?

- Is the taper plan I've described feasible in your opinion? Are there any changes you would recommend?

- Would you be willing to prescribe this alternative medication: _____?

Remember to thank them for their time and support. If they are not willing to help you taper off your medications, you may wish to find a different prescribing provider; you could ask the current one for a referral.

TAPER CALENDAR

Client Worksheet

PURPOSE

This worksheet will help you and your therapist plan your taper process.

BACKGROUND

Setting a schedule with the guidance of your therapist is crucial for tapering off medications effectively and safely. This does not mean the schedule is written in stone; it can change as needed, usually to slow down the process. Tapering is a marathon, not a sprint. There's no rush. If it takes a year, or multiple years, that's perfectly fine! You will be successful. When you feel impatient, repeat this mantra: *Take your time tapering.*

INSTRUCTIONS

With your therapist, complete the following chart to set your goals for tapering off medications (you can make as many copies as needed). Include the specific dosages for each week. As you enact your tapering plan, make notes of how you are feeling (emotionally, mentally, and physically). Bring this chart to your follow-up appointments to discuss with your therapist.

WEEK	DOSAGE OF MEDICATION(S)	NOTES (HOW ARE YOU FEELING?)

NICOTINE WITHDRAWAL

Clinician Handout

PURPOSE

This informational handout provides integrative and nutritional methods to relinquish tobacco addiction.

BACKGROUND

Smoking tobacco is often a form of self-medication. Nicotine is a stimulant that releases dopamine, the pleasure chemical, in the brain. It enhances mood and cognitive function and stimulates metabolism. Nicotine is highly addictive—as addictive as heroin.

Withdrawal from nicotine generally begins within 30 minutes of smoking the last cigarette; physical symptoms peak within three days and last for four weeks. Because nicotine is an antidepressant, cessation often triggers depression. It's essential to remember that nicotine suppresses traumatic memories. Nicotine also speeds metabolism, and weight gain usually follows withdrawal. People are also subject to low energy and depressed cognitive function during the withdrawal process. Planning with diet, nutrients, and exercise can mitigate these effects.

REPLACE RITUALS

Many addictive substances have a sacred ritual use, which can inform your client's nicotine withdrawal process. Encourage your client to consider how they might be using tobacco in a ritualistic way and to explore alternatives. For example, instead of having a cigarette with coffee or tea in the morning, they might take a few minutes to practice the "breath of fire" pranayama (see **Breathing for Depression and Fatigue: Kapalbhati**, p. 301). Or, if cigarette smoking is attached to socializing and social drinking, they might switch a cigarette for a glass of sparkling water with fruit or a piece of chewing gum.

In my clinical experience, many people can withdraw successfully from tobacco by substituting cannabis during the acute withdrawal period. Both THC and CBD are associated with a reduction of somatic symptoms of nicotine withdrawal (Smith et al., 2021). The inhalation process likely contributes to the efficacy as well, as it maintains the client's smoking ritual.

The following table also presents different presents different methods you can use to help clients navigate nicotine withdrawal using the Brainbow Blueprint.

BRAINBOW BLUEPRINT	PROTOCOL
Culinary Medicine	• Balance blood sugar and oral needs • Eat high protein and healthy fat meals • Eat dopamine-rich foods (e.g., chocolate, coffee, bananas, walnuts)
Nutritional Supplements	• Take B-complex, multiminerals, niacin, zinc, taurine, tyrosine, vitamins A, C, D, E, and K • Take omega-3 fatty acids, choline • Consider taking adrenal, pituitary, hypothalamus, and lung glandulars
Herbal Medicine	• Use extract of lobelia, oat milk seed, St. John's wort, passionflower • Obtain licorice root sticks and suck on them instead of a cigarette (licorice can raise blood pressure, so monitor it) • Use cannabis during the acute withdrawal stage (1:1 ratio of CBD to THC) • Use kava for its anxiolytic effects (during the day, not in the evening) • Put black pepper essential oil in a diffuser • Add lavender oil to a hot magnesium sulfate bath
Hydrotherapy and Detoxification	• Do constitutional hydrotherapy every other day
Exercise; Breath	• Practice high-intensity interval training daily • Practice 4-7-8 breathing three times a day or as needed (see chapter 14) • Use a komuso breathing device
Somatics and Bodywork	• Do a diaphragmatic massage • Get a reflexology foot massage • Schedule cranial sacral and visceral manipulation therapy • Practice the NADA acupuncture protocol daily • Try PEMF (pulsed electromagnetic) therapy
Altered States and Psychedelic Medicine	• Consider psilocybin therapy

12
EXERCISE

In earlier times, movement was inherent in being human—our ancestors were foraging, running, walking, stretching, lifting, and bending throughout the day. In our modern world, however, many of us lead sedentary lives and need to intentionally make time to move and exercise. We may even buy a special mat, join a class online, or go to the gym. To reach a state of balance and health, it's critical that we move our bodies.

Yet how do we broach the topic of exercise with a client who is disinclined, had negative early life experiences, or believes they are "uncoordinated"? Or one who has challenges with certain movements, has a phobia about exercise, or is in recovery from body dysmorphia? Similarly, how do we know which type of exercise, and for whom, and for which type of distress? Making decisions about movement is both an art and a science and involves both objective and subjective experiences. There are also genomic influences on the kinds of exercises we are drawn to—exercise, like diet, is bioindividual.

Fortunately, a wealth of knowledge is available to help us understand the benefits of different forms of exercise so we can work with clients to make tailored recommendations. In this chapter, I share some fun, innovative exercises that you can share with your clients. Even clients who are already in the habit of exercising can still benefit from specific methods to address depression, anxiety, or insomnia. Let's begin by exploring some of the major types of exercise.

TYPES OF EXERCISE

Aerobic Exercise

I often remark that if our clients did aerobic exercise for an hour a day, we mental health care providers would likely be out of a job! Scientific research confirms that walking, running, swimming, or using a treadmill, elliptical, or rowing machine increases chemicals that protect the brain, circulates more oxygen throughout the body and brain, and aids lymphatic circulation. Most people will do well working between 55 percent and 80 percent of their maximum heart rate. However, differences in mobility, age, and well-being may require starting lower and working up to 55 percent.

Anaerobic Exercise

Anaerobic means "without oxygen." Anaerobic exercise breaks down glucose without using oxygen. It is typically fast and intense. Like aerobic exercise, anaerobic exercise improves mood. It also increases mitochondrial function, muscle mass, and muscle strength, which in turn all increase energy. Examples include weightlifting, resistance training, and strength training exercises, along with high-intensity interval training. Special core exercises like Pilates and circuit training are also anaerobic.

Stretching

Stretching keeps muscles flexible and strong. It also increases serotonin and thus enhances mood. A combination of stretching and core work can help with balance and posture, while stretching combined with balance and coordination exercises can have special benefits for people working to improve cognitive function, as with traumatic brain injury. Yoga has been well-studied for its positive effects on brain structure and cognition. Numerous types of yoga—including trauma-informed yoga, chair yoga, and yoga combined with meditation and breathing—can be identified to address each client's needs.

Energetics

The energetic traditions include chi gong, tai chi, and combination exercises like polarity, yoga, and bioenergetics. These exercises enhance awareness of the energetic body and the energy field. They may include the use of sounds and incorporate balance. Many, though not all, are derived from the Eastern traditions.

Special Exercises

The martial arts, including fencing, represent a combination of exercise training that may combine aerobic, anaerobic, and energetics. These forms of exercise are especially good for focus and attentional issues.

CHOOSING THE RIGHT TYPE OF EXERCISE

We tend to do the exercises that we are good at and avoid others. For example, someone who is naturally flexible may love yoga and avoid aerobics. Our decisions about exercise are partly driven by genetics and their influences on our brain chemistry. Just like there is intuitive eating in which we trust our "gut" to make choices about what foods we want to eat, there is intuitive exercise in which we don't follow a routine per se but tune in to what we need daily for movement. Understanding the complexity of movement and exercise for each person gives us numerous options for supporting the inclusion of movement in daily life.

Janelle's Story

Janelle told me that she hated to exercise and that there was no way she would do it. She had grown up in a family of athletes and had been forced to play every sport when all she really wanted to do was read. However, one day she was telling me about her decision to detoxify her home and clean using "green" products. She said how much she enjoyed cleaning, so I suggested that she consider cleaning her home as part of her exercise—that she bend and lift and twist, reach and squat, and while doing this, breathe and ensure that her abs were tightened in order to protect her back. I also suggested that she might enjoy listening to music while cleaning, opening the windows, and adding essential oils to her cleaning agents. Janelle's self-concept as someone who hated to exercise changed when she recognized that she enjoyed movement—when *she* chose it.

When helping a client choose the right type of exercise for them, it is also important to keep in mind whether a client has limited mobility, disabilities, or a chronic illness. Often, we work with people with depression, chronic pain, autoimmune diseases, and various disabilities, which requires us to consider a client's ability level and make adaptations as needed. Many of the exercises I've included in this chapter can be adapted to the upper body or lower body and can be done while seated or lying down.

When working with clients who have chronic pain or autoimmune illnesses, there are also challenges to adherence, as people can experience a flare-up of symptoms. This can be prevented by titrating movement and finding what works for each person. Special courses designed for autoimmune exercise or fibromyalgia can also be helpful.

You do not need to develop an expertise in exercise science to help your clients; you can collaborate with the client's trainer or refer them to an organization such as the YWCA. As a team, explore methods to address the client's particular concerns, such as body dysmorphia, chronic pain, anxiety, or depression. You can also help identify the obstacles to compliance and adherence. Exploring the client's history, readiness, motivation, ability, and goals for movement is essential to success. For clients who experience dissociation and spend time "outside their bodies," I also focus on identifying what about exercise could help them live comfortably and pleasurably in their bodies.

The exercises included in this chapter involve minimal space and equipment, so you may be able to teach them to your clients in session. You might also consider making movement part of your regular practice. Walking therapy (also called walk-and-talk therapy) involves walking, ideally outdoors, during therapy sessions. It combines the best of counseling, movement, and the benefits of nature and sunlight.

Exercise at a Glance

WELLNESS TARGET	RECOMMENDATIONS
Depression	• Aerobic exercise • Yoga (emphasize right-nostril pranayama)
Anxiety and panic	• Aerobic exercise and breathing retraining, such as the flying dragon (p. 250) or "ha" breath wood chopper (p. 291)
OCD	• Alternate aerobics, weights, and yoga and chi gong each day • Track benefits and improvement
Bipolar disorder	• Exercise outside at midday with natural light
Insomnia	• Aerobic exercise before 3 p.m.
Stress, trauma, and PTSD	• Balance hard aerobic exercise early in recovery with anaerobic exercise 4 days a week • Yoga and meditation
ADHD	• Martial arts, fencing, high-intensity interval training (HIIT), BOSU® balance exercise, surfing
Chronic pain	• Spectrum ranging from gentle to core to HIIT • Special autoimmune exercises
Substance use disorder	• Depends on the stage of recovery; try early morning aerobic exercise, build up to high intensity, use anaerobic exercise for dissociation and early evening yoga for relaxation
Cognition and memory	• Aerobic, high-intensity, and balance exercises • Broomstick stretch and balance exercises (p. 258) for right-brain/left-brain balance
Autism spectrum and neurodivergence	• Exercise in nature—along narrow mountain paths, skipping across stones or a bridge over a river • Emphasize exercises that require hand-eye coordination
Body image and eating disorders	• Core exercises, anaerobic resistance training, vinyasa yoga • Limit aerobic exercise if the client is dissociative
Digestive disorders	• Uddiyana bandha, hula hoops (IT band contact stimulates digestion)

EXERCISE, MITOCHONDRIAL FUNCTION, AND MENTAL WELLNESS

Clinician Handout

PURPOSE

This informational handout will provide you with background on some of the novel benefits of exercise that you can share with your clients.

BACKGROUND

There are so many established benefits for exercise, they need not be listed. I find that most of my clients are knowledgeable about the benefits and importance of exercise, but they may not know which types of exercise are best for them or may have challenges actually doing them. In addition to the adherences strategies I discuss in chapter 18, I find that educating clients about some of the novel benefits they may be unfamiliar with enhances motivation.

BENEFITS

Emerging evidence suggests that one oft-neglected benefit of exercise is the changes in mitochondrial function and brain-derived neurotrophic factor (BDNF). Mitochondria are our little energy machines within each cell. A variety of insults—including certain medications, infections, aging, acute and chronic stress (including PTSD), and toxic exposures—can damage the mitochondria. BDNF is a protein that ensures the growth and integrity of neurons, helping the neurons make new connections.

Many chronic mind-body challenges involve mitochondrial dysfunction and BDNF. These sensitive organelles are affected in a large range of illnesses, including fibromyalgia, Epstein-Barr, depression, PTSD, and long COVID. Decreases in BDNF are highly associated with PTSD and chronic stress. Exercise both enhances mitochondrial function (Sorriento et al., 2021) and increases BDNF, which may contribute to exercise's antidepressant and anxiolytic effects. In particular, high-intensity aerobic exercise, such as high-intensity interval training (HIIT), is one of the best methods to enhance cognition and reduce depression and anxiety (Borrega-Mouquinho et al., 2021).

EXERCISE HISTORY INTERVIEW

Clinician Handout

PURPOSE

This client interview will help you deepen your understanding of your client's experiences, attitudes, beliefs, and interests related to exercise and movement. This will enable you to tailor recommendations and referrals and to enhance adherence and success.

BACKGROUND

It's harder to motivate a client and get them engaged with exercise if they don't have a history with exercise or there are factors that prevent them from moving their body. A thorough understanding of your client's history, experience, beliefs, and goals will help you find an optimal approach with their exercise program. Remember, exercise is bioindividual, and any exercise that the client will do is the right exercise for them.

INSTRUCTIONS

Use the following process to guide you as you explore your client's relationship with exercise and movement.

1. Before you bring up the topic of exercise with your client, revisit their intake form to identify their current exercise habits —the types of exercise they engage in and how often they do so. I also assess how important exercise is in the client's life by asking them to rank all the Brainbow areas in order of priority. This information can be used as a starting point to determine when you should discuss exercise with the client and to begin your exploration.

2. Explain to the client that you would like to discuss the role of exercise in their health plan. Ask them to confirm or update the information you had gathered about their exercise habits.

3. Explore why the client engages in the types and amount of exercise that they do. If the client has a full movement schedule, I make this segue by congratulating them and asking them to share the benefits they experience—I then ask if it might be time to try something new. If the client has limited activities, I invite them to share their experiences and concerns regarding exercise. Other helpful questions include the following:

    o   How much do you know about exercise? Are you ready to learn some new methods to improve your health?

    o   What kinds of exercise or movement do you like to do, and why? Which ones do you not like to do, and why?

- ○ Are there any physical injuries, illnesses, or limitations to consider? How does this affect the types of exercise or movement that you would be comfortable trying out?

- ○ What are your feelings regarding exercise?

- ○ What have been the greatest influences on your views toward exercise? (It is helpful to consider the influences of the client's caregivers on their attitudes and exposure to athletics; their experiences in school, such as physical education classes; their inclusion or exclusion from team sports in competition; any injuries resulting from exercise; and so forth.)

Exploring the underpinnings for the client's attitudes will help you assess motivation and adherence, and to define the potential for next steps and specific exercises.

FLYING DRAGON

Client Exercise

PURPOSE

This exercise helps open up your respiration by opening the chest and stretching the shoulder blades.

BACKGROUND

Combining breath retraining with stretching has many benefits for treating anxiety and panic. The "flying dragon" is a simple exercise that you can incorporate into your routine.

INSTRUCTIONS

- With your feet spread shoulder-width apart, bend your knees slightly and slowly lift your arms up over your head.

- Bring your arms around to the back of your body and clasp your palms together, squeezing your shoulder blades together and stretching the pectoral muscles in your chest.

- Slowly bend over, keeping your knees slightly bent. Stabilize your back by tightening your abdomen.

- Bend over until you're parallel to the ground (and no further). As you bend over, keep your palms clasped and lift your arms up overhead straight behind you.

- As you lift your head straight out, remaining parallel to the ground, breathe into your chest and back. Slowly let your arms drop, release the stretch, and raise your torso back to an upright position.

THE KINESTHETIC BODY EXERCISE*

Client Exercise

PURPOSE

This exercise introduces gentle movement that explores the physical body and the kinesthetic body.

BACKGROUND

The kinesthetic body (also called the energetic or imaginal body) calls on your active imagination—your inner felt sense of where you begin and where you end, your matter and your motion, inside and outside of the physical definitions you call your body. This sense allows you to imagine your body moving when you are not moving at all.

Beginning movement with the kinesthetic body will help you identify the range of your physical body. While you may think you know where your body begins and ends, those boundaries are very subjective. Consider how your body feels after you have a shot of anesthetic, or if you have too much alcohol, or during feelings of dissociation. So much mental distress—pain, addictions, dysmorphia—involves feeling outside of the body or not feeling comfortable in the body. The kinesthetic body can help you explore these sensations and variations.

It will be difficult to do this activity while reading the instructions, so ask your therapist (or a friend, family member, etc.) to read the instructions out loud to you or make a recording.

INSTRUCTIONS

- Stand with your weight evenly balanced on both your feet. Notice all your muscles—is there any unnecessary tension, particularly in your shoulder and neck area? If so, relax this tension.

- Raise your real right arm and stretch. Feel the stretch in your fingers, your hand, your shoulder, your torso. Now lower your arm. Repeat this several times.

- Now stretch your kinesthetic right arm. To do so, keep your real arm still but imagine, as vividly as possible, that you are raising your arm. Recall all the same sensations. Try to experience your kinesthetic arm with as much reality as your real arm.

- Stretch again with your real right arm, then your kinesthetic right arm. Alternate several times between stretching with your real arm and your kinesthetic arm.

---

* Adapted from *The Possible Human: A Course in Enhancing Your Physical, Mental, and Creative Abilities* (Houston, 1997).

- Do the same thing with your left arm: Stretch your real left arm several times, then keep your real left arm still and stretch your kinesthetic left arm. Alternate several times between stretching with your real arm and your kinesthetic arm.

- Let your real arms and shoulders circle in a round forward movement. Then do the same thing with your kinesthetic arms and shoulders. Then alternate between your real and kinesthetic arms and shoulders.

- With your real body, lunge to the right. Come back to the center. Repeat this several times. Now lunge to the right with your kinesthetic body. Come back to the center. Alternate several times between your real and your kinesthetic body.

- Do the same thing to the left: With your real body, lunge to the left, then come back to center. With your kinesthetic body, lunge to the left, then come back to center. Alternate several times.

- Follow this sequence:

    o Real body lunges right, then comes back to the center.

    o Real body lunges left and comes back.

    o Kinesthetic body lunges left and comes back.

    o Real body lunges left and comes back.

    o Kinesthetic body lunges right and comes back.

    o Real body lunges right and comes back.

    o Real body lunges left and comes back.

    o Now, *at the same time*, your kinesthetic body lunges right and your real body lunges left.

    o Come back to the center.

    o Now lunge with your real body to the right and your kinesthetic body to the left.

    o Come back to center.

- Rest for a moment.

- Raise both of your real arms over your head and hold them there.

- At the same time, feel your kinesthetic arms hanging at your sides. *Slowly* lower your real arms while you raise your kinesthetic arms.

- Then lower your kinesthetic arms while you raise your real arms.

- Lower your real arms while you raise your kinesthetic arms.

- Continue with this until the raising and lowering of your kinesthetic arms becomes almost indistinguishable from the movement of your real arms.

- Rest for a moment.

- Be aware of the space several feet in front of you. Now, with your real body, jump as high as you can into that space. Then jump back. Do it again with your real body, jumping as high as you can, forward and back.

- Do the same thing with your kinesthetic body, jumping forward and back, as high as you can.

- Repeat with your real body. Jump forward and back three times in a row.

- With your kinesthetic body, jump forward and back once.

- Jump with your real body.

- Jump again with your kinesthetic body.

- Jump forward with your kinesthetic body and stay there.

- Now, jumping as high as you can, jump with your real body *into* your kinesthetic body!

- Standing still, notice how you feel. Scan your body. Is there greater awareness now in your body?

- Begin to walk around. Notice your awareness.

- Opening your eyes, see if your perception of the external world and others has changed.

DRUMSTICK EXERCISES

Client Exercise

PURPOSE

This exercise combines movement, toning, and emotional release through rhythmic sound. It is a lot of fun because the sticks are an energy receptor and help to release stress, anger, and fatigue.

BACKGROUND

The addition of drumsticks to any movement enhances rhythm and balance and provides a great upper body workout. Moving the trunk of the body, arms, and feet at different times aids coordination and integration of the right and left brain hemispheres.

INSTRUCTIONS

Drumstick Hit to the Side

This exercise can be done seated or standing.

- Take two drumsticks.

- Grab the sticks from the lower end, not by the middle. Hold one stick with your arm outstretched, and with the other stick, hit the first stick in the middle.

- If you are standing, as you do the lateral movements, move the tip of the foot toward the center along with the knee. Now combine a step in the same place with your right toe and one hit to the right. Hit with your left hand.

- Optional: As you hit, make the *ha, ha, ha* sound as loud as you can, and feel your emotions release and dissipate.

Drumstick Front and Back

In this exercise, you will combine core strengthening with a release of stress by using drumsticks to bang on the floor surface.

- Place a yoga mat on the floor and grab two drumsticks.

- Sit down on the mat, with your legs in front of you and your knees bent so that your heels are on the floor. Your legs should be hip-width apart. Make sure your legs are engaged at all times.

- Then curve your chest in so you feel your tightened abs working.

- Hold a drumstick in hand and with your hands next to your hips, hit the floor in front of you, reaching past the side of your knees.

- Then reach behind you and hit the floor in the back, by swinging your arms behind you and slightly lowering your chest. Don't forget to keep your back slightly curved at the chest and keep your abs tight.

- Continue alternating between hitting in front of you and behind you for 30 seconds.

- Optional: As you bang, yell *oh, oh, oh.*

Drumstick and Squat

This exercise combines the movement of squats while you hit the floor with the drumsticks and then hit in the air with the drumsticks. It is like playing drums. It works your legs, reduces back pain, and releases anger.

- Stand tall with your feet two times your shoulder-width and your feet pointing out.

- Then move your glutes back a bit and lean slightly forward, with your knees slightly bent and your abs firm.

- Extend your arms in front of you and hit the drumsticks against each other, then go down with a squat and hit the floor with the sticks.

- Rise back up and repeat the sequence for 30 seconds.

HULA HOOP ON THE FLOOR

Client Exercise

PURPOSE

This exercise improves rhythm and coordination as it strengthens your legs.

BACKGROUND

The hips can become very tight from sitting or lack of diverse movement like rotation. Some societies, like Indigenous Hawaiians, use hip rotation in ritual dance and celebrate this movement. Other societies frown upon this type of movement, leading to inhibition. Tight hips can also cause tense lower back muscles—and, conversely, when the hips are flexible, the lower back is also supple.

INSTRUCTIONS

Circular Steps

- Place the hula hoop on the floor and stand in the center of it.

- You will be stepping in a sequence; it's essential to always step with the whole sole of your foot.

- Keep your left leg in place. With your right leg, step in front of the hoop, then step back to the center. Step to the right, then back to the center. Finally, step behind the hoop, then back. Move your arms as you step, allowing them to swing and letting the elbows be bent.

- Repeat on the opposite side: Keep your right leg in the center of the hoop. With your left leg, step forward, to the left, and then backward, returning to center after each step.

- Repeat for four circuits on each side.

- For a more advanced variation, do not return to center after each step—always keep your stepping foot outside the hoop. If you have a hard time moving your arms along, place them level with the height of your shoulders.

Side Jumps

- Stand in the center of the hula hoop and bend over slightly.

- Jump to the right so you land outside of the hoop, then jump back to the center. Repeat on the left side.

- Continue alternating between the right and left, aiming for 16 jumps to each side.

- If you can't do it fast, don't worry. Do it slowly and build your speed as it feels comfortable.

Lunges

- Start in the center of the hula hoop.

- Make short backward lunges going behind the hula hoop, while raising your arms.

- Do 16 repetitions, alternating between left and right.

Step to the Front

- Start in the center of the hula hoop.

- With your right leg, step forward outside the hoop while you rotate your whole arm and turn slightly to the side, as if you are boxing. Return to center and repeat with the left side.

- Complete 16 repetitions, alternating between left and right.

Combination Step and Lunge

- Do a right backward lunge, then a left backward lunge, then a right "step to the front," and finally a left "step to the front."

- Repeat this circuit four times.

Client Exercise

PURPOSE

These exercises enhance physical and right-brain/left-brain balance.

BACKGROUND

Each of these exercises can be completed in about one minute, and the only equipment you need is a broomstick (or a similar support item).

INSTRUCTIONS

Horizontal Stretch on One Foot

- Hold the broomstick vertically with your left hand, with one end on the floor.

- Slightly bend your left leg.

- Do a back lift of your right leg as you extend your right hand to the front.

- Lower as slowly as you can and allow yourself to feel your balance.

- Contract your abs as you lower.

- As you go down, your hand can slide down on the broomstick too.

- Hold this posture for 10 seconds.

- Repeat the process with the other side of your body.

- As your balance improves, increase the holds to 30 seconds each.

Diagonal Stretch on One Foot

- Place your right hand on your hip.

- With your left arm, hold the broomstick and stretch this arm out to the side for support.

- Lean to your left, and raise your right leg and arm. You may need to adjust the broomstick as you stretch.

- Stretch your arm and try to touch the tip of the broomstick with the palm of your hand.

- Stay there for 10–30 seconds, lower, and then raise back up—first the leg, then the arm.

- Repeat this exercise on the other side.

Advanced Horizontal Stretch on One Foot

- Hold the broomstick horizontally with both hands.

- Slightly bend your left leg and raise your right foot off the ground behind you. Stretch your body out horizontally, moving your hands out to the front.

- Bend over as much as possible, and contract your abs, until you reach a horizontal position.

- Hold this posture for up to 30 seconds.

- Repeat with your other leg.

Advanced Diagonal Stretch on One Foot

- Hold the broomstick horizontally with both hands and look at the floor.

- Elevate your right leg to the side, while moving your hands to the left.

- Stretch until you reach a deep diagonal—almost horizontal—line that includes your arms, body, and leg.

- Hold this position for up to 30 seconds.

- Repeat on the other side.

Client Exercise

PURPOSE

This set of exercises stretches the shoulder blades, the arms, the entire spine, and the lower back and legs to release emotional stress and recuperate from the effects of sitting.

BACKGROUND

You will need an exercise ball (or a chair) for these exercises. Each exercise takes less than a minute.

INSTRUCTIONS

Downward-Facing Dog

- Place the exercise ball in front of you.

- Stand and open your legs to the side as far as you comfortably can.

- Tighten your abs.

- With your knees bent and your hips back, place your palms on the ball in front of you and walk the ball forward with the palms of your hands.

- Push forward, put your head in the middle of your arms, lower your head, and relax and stretch.

- You can relax a bit more and swing back and forth.

- Hold this position for 30 seconds.

- When you return to the initial position, go up in the cat position by rounding your back.

- A variation of this exercise is to use just your fingertips, rather than the palms of your hands, to move the ball. Drop down as far as you can so you can relax your upper body: chest, back, shoulders, biceps, triceps, trapezius. Hold for 30–45 seconds before returning to the initial position.

Rotation to the Side and Front

- Stand with the exercise ball in front of you and your feet spread as far as you can comfortably manage.

- Place your left hand on your left leg.

- With the palm of your right hand, walk the ball to the left as far as you can, leaning your upper body to the front as you move. Now rest your head on your left arm.

- Hold this position for 15 seconds.

- Return to the center and start stretching to your right. Lean your right hand in on your right leg so you don't hurt your back.

- Bend down, lay your head on your arm, and stretch.

- Rest for 15 more seconds.

- Go back to the initial position and stretch again to the front in a downward-facing dog position, with your fingertips on the ball, for 15 more seconds.

- When you come up, do it in a cat pose, with your back rounded. Move slowly so you don't get dizzy.

- Take a moment to sit and relax.

BALANCE THE BRAIN, BALANCE THE MIND: EXERCISES FOR SELF-INTEGRATION

Client Exercise

PURPOSE

These fun and dynamic physical exercises increase communication between the brain's left and right hemispheres, bringing your intuitive and analytic sides into harmony.

BACKGROUND

Our brain's right and left hemispheres see the world a little differently. Both hemispheres can engage in most functions—in fact, when one hemisphere has been damaged by a stroke or traumatic brain injury, the other can fill in. You have likely heard about right or left brain "dominance." While laterality determines hand and eye dominance and contributes to language and movements, the dominance of one hemisphere over another has been linked to cognitive imbalances and other mental and physical health issues.

You may have already tried forced-nostril breathing (see **Ultradian Rhythm Exercises: "Hello, Brain,"** p. 82), which uses intentional hemispheric dominance to alter your consciousness. The following exercises will engage both hemispheres of your brain and increase communication between them. This has many benefits: It expands your perspective; jump-starts your creativity, focus, and mental stamina; and helps you decompress and release frenetic mental energy at the end of the day.

DID YOU KNOW?
Cross-lateral movements allow us to cross the body's midline to integrate the left and right hemispheres.

INSTRUCTIONS

These exercises are best performed twice daily: once in the morning and once in the evening. Choose at least one exercise to practice regularly for a week. Whichever exercise you choose, do it for 1–2 minutes or 30 repetitions. Most importantly, do it slowly and deliberately—resist the urge to rush. You can also do these exercises to music you enjoy. Listening to music integrates the left and right brain hemispheres; Sufi meditation music and binaural beats are especially helpful.

The Cross-Crawl

- Stand with your feet planted slightly wider than hip-width apart and your arms outstretched to either side, parallel to the ground.

- Lift your right knee to hip height and touch it with your left hand or elbow.

- Lift your left knee to hip height and touch it with your right hand or elbow.

The Heel Touch

- Stand with your feet planted slightly wider than hip-width apart and your arms outstretched to either side, parallel to the ground.

- Swing your right heel behind your left calf. Reach down to touch your heel (or ankle) with your left hand.

- Repeat on the other side, swinging your left heel behind your right calf and reaching down to touch it with your right hand.

Shoulder-to-Shoulder

- This variation is beneficial if you have decreased mobility in your lower body.

- Stand or sit with your arms outstretched to either side, parallel to the ground.

- Bend your right elbow and touch your right fingertips to your left shoulder.

- Re-extend your right arm, bend your left elbow, and touch your left fingertips to your right shoulder.

Toe-Touches

- Stand with feet your planted wider than hip-width apart and your arms extended to either side, parallel to the ground.

- Swing your right arm down and across your body until your fingertips touch your left ankle, foot, or toes. Return to starting position.

- Repeat on the other side, swinging your left arm down and across, touching your right angle, foot, or toes with your left fingertips. Return to the starting position.

Leg Extensions

- Stand with your hands on your hips or gripping a ballet bar or other support. Place your feet hip-width apart.

- Extend your right leg, keeping the toes on the ground or lifting the foot into the air so that you cross the left leg completely. Imagine standing in the middle of a square. Extend the right leg so that you would touch your right toes to the front left corner of the square. (If you are somewhere with tiled or linoleum flooring, you may be able to find an actual square to stand in and use as a guide.)

- Repeat on the other side, touching your left toes to the upper right corner of your imaginary square.

- Seated modification: Place your feet under your knees so that your legs form a 90-degree angle. Extend your right leg across your left leg, touching your right toes to the floor beyond your left foot. Repeat on the other side, touching your left toes to the floor beyond your right foot.

Mismatched Motions

Variation 1

- Place your right hand on top of your head and your left hand over your navel.

- Move your right hand up and down, patting the top of your head. Sustain that movement while moving your left hand in a circular motion, rubbing your belly. Continue for a full minute.

- Now switch hands! Pat your head with your left hand and rub your belly with your right hand. Do so for a full minute.

- Notice whether it was difficult to make the mismatched motions at the same time, and whether one hand had a more challenging time staying "focused" on its task than the other.

Variation 2

- While seated, circle your right ankle in a clockwise direction. Now, maintaining the ankle motion, draw the number "6" in the air with your right hand. Did your foot change direction?

- Go slowly and see if you can sustain the mismatched movements of your foot and hand.

- Switch sides—circle your left ankle clockwise while drawing a "6" in the air with your left hand. Could you do it? Was one side harder than the other?

Unexpected Movements

Unexpected movements are unpracticed variations of familiar movements—in other words, doing your usual activities but in an unusual way. Here are some ideas:

- Reach for items with your nondominant hand.

- Step with your nondominant foot first.

- Place your feet in a different (but still safe and stable) position while you brush your teeth.

- Cross your legs under you while you work at your desk (just for a minute or two).

- Write notes using your nondominant hand.

- If you practice yoga, try changing up the positions:

  - Take a locust pose and extend your right arm behind you.

  - Move from a downward-facing dog to a three-legged dog (right leg lifted) and then through the plank pose (chaturanga), keeping your right leg lifted until you get to an upward-facing dog. Lift the left leg as you move back into down-dog from up-dog, assuming a three-legged dog on the other side. Now, repeat this short flow with the left leg lifted.

REFLECTION

After practicing your hemisphere integration exercise(s) regularly for one week, reflect on the following questions.

Did you notice any changes in your mental focus, stamina, or creativity this week? Did you notice yourself thinking integratively—in whole systems rather than in parts?

_____

_____

_____

How soon after doing the exercise did you experience this change? How long did it last?

_____

_____

How hard or easy was it for you to perform the exercise(s) you chose? Were some exercises more challenging than others?

_____

_____

_____

What are your favorite exercises?

_____

_____

13
SOMATICS AND BODYWORK

The body has a story to tell; it carries memory and meaning, often over rough terrain. As movement therapist Bonnie Bainbridge Cohen has said, "The mind is like the wind and the body like the sand: If you want to see how the wind is blowing, you can look at the sand."

In the previous chapter, we explored the role of exercise and movement that moves muscle and lymph, elevates our neurohormones, and cheers our brain chemicals onward. This chapter provides exercises that give the body a quieter, inward vista—a safe space to engage body and mind, soma and psyche. Done solo, or in dyads or groups, these practices lead to profound experiences of empathy (for oneself and others) and attunement to one's deeper needs.

I began my 45-year clinical career as a bodyworker, doing polarity therapy, craniosacral therapy, and deep tissue massage. I discovered the various ways the body tells the story of life's events, including traumatic events. I would touch my clients' pain, tension, constriction, spasms, constipated bowels, and more—and as I did, the stories, memories, and meanings emerged. These experiences led me to train as a psychotherapist and practice as a somatic therapist specializing in trauma. Very few mental health clinicians will touch the client's body—nor should they generally, especially with clients whose boundaries have been violated—unless under particular circumstances. Instead, they will refer their clients to licensed somatic therapists.

However, dually training in somatics provides a potent opportunity for integration, the oft-missing piece in any therapy. It allows you to teach your clients a variety of therapeutic body-based techniques, such as how to perform a foot massage, or how to rock their partners and children to induce vagal response and deep sleep. Teaching these techniques requires a simple skill set. This contrasts with medical massage and therapeutic manipulation of the body, including the viscera, which require training and licensures. It is much like the difference between listening to a friend discuss their problems and having the skills of a psychotherapist.

There are as many types of bodywork therapies as there are psychotherapies, and this variety provides opportunities to make referrals based on what methods are most suited to both the individual and the goal of intervention. The exercises in this chapter are a good starting point for clients to begin to tune in to and explore their somatic needs—and of course these are bidirectionally related to mental health.

SOMATIC EMPATHY AND SYNCHRONY

When I developed the idea of somatic empathy, it arose from my experiences combining psychotherapeutic, somatic, and energetic work with clients, leading to interpersonal synchrony. This synchrony was reflected in empathy that went beyond emotion to engage the energetic field. I have written about this previously in depth (Korn, 2013/2022) as I sought psychological and biological explanations for these profound, healing experiences.

Ongoing science about the human nervous system shows how brain neurons and brain waves synchronize. Brain waves synchronize within individuals, within dyads, and even within groups. The synchrony of brain waves appears to enable new learning and adaptation, while an inability to synchronize has been observed in mental illnesses, including schizophrenia and autism (Uhlhaas & Singer, 2006).

While the science has yet to be fully elucidated, research suggests that activities and interventions that actively support synchrony across the hemispheres lead to more flexible thinking (Cho et al., 2020). Many of the integrative methods I explore in this book are meant to foster synchronic function. Still other methods include binaural beats, neurofeedback, psychotherapy, dance, energetic methods of bodywork, acupuncture, and various rituals. This mirroring effect between dyadic brain nodes occurs only in the clinical interaction where rapport is already established, and it can lead to profound physiological changes, including analgesia in pain patients (Ellingsen et al., 2020).

Brain-to-brain synchrony has also been studied between students and teachers, with the finding that closer relationships lead to more synchronization (Bevilacqua et al., 2019). Thus, as psychoeducators, we recognize the power of eye contact to awaken empathy in the social brain, through activating the cerebellum of each gazing individual simultaneously. This also activates the limbic system when we move any part of the body (including the eyes), and when we observe someone else's movements. Even clients who have physical challenges to movement can achieve synchronization; the science suggests that our mirror neurons activate motor neurons (Yuan et al., 2015) regardless of whether the motor neurons activate movement.

Therefore, we can promote synchrony through either shared physical movement or imaginal exercises, such as those proposed by Jean Houston (1997) in her groundbreaking work on kinesthetic exercises and Ilene Serlin's (2014) concept of dancing for the imaginal self. This may explain the Indigenous Kenyan practice of long-distance runners training as much by visualizing their runs while resting in a hammock as doing their physical running. This mindful approach to somatics—emphasizing *being* (not doing)—leads to intrapersonal and interpersonal synchrony. We can reenact the ancient, hardwired templates of our diverse ancestral and Indigenous ritual traditions that engage interpersonal coherence at a community-wide level (D'Aquili et al., 1979).

THE ART OF SOMATIC AND BODYWORK REFERRALS

Not all touch is created equal. Different kinds of touch and different degrees of pressure are used in somatic work to produce different results. For example, an individual with depression may benefit from a deep pressure massage, while an anxious client will benefit from lighter touch.

Many people may also receive tremendous benefits from subtler forms of somatic work, like cranial electrotherapy stimulation (CES). In CES, a small, FDA-approved, prescription medical device is used to deliver a low-intensity electrical current via a pair of electrodes attached to the earlobes. This modulates central and peripheral nervous system activity and can improve symptoms of anxiety, insomnia, depression, PTSD, and pain. I recommend that clients use it for 20–60 minutes at a time. CES devices should not be used by people with cardiac implants, like pacemakers or defibrillators.

Unless your clients have had significant previous experience with somatic work, they may not know what will be of benefit to them in this realm. Your role may then be twofold: to explore and discern the methods that will bring relief and balance, and to refer clients to expert bodyworkers who can augment the work you are doing together. The best way to identify professionals in your area for massage, bodywork, and other somatic therapies (Feldenkrais, Trager, lymphatic massage, somatic experiencing, etc.) is to make an appointment yourself and explore your own experience and response.

Somatics and Bodywork at a Glance

WELLNESS TARGET	RECOMMENDATIONS
Depression	• Apply stimulating pressure (apply deep pressure point or massage where it feels good but may be slightly tender) • Receive deep reflexology • Do guided body scan exercises
Anxiety and panic	• Encourage light touch bodywork, especially to the neck and diaphragm • Breathe into the pelvis and connect with core muscles
OCD	• Do belly rocking and side rocking with the hands on the sacrum and shoulder blades
Bipolar disorder	• Practice yogic breath holding to reduce depression • Apply moxibustion
Insomnia	• Practice relaxing bodywork • Receive and give body rocking • Practice yoga asanas that activate the parasympathetic nervous system (such as lotus or corpse pose)
Stress, trauma, and PTSD	• Understand pelvic anatomy and muscular restrictions (see **Discover Your Pelvis**, p. 271) • Do a belly self-massage (see **Discovering Your Digestion with Touch**, p. 135)

WELLNESS TARGET	RECOMMENDATIONS
ADHD	• When agitated, rock while lying on the right side • Practice guided somatic visualizations • Do a polarity facial massage
Chronic pain	• Explore pelvic awareness; contact pubis symphysis points • Do a facial and deep tissue massage • Get acupuncture, electro-acupuncture • Use a cranial electrotherapy stimulation (CES) device
Substance use disorder	• Use a CES device • Do acupuncture, moxibustion, and exercises to decrease dissociation
Cognition and memory	• Schedule a craniosacral therapy appointment • Receive a grounding massage treatment, focusing on the feet and hands
Autism spectrum and neurodivergence	• Rocking, rocking, and more rocking! • Do guided body scans, grounding exercises, touch therapies on the hands and feet, and craniosacral therapy
Body image and eating disorders	• Receive visceral manipulation therapy • Do diaphragm and pelvic work • Practice breath holding, uddiyana bandha
Digestive disorders	• Do gentle visceral manipulation, emphasizing the dan tien point (see **Dan Tien: The Elixir of Life**, p. 136)

DISCOVER YOUR PELVIS

Client Exercise

PURPOSE

These exercises will help you understand and connect somatically and compassionately with the pelvic region.

BACKGROUND

The pelvis is a skeletal structure that links the upper and lower body. It is the foundation—the fulcrum—of the body and the psyche. The pelvis affects how we feel, sit, stand, and walk, along with how we experience pain. The muscular connections in and around the pelvis are fundamental to core stability and functional strength.

Paying attention to the pelvis helps us address pain related to the bladder, prostate, or menstrual cycle. The hips and pelvic region, like all regions of the body, potentially hold memories. If you have experienced trauma related to the pelvic area (such as sexual assault), opening, releasing, and strengthening this area may help in your recovery. Paying attention to the pelvis will help you attune to your whole body, from the inside out.

INSTRUCTIONS

For the following activities, you will need a space where you can move around, sit, and lie down comfortably—a yoga mat on the floor would be ideal.

Activity 1: Find Your Pelvis

The term *pelvis* refers to two fused pelvic bones called the os coxae, the innominate bones, or the coxal bones. Each pelvic bone has three parts: the ilium at the top, the ischium below, and the pubis in front.

Iliac Crests

- While seated or standing, place your hands on your waist so that the C-shapes created by your index finger and thumb rest firmly against either side of your middle torso.

- Press your hands on your body, suck in your stomach in and up to lengthen your waist, and slide your hands down until you reach the hard bone. If you press the pads of your thumb and forefinger in here, you should feel the top of an arch of bone on either side of your lower torso. These are your iliac crests, the uppermost part of each ilium.

Ischial Tuberosities

- Sit down on a firm chair or another hard surface.

- Reach your fingers under one side of your buttocks, pressing firmly into the very middle of the fleshy part of your backside, and then lower the cheek down. You should feel a hard bone there—this is the ischial tuberosity, or the "sits bone." It is the base of the ischium, which is the posterior and distal portion of the os coxae.

- Repeat this process to find the ischial tuberosity on the other side.

Pubic Symphysis

- You can stay seated, but it may be easier to lie down or stand up for this portion.

- Press into the area of the body where you grow (or would grow) pubic hair. Gently migrate your fingers down this area until you hit hard bone—it is in fact cartilage, but it bridges the two pubis bones. This is called the pubic symphysis, where your two ox coxae join to create the pelvis. This structure protects your sexual organs.

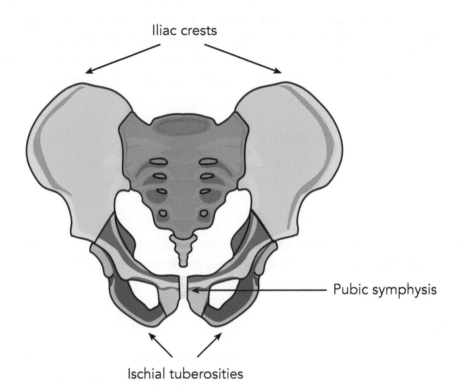

Iliac crests

Pubic symphysis

Ischial tuberosities

Activity 2: Check-In

When describing your sensations throughout this exercise, you may find these sense words helpful:

Tense	Tight	Crunchy	Dull pain
Numb	Open	Fluid	Shooting pain
Neutral	Weak	Sore	
Stiff	Imbalanced	Sharp pain	

- Stand up and stretch your arms up over your head while pressing your feet down into the ground.

- Begin to "crawl" as if you could climb into the air, stretching one arm higher than the other, extending down through the corresponding leg as you reach up with each arm.

- How does this feel in the low back and the front of the hips? In the rest of the spine? In the front and back of the thighs?

- Lower your arms and slowly roll down through your spine, reaching your fingers toward the ground. Bend your knees. Experiment with reaching down lower and raising up higher, holding on to your legs at different levels for support, stretching and curving your tailbone back, up, and down. What sensations are these movements prompting in your pelvic region? In the connected parts of the body?

- Get down on your hands and knees, and begin a few rounds of the cat-cow yoga pose: Arch your back, tuck in your tailbone, and let your head curl down in the cat pose, then bring your head up and let your back drop down in the cow pose. What are you sensing in your hips, back, abs, legs, buttocks?

- Finally, lie down on your back. Start with your feet planted on the floor in front of your hips. Plant them closer and farther away. Move your knees and hips around, searching for fluidity and points of tension. What do you feel in the pelvic region?

DID YOU KNOW?

The action of the pelvic floor mirrors the movement of the diaphragm. That is, as we inhale and the diaphragm lowers to increase lung capacity, the pelvic floor muscles lower too. As we exhale, the opposite motion occurs. Because of this, diaphragmatic breathing can help the pelvis gain fluidity and release.

Activity 3: Breathe In Butterfly

- Lie on your back, with your legs in a butterfly position (with the soles of your feet touching and the knees relaxing outward). Place a bolster, pillow, or rolled-up blanket or towel under your knees on both sides. You can also keep your legs extended and place the support under your knees in that position.

- Breath to a count of 4-4-4-4, as follows: Seal your lips. Breathe in through your nose for a count of four, and hold your in-breath for a count of four. Then exhale for a count of four, and hold your out-breath for a count of four.

- Repeat several rounds of this breathing, or use your own favorite breath exercise. You can set a timer for 3–5 minutes (or more) if that helps you relax into the pranayama.

Activity 4: Go Deeper

Based on what movements feel good and what you need, choose from the following practices.

If you need opening, comfort, or relief from pelvic pain:

- Make a heating pad by filling a sock, pillowcase, or piece of fabric with dry rice or sand gathered from a beach. Sew or tie it shut and microwave it for 1–3 minutes. Place it under your sacrum, on your pubis, or a little higher on your low belly. You may also rub some CBD salve on the area first.

If you need movement and strengthening:

- Repeat the cat-cow pose described in activity 2.

- Try the bird-dog pose:

    ○ Start on your hands and knees, with a neutral spine position.

    ○ Raise your right arm and left leg, keeping your shoulders and hips parallel to the floor and tucking your chin into your chest. Hold for a few seconds, then return to the starting position.

    ○ Repeat with your left arm and right leg. This completes one round.

    ○ Do several more rounds.

DID YOU KNOW?
Our pelvis helps us stay grounded. Recipes with root vegetables can provide an important complement to these somatic explorations (see **Grounding with Roots: Parsnip Purée**, p. 176).

POLARITY FACIAL MASSAGE

Client Exercise

PURPOSE

This worksheet explains how to give yourself a polarity facial massage to promote relaxation and well-being.

BACKGROUND

We spend so much time focusing, looking, seeing, and being exposed to the blue light of computers that it's good to have a chance to relax our faces. Polarity points are unique energy points on the body, like acupuncture or marma points. Massaging the polarity points on the face and scalp creates a deeply energizing, yet relaxed, sense of well-being.

INSTRUCTIONS

- Close your eyes, place your fingers on your jawline, and begin gently tapping outwardly with all your fingers. Move up to the jaw, feeling the temporomandibular joint (TMJ—where your mouth opens and closes on a hinge joint), and even tap up to the lower temples.

- Do this three times. On the final time, stay on the TMJ and tap, letting your jaw open slightly and relax.

- Next, begin by tapping just below the bottom lip and following that line up toward the jaw, now passing over your cheekbones. Again, do this three times.

- Next, tap gently on your temples 30 times.

- Now, take your first two fingers and gently tap on the eyebrow, moving from the inner brow to the outer brow. Do this three times and then move down to the cheekbones, moving from the nose outward along the bone, tapping as you go, for three rounds.

- Next, bring the tapping around your eye bones. Complete a full circle three times. As you tap, feel your face relax, and feel for any areas that you notice are feeling swollen or tense. Take a moment to rest and feel the sensations.

- When you are ready, start at the third eye in the middle of your brow and very gently tap 30 times.

- Next, bring your fingers up and tap from the middle of your forehead to the edge of your face. Do this three times, along several imagined horizontal lines along your forehead, until you rise to the hairline.

- When you reach the hairline, move your tapping fingers along the midline of your head, tapping as far back as you can, coming down to your neck.

- When you finish, let your eyes remain closed. Take a moment to feel the sensations. Breathe, relax, and feel the aliveness. When you are ready, open your eyes.

V IS FOR VAGUS AND VITALITY

Client Exercise

PURPOSE

This vagus nerve stimulation exercise promotes vitality and relaxation.

BACKGROUND

The 10th cranial nerve, known as the vagus nerve, comes to the surface along the auricle (the external part of the ear). In Chinese medicine, the earlobes denote the center of vitality and suggest the amount of energy we bring into this life. Western medicine has also connected this area to vitality; for example, diagonal creases in the ear often signify heart disease. Piercing the ears is also related to our vitality. The practice began in Africa, where placing gold or silver in the earlobe was believed to attract solar or lunar energy, respectively, thus enhancing the life force. (However, too many piercings are considered to bisect energy flow and are ill-advised.)

Auricular acupuncture or acupressure is a potent way to stimulate vitality and release blocked energy in the form of tension or pain. Auricular acupuncture is also the basis for the NADA protocol that treats addictions and cravings. There are many benefits to this exercise, and you will discover them as you explore the variations by doing this for just a few minutes daily.

INSTRUCTIONS

- Begin by applying some pressure with your thumb and forefinger to each earlobe. It might be sensitive, but it should also feel good.

- Explore any areas in your ear that have points of pain or discomfort. This is a sign of energy blockage. Putting pressure on these points, massaging them, and stretching them releases the blockage and increases your vitality. It also enhances relaxation.

- Pull down on your ears and stretch them out at a 45-degree angle while applying pressure. This releases any tension that you have in your jaw. If you experience temporomandibular joint (TMJ) pain while doing this, breathe and relax.

- Slowly make your way up the outer edge of your ears, from your earlobes up to the point where your ears reconnect to your head, applying pressure. You should feel some areas that are more responsive; they may feel warm or have a tingling sensation. Don't forget to breathe during the practice!

- Afterward, put your hands in your lap and take a moment to notice how the exercise made you feel.

IMMUNE BOOST

Client Exercise

PURPOSE

This simple, fun exercise helps to stimulate immune function. It can be done daily.

BACKGROUND

Our little thymus gland does a powerhouse of a job. Among other things, it keeps our immune system healthy and responsive. But the thymus weakens and atrophies as we age. In effect, it can doze off—and we want to wake it up! Free radicals can age the thymus, but vitamins A and C, the minerals selenium and zinc, and the herb astragalus can counteract the oxidative stress on this gland and restore immune strength. Tapping on the thymus, as you will do here, can also help.

INSTRUCTIONS

- Feel for the slight soft indentation on your neck where your collarbones (clavicle) meet.

- Measure a two-finger width below that. This is where your thymus is located.

- Take your pointer and middle fingers and gently tap on the thymus for 30–60 seconds. Breathe and relax while tapping.

- Remind yourself that you are supporting your immune system. You might also address your thymus gland: "Hello, thymus! Wake up!"

- When you have finished tapping, feel this area of your body. You may notice an awakening awareness, a tingling sensation, a release, or the urge to let out a long sigh.

GRIEF POINT

PURPOSE

In this simple exercise, you will touch the center of grief in your heart.

BACKGROUND

We carry so much grief within us—ancestral, intergenerational, and personal losses and pain. Grief makes the heart ache, and we typically want to ignore, suppress, and just not feel it. Along the sternum, over the heart, is one point that is more sensitive than the others. This is your grief point. Gently touching it will help you feel and release the pain.

INSTRUCTIONS

- Feel for the slight soft indentation on your neck where your collarbones (clavicle) meet. Come down six finger widths below that spot.

- Use your middle finger to feel for areas of tension on the breastbone; this is the grief point.

- Apply gentle pressure to the grief point, close your eyes, and breathe. Allow yourself to feel the losses that you've had. Do not fight or resist them.

- Now allow yourself to mindfully enter into the heart, where grief is held. You may feel a softening or lightening of pain or tension. Continue to pay attention and allow yourself to feel whatever you feel, with no judgment, seeking, or yearning. Do this for one full minute.

- Take your hand away and give yourself a moment, then open your eyes.

RIDE THE THIRD WIND

Client Exercise

PURPOSE

This exercise may be done any time of the day when you feel fatigued.

BACKGROUND

When you've already pushed through your "second wind" of the day and need another energy boost, stimulating the Ayurvedic energy points on each side of the deltoid will help you ride your "third wind."

INSTRUCTIONS

- Locate the energy points by measuring a two-finger width below the shoulder bone in the center of each upper arm.

- Apply some pressure to these points; you may feel tension.

- Cross your arms, find the point again on each arm, and give them a deep, vigorous massage in one direction.

- Now go in the opposite direction, applying pressure, tension, and rotation. Do this for 30–60 seconds.

- Pay attention to how you feel afterward.

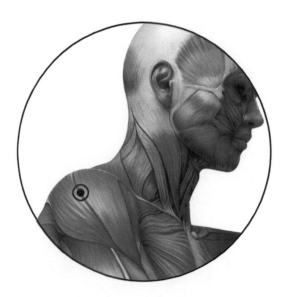

BODY ROCKING: A TWO-PERSON EXERCISE

Client Exercise

PURPOSE

This easy, yet potent, exercise alleviates insomnia, anxiety, and distress.

BACKGROUND

Rocking is a universal behavior that begins when we are rocked to sleep as infants. An adult holds the baby, patting the sacrum at the bottom of the spine in a gentle, rhythmic way with one hand and cradling the brachial plexus at the lower neck with the other. They may also hold the baby close while relaxing in a rocking chair or place the baby in a hammock.

We don't generally receive rocking as adults, but we should! Rocking engages the healing template of touch and the inner infant. It synchronizes the brain and accelerates and improves sleep quality in several ways: It increases sleep spindles, which are associated with being able to sleep through environmental noise; strengthens deep sleep via neural entrainment; and enhances memory consolidation during sleep (Bayer et al., 2011; Perrault et al., 2019). Rocking is also very soothing, and the person doing the rocking relaxes almost as much as the person being rocked.

INSTRUCTIONS

This exercise requires two people. You may wish to use it to help a loved one, or you might share these instructions with someone who can apply the treatment to you.

- To begin, have the person receiving the treatment lie on their right side (if they are comfortable this way). Being on the right side activates the rest cycle of the right brain hemisphere, which will induce sleep more quickly. Place a pillow under their neck for added support. Some people also feel comfortable hugging a pillow at their belly.

- Sit behind your partner. Take your left palm, fingers pointing upward (toward the sky), and place it directly over their sacrum (the bone that is just above the cleft of the buttocks). Your left palm should be covering the sacrum but not touching the buttocks; the outer edge of your little finger should be just above the cleft and your thumb should be around the sacro-iliac line (the joint between the sacrum and ilium).

- You can place your right hand on the person's neck, on the cervical vertebrae, such that your hand will cup very naturally around the neck. The quality of touch should be very light, with no pressure.

- Very gently, begin rocking the sacrum by pushing rhythmically and slowly with your left palm. Your right hand should maintain a gentle, firm pressure and should not move. You don't need to generate a lot of movement for this to work, and your movement should be adjusted for the comfort of your partner. Also remind them to breathe throughout.

- Continue for 10–20 minutes, until your partner falls asleep or is sufficiently relaxed.

14
BREATH

THE LIFE FORCE OF THE BREATH

To breathe correctly is perhaps the most powerful intervention we can do for our emotional and physical well-being. Along with our beating heart, our breath is the governing rhythm of our lives. We tend to ignore it, yet it is the major automatic behavior that we can control, and it can transform our health and our mood (Brown et al., 2013). This chapter provides a brief assessment for disordered breathing, along with several breathing exercises that have the power to transform mental distress. I find it helpful to teach these to clients and practice them together in session.

Many of these exercises come from the venerable yogic tradition of pranayama. The term comes from the root word *prana*, which means "life force." More than mere oxygen, our breath is identical with the force of spirit. Yoga scholars from the second century BCE wrote that if you control the breath, you control the mind. Gaining control of the breath is key to regulating the autonomic nervous system, and it is especially important as a method to alter consciousness and enhance or decrease right or left hemispheric brain activity to achieve changes in consciousness.

Pranayama consists of three phases: inhalation, breath retention, and exhalation. Retention, or kumbhaka, is the most important of these. Traditional yoga suggests the time to be allotted to the three steps is 1:4:2. Pranayama provides an accessible foundation for clients' self-care and the restoration of balance where mental distress co-occurs with body-mind dysregulation.

In anxiety and chronic stress, the individual uses the neck, shoulders, and chest to breathe; it is shallow and often rapid. This regular overbreathing, also known as hyperventilation, increases oxygen (O_2) intake and CO_2 output. CO_2 is a blood gas that relaxes and induces a parasympathetic state. Excess O_2 leads to a sympathetic or fight-or-flight state. This influence is bidirectional—overbreathing can cause panic and panic leads to overbreathing. In yogic breathing and respiratory rehabilitation, the goal is to have balance. Kumbhaka restores levels of CO_2, which promotes relaxation. Most breathing exercises include this phase, though they vary in how long the breath is retained and whether retention occurs at the inhalation or exhalation cycle. Some, like the kumbhaka exercise in this chapter, focus solely on breath retention to increase tolerance to CO_2 and reduce anxiety.

Breathing exercises and rehabilitation methods are found in many traditions in addition to yoga. Behavioral medicine—the science of applied psychophysiology—uses self-regulation methods like breathing to address anxiety and retrain the breath for psychosomatic illnesses such as asthma, cardiovascular disease, panic, pain, and chronic fatigue. And, because SARS-CoV-2 affects respiratory health, there is significant opportunity to apply breath retraining in post-COVID and long COVID recovery.

Simple diaphragmatic breathing may be the best way to introduce breathing exercises. This approach begins with a gentle contraction of the diaphragm, expansion and release of the belly, and deepening of inhalation and exhalation. This slows the breath and balances blood gases. Just realizing that their breath is under their conscious control is a good first step for clients.

However, making breathing conscious is easier said than done. Under conditioned stress, the muscles of respiration—the diaphragm and the neck and shoulder muscles, like the scalenes, sternocleidomastoid, and trapezius—become rigid and unresponsive to our intention to breathe and relax. Exercises using the "ha" breath are helpful to open and release these muscles. A skilled bodyworker can also assist by releasing the scapula (shoulder blades), which are meant to move or massage the diaphragm. Physical exercise—especially aerobics—is another avenue for gaining awareness and control of the breath.

Because breathing pattern disorders and mental distress so often co-occur, breath work can be very effective at aiding symptoms of both.

BREATHING AND CHILDREN

Breathing exercises are a form of biofeedback in which children can experience real-time responses to their emotional state as well as their physiological functioning; the goal is awareness and self-regulation. Breathing exercises have been found to aid focus and attention, including helping children with ADHD manage their symptoms (Amon & Campbell, 2008; Ma et al., 2017). Children tend to respond very well to these exercises, especially when the methods are adapted to be fun and engaging. For example, you might have the child lie down and place a small stuffed animal or toy on their belly, which they can watch rise and fall with each breath. The straw breath exercise (p. 298) is also effective.

CLINICAL PEARL
People who have cardiovascular disease or COPD, as well as people who are pregnant, should refrain from certain breathing exercises unless they are under the guidance of a skilled practitioner. Make sure you (or your client) discuss these with their provider.

The variety of exercises in this chapter will help you explore your clients' experiences with breathing and identify the most helpful interventions for each client. Alternate-nostril breathing is another exercise you will want in your toolbox; instructions for this pranayama can be found in **Ultradian Rhythm Exercises: "Hello, Brain"** (p. 82). As you reflect on your clients' needs, you should be guided by the following questions:

- What is the breathing pattern of this client?

- How long has this pattern been in place?

- How do the client's posture and musculature reinforce this pattern? How might somatics, stretching, and yoga serve as adjuncts to opening musculoskeletal function?

- What symptoms does this breathing pattern reinforce?

- What methods will be most appropriate, and in what order?

- Might there be emotional triggers that arise when doing these exercises?

- Are there any obstacles to adherence?

Breath at a Glance

WELLNESS TARGET	RECOMMENDATIONS
Depression	• Right-nostril forced breathing upon awakening and at midday • For anxious depression, use the straw breath
Anxiety and panic	• Three-part breath • Long, slow breathing; practice kumbhaka • Use komuso tool
OCD	• Left-nostril forced breathing • Use komuso tool or straw breathing
Bipolar disorder	• Balanced pranayama breathing • If depressed, emphasize right-nostril breathing • If manic, emphasize left-nostril breathing
Insomnia	• Do the 4-7-8 breath while resting in bed
Stress, trauma, and PTSD	• Do the 4-4-4-4 breath and then advance to 4-7-8, or the "ha" breath
ADHD	• Do the 4-4-4-4 breath and then move into 4-7-8 breath • Practice kapalbhati breathing
Chronic pain	• For acute pain: kapalbhati • For maintenance: straw breath
Substance use disorder	• Breath of fire • Manage anxiety or depression by breathing in through the nose and out through the mouth while actively increasing the heart rate to 65% of maximum

Cognition and memory	• Kapalbhati; practice balanced pranayama for five minutes twice daily • Practice kumbhaka
Autism spectrum and neurodivergence	• Combine breathing with walking exercises, yoga, and movement activities
Body image and eating disorders	• Uddiyana bandha • "Ha" breath to release the diaphragm
Digestive disorders	• Practice 4-4-4-4 breathing for 6 cycles prior to eating • Mindful breathing between bites

ARE YOU OVERBREATHING?

PURPOSE

This worksheet will help you determine whether you have symptoms of breathing dysfunction.

BACKGROUND

Breathing is the most direct route to balancing your mental and physical function. Healthy breathing is about the balanced exchange of gases in our blood. Overbreathing, rapid breathing, shallow breathing, and upper-chest breathing all lead to exhaling too much carbon dioxide (CO_2), which alkalizes the blood pH and contributes to increased anxiety and pain sensitivity. If you restore the breath, you can decrease the anxiety, panic, and pain.

INSTRUCTIONS

The Nijmegen questionnaire is a diagnostic tool that will help you determine if you are overbreathing. Fill in your answers in the following table. If your results suggest that you are overbreathing, a simple breathing exercise is provided in the **Three-Part Breath** worksheet (p. 289) that will help you manage your symptoms.

Provide a rating for each symptom using this scale:

0: Never   1: Rarely   2: Sometimes   3: Often   4: Very often

SYMPTOM	RATING	NOTES
Chest pain		
Feeling tense		
Blurred vision		
Dizzy spells		
Feeling confused		
Faster/deeper breathing		
Shortness of breath		
Tight feelings in the chest		
Bloated feeling in the stomach		
Tingling fingers		
Unable to breathe deeply		
Stiff fingers or arms		
Tight feelings around the mouth		
Cold hands or feet		
Palpitations		
Feelings of anxiety		
Total		

Add up all the numbers in the rating column. A score of over 23 suggests a positive diagnosis of hyperventilation syndrome—in other words, you are overbreathing. Another sign of hyperventilation syndrome is if you cannot hold your breath for more than 20 seconds at a time.

THREE-PART BREATH

PURPOSE

This worksheet includes an activity to introduce and guide you through the three-part breath, followed by a few prompts for reflection.

BACKGROUND

Three-part breath is a pranayama (breathing method) that can be helpful for disordered breathing and anxiety. It may also be of use to those who struggle with binge eating, as inflating and paying attention to the belly area may foster a sense of satiety and easy calm.

INSTRUCTIONS

The first time you practice this pranayama, it will likely be easiest to do so while lying down on your back. You can place your feet flat on the ground with your knees pointing up. Alternatively, you can arrange your legs into a butterfly or diamond shape by placing the soles of your feet together and letting your knees fall out to the sides.

- Once you find a comfortable position, place the palms of your hands on your belly, on either side of your navel.

- Seal your lips. Breathe in slowly through your nose.

- Think first about inflating the space beneath your hands with air.

- When the belly space feels full, think about expanding your ribs with air. Imagine you've "topped off" your belly with breath, and now the second part of your inhalation has no choice but to fill up the space between your ribs.

- Finally, imagine the last portion of your inhalation filling your chest, making your breastplate rise. You are now completely full of your inhalation.

- To release the air, follow the same pattern: Softly contract your abdomen to help the air exit your belly. Next, allow the air to leave the space between your ribs, pulling them in toward each other. Finally, let your chest fall as the last of the air leaves your torso.

- Repeat as many or as few times as you like. You can experiment with holding the full inhalation for a few counts before exhaling. You can also try holding the complete exhalation before inhaling again.

REFLECTION

What did this pranayama change about your breathing? Did you feel a change in the quality of your breath? In its sound or its depth? If you were experiencing anxious energy or an urge to binge before practicing the three-part breath, how are you feeling after practicing it? Has the level of tension in your chest and neck muscles changed after doing this exercise?

_____

_____

_____

_____

_____

_____

_____

THE "HA" BREATH
WOOD CHOPPER

Client Exercise

PURPOSE

This is a fun, active exercise that reduces anxiety and enhances breath.

BACKGROUND

This exercise integrates movement and sound to engage and activate the diaphragm and release emotion. It is especially useful to teach to children or teens, who may find it difficult to express and release feelings such as anger and frustration.

INSTRUCTIONS

- Stand with your feet shoulder-width apart, your feet pointing outward, and your knees slightly bent.

- Imagine yourself to be chopping wood. Breathing in, lift your arms over your head as if you were holding an ax. Your pelvis should tip forward so that your back is arched slightly. Take care not to overextend your shoulders backward.

- As you breathe out, bring your arms forward while simultaneously bending forward, tilting the hip, and curving your head down as if you were chopping wood. On the downward thrust, make a loud "Ha!" sound. Let your arms swing toward the ground and through and between your legs.

- Repeat each movement 5–10 times. You can do this exercise more slowly or quickly according to your comfort level.

KUMBHAKA

Client Exercise

PURPOSE

This exercise restores balance to the breathing rhythm and reduces anxiety by causing a slight, temporary buildup of carbon dioxide in the blood.

BACKGROUND

Kumbhaka is the practice of retaining your breath following an inhale or maintaining empty lungs following an exhale. It can be done alone or incorporated into another form of pranayama or moving yoga practice. Use the after inhale version when you are feeling fatigued and the after exhale version to reduce anxiety, panic, and stress. For balancing, use both versions equally. Experiment with the different versions and notice how you feel.

To improve your breath-holding capacity, test your breath-holding time at least once a week. As the weeks pass, and your carbon dioxide tolerance increases, the breath-holding period should gradually increase. Kumbhaka for more than 20 seconds should be undertaken gradually, once other breathing methods are well practiced. If you have a heart condition, are pregnant, or are acutely ill, you should avoid prolonged breath holding unless you are working under the guidance of an experienced yoga teacher.

INSTRUCTIONS

After Inhale (Antara Kumbhaka)

- Find a comfortable seated position. You may also try this lying down.

- Take a smooth, deep, rib-expanding inhale through your nose.

- Retain this breath: Seal your lips, hold it in, and do not exhale. Close your eyes or soften your gaze. Do not strain. Remain without tension in the neck, face, or shoulders. Begin with holding for 20, 30, or 40 seconds and build capacity to maintain the hold for as long as you can.

- When you are ready to release the breath, open your lips and blow it out as smoothly as you can.

After Exhale (Bahya Kumbhaka)

- Find a comfortable seated position. You can also try this lying down.

- Take a smooth, deep, rib-expanding inhale through the nose, and then exhale all the air from your lungs through your slightly opened mouth. You may gently contract your abdomen to assist this emptying.

- Retain the emptiness: Seal your lips, and do not inhale. Close your eyes or soften your gaze. Begin with 10 seconds and slowly build capacity to maintain the hold for as long as you comfortably can.

- When you are ready to inhale, draw in a new breath smoothly and slowly through your nose.

BUMBLEBEE BREATH

Client Exercise

PURPOSE

This exercise activates the right brain and synchronizes it with the left.

BACKGROUND

Bhramari pranayama, or bumblebee breath, is an enjoyable yogic breathing technique that involves humming. It opens up the right brain, reduces anxiety, and enhances nitric oxide function—and thus improves heart health, psychological well-being, and longevity. The practice also enhances blood flow to the brain and ventilates and drains the sinuses.

INSTRUCTIONS

- Sit comfortably and close your eyes. Place your thumbs in your ear canals to gently block them. Place your index fingers over your eyebrows, and let the rest of your fingers rest over your eyes, covering them.

- Take a deep breath in, then exhale slowly through your nose while making a loud humming sound in your throat and focusing your attention on the area between your eyebrows. Repeat this five times.

- As you continue to practice, build up to 5–15 minutes once, and then twice, per day.

BREATHING FOR ANXIETY AND EATING DISORDERS

Client Exercise

PURPOSE

These breathing exercises are helpful for those with anxiety and eating disorders.

BACKGROUND

The three parts of this exercise should be completed in order. You may want to space them out, rather than attempting to complete all three parts at once. The third practice, uddiyana bandha, is a pranayama and movement that can be uniquely helpful for bulimia. Also called an "abdominal lock," it can simulate the sensation of heaving as well as the desired sedative effect of purging.

INSTRUCTIONS

Part 1: Breathing on Your Stomach

- Lie on your stomach and rest your head on your hands to allow room to breathe.

- Close your lips and place your tongue on the roof of your mouth.

- Breathe in through your nose and pull air down into your stomach. Try to focus on your stomach pushing down as you breathe.

- Slowly exhale your breath through your nose.

- Continue these deep breaths for a full minute.

Part 2: Release the Breath with Visceral Self-Massage

- Lie on your back on a bed or couch and place a pillow or two under your knees. This helps to soften the diaphragm.

- Take both hands and begin to feel for the bottom ribs on both sides. Follow them with your fingertips from their edge alongside the chest to where they meet at the tip of the soft breastbone (called the xiphoid process).

- Focus your breathing so that as you inhale, your hands rise and you release pressure, and as you exhale, allow your hands to gently massage and go underneath the ribs, feeling for tension and pain and gently releasing the tension as you massage. Align the rhythm of your breath with the movement of your hands. If you feel a taut area, let your hands gently rest there.

- You may also apply a hot-water bottle to relax the muscles.

Part 3: Uddiyana Bandha

- Stand up with your hands on your hips, with your knees bent with your feet slightly apart.

- Start by taking a deep breath in, then exhale all the air out of your body.

- Hold your exhale out, and pull your navel in and up, as if you could tuck your belly under your ribs. Imagine your diaphragm and pelvic floor sucking in and up as well.

- Hold this position for as long as you can.

- When you feel the need to resume your breath, first release the abdominal lock by pushing your navel out. Your body will resume its normal pattern of breath.

- The first time you practice uddiyana bandha, just do it once. Work up to practicing it three times in succession, giving yourself plenty of time to resume normal breathing in between.

REFLECTION

Take a few moments to reflect on your experience with uddiyana bandha: If you were experiencing the urge to purge or binge before practicing this pranayama, how are you feeling after practicing it? Do you notice any other changes in your physical and mental state after practicing uddiyana bandha?

BREATHING FOR ANXIETY AND FATIGUE: RIB BREATHING WITH SHAVASANA

Client Exercise

PURPOSE

This breathing exercise alleviates fatigue and aids deep relaxation.

BACKGROUND

For people with disordered breathing, deep breathing (that also extends up to the shoulders and neck) is contraindicated because these breaths continue to overuse the upper respiratory muscles. This is where rib cage breathing can be of benefit. Practiced by singers to gain control over the breath, this type of breathing expands the rib cage in all directions and keeps the upper respiratory muscles from engaging. Rib breathing also helps with anxiety, since hyperventilation (overbreathing) is connected to anxiety and deep breathing to a calm mind and body.

This exercise combines rib breathing with a traditional yoga position, shavasana, to promote energy and relaxation. Rib breathing engages muscles you don't usually use, so take it slowly and practice every few days. It may be difficult at first, but with practice it will become easy. It is a wonderful tool to use when you are feeling anxious or stressed.

INSTRUCTIONS

- Lie down on your back (or sit in a comfortable position).

- Place your palms on your lower ribs. Breathe normally for a moment, feeling the slight movement of your ribs as you breathe in this position.

- Now, while inhaling, tighten your front abdominal muscles just enough to prevent your belly from rising. Continue inhaling without allowing your belly to rise or fall. Your diaphragm will draw your lower ribs up and apart, so you will feel your fingertips expand. Feel the expansion of the ribs outward, and notice how this is different from your regular breathing.

- Exhale, keeping your abdomen completely level as you allow your ribs to return to their starting position. At the end of the exhalation, release a little extra air, without forcing it, by consciously allowing your lowermost ribs to swing down and in a little more, while fully relaxing your abdomen.

- Practice for several breaths. Make sure you do not engage the neck or shoulder muscles as you breathe. If it is difficult, rest and then begin again. Marvel at your capacity to feel your rib cage expand, and know that with practice you will improve and increase the benefits.

BREATHING FOR ANXIETY AND PAIN: STRAW BREATH

Client Exercise

PURPOSE

Straw breath is a pranayama that can be helpful for anxiety and pain.

BACKGROUND

Slowing down the breath begins to alter blood gases and increase carbon dioxide levels. This is an excellent exercise for stress or anxiety, and it is simple enough that children can practice it, as well.

INSTRUCTIONS

- Find a comfortable position to rest in—you can be seated, lying down on your back, or standing with your legs at least hip-width apart and your knees slightly bent. Alternatively, you can do this pranayama while in motion, perhaps while walking outdoors.

- Shape your mouth as if you were sucking liquid through a straw.

- Breathe in through your nose and out through that straw shape. You may make a hissing noise as you exhale. Notice how the shape naturally slows down the rhythm of your breath.

- You can use this mouth shape with the natural rhythm of your breathing or with an intentional structure:

  o 4-4-4-4: Inhale for a count of four, hold in for a count of four, exhale for a count of four, then hold out for a count of four

  o 4-7-8: Inhale for four counts, hold for five to seven counts, then exhale for eight counts.

- Build up to 20 repetitions of each full cycle.

REFLECTION

What did this mouth shape change about your breathing? Did you feel a change in the quality of your breath? In its sound? In its depth?

_____

_____

_____

_____

_____

If you were experiencing anxious energy or physical discomfort before practicing straw breath, how are you feeling after practicing it?

_____

_____

_____

_____

_____

Client Exercise

PURPOSE

This breathing exercise will help you achieve a full exhale and enhance lung efficiency. It also helps with chronic stress and chronic pain, such as fibromyalgia.

BACKGROUND

The renowned osteopath and naturopath Leon Chaitow has written extensively about breath rehabilitation as the key to addressing chronic pain. He maintains that learning to exhale completely is the first step to learning how to breathe correctly. This exercise builds on the previous one, **Breathing for Anxiety and Pain: Straw Breath** (p. 298). As you practice this more advanced exercise over time, feelings of anxiety and sensations of pain should diminish.

INSTRUCTIONS

- Get into a comfortable position, either sitting or lying down, and begin to exhale slowly, and as fully as is comfortably possible, through pursed lips.

- While exhaling, visualize a candle flame about six inches from your mouth. Exhale at a strength that would flicker the flame but not blow it out. Continue to exhale until the first sign of a need to inhale.

- Pause for one second, if possible, before inhaling through your nose.

- Without pausing to hold the breath, exhale again, starting the next cycle. Each exhalation should be slow and continuous.

- Repeat the sequence 30 times, in the morning and the evening.

- After some weeks of daily practice, the inhalation phase should be found to comfortably last 2–3 seconds, and the exhalation phase 4–5 seconds, without strain.

When you begin this breathing practice, your carbon dioxide (CO_2) tolerance might be low. This can result in one or both of the following:

- You may feel increased anxiety or panic after just a few cycles of this breathing practice. If this happens, stop the exercise and briefly try it again later that day. Over time, as your CO_2 tolerance increases, this sensation will disappear.

- After the breathing exercise, you may feel light-headed due to increased oxygen reaching the brain. If this happens, sit quietly for a few minutes until it passes.

BREATHING FOR DEPRESSION AND FATIGUE: KAPALBHATI

Client Exercise

PURPOSE

This breathing exercise improves mood and energy levels.

BACKGROUND

Kapalbhati, or "skull-shining breath," is pranayama that can be helpful for depression. It is an energizing breathing method that activates the whole body and enhances oxygen levels and circulation. It releases prana, the life force, and stimulates kundalini, the she-serpent who sleeps at the base of the spine. Kundalini awakens in response to consciousness practices and rises through the chakras, or energy centers. This technique is a stimulating and cleansing pranayama practice.

Be sure to do this exercise on an empty stomach. If you are pregnant, have high blood pressure, or are acutely ill, you should not attempt this exercise.

INSTRUCTIONS

- Start by taking a deep breath in.

- Then exhale all the air out of your body.

- Inhale again, then exhale sharply while quickly drawing in your navel.

- Repeat the sharp exhale again and again, "pumping" your navel with your breath. Your inhale will be passive during this exercise, meaning you should let your body take care of the inhale and focus consciously on the sharp exhale and accompanying navel pumping.

- Take as many breaks as you need, and go as slowly or as quickly as you wish to start. During subsequent practice, gradually increase the speed of the breath and pumping.

- Begin with 20 cycles and gradually increase to as many at 120. As you improve, you may end your session with a few deep breaths and moderate breath retention.

- Practice kapalbhati once a day, at the same time of day, for seven days. Rest for three days before beginning the cycle again.

REFLECTION

Compare your mood and energy levels before and after practicing kapalbhati. How do you feel after one week?

_____

_____

_____

_____

_____

_____

15

SPIRITUALITY AND MEANING-MAKING

Your clients may have a broad range of religious or spiritual beliefs, practices, and experiences. These reflect the great existential challenges of life and death: making meaning of our lives, connecting to a higher power, and engaging in experiences that inspire awe, hope, purpose, and service. However, mental and physical distress can challenge these beliefs, especially when illnesses become chronic, or when people have tried many approaches yet had limited success.

As a clinician, how do you activate and supercharge meaning-making and empower your clients to find meaning and translate that into purpose and power? How do you engage these robust belief systems to activate profound psychobiological change? My approach to spirituality in the Brainbow is like everything: I believe therapists must delve into each individual client's spiritual beliefs and behaviors to understand their impact on the client's mental and physical health outcomes.

DISENTANGLING BELIEF SYSTEMS

Clinicians are increasingly challenged to help clients disentangle belief systems, often rooted in spiritual or religious ideas, that blur the lines between magical thinking and magic. While you should question outrageous beliefs that doubt the rational material universe, you should also recognize that there are unexplained forces—in psychology, this is called the study of the paranormal. The danger is the merging of an openness to truth with conspiracies and paranoia. While it is beyond the scope of this book to explore these questions in depth, it is beneficial to explore how your own beliefs can consciously and unconsciously affect your work with clients.

Luke's Story

I was supervising a psychology intern named Luke, when one day he came to me and said, "I am treating a 9-year-old boy named Daniel, and I think he is psychotic." I asked why and he replied, "He believes in ghosts, and when I raised this with his mother, she said she believes in ghosts also and did not see the problem." I asked if Daniel showed any other signs of psychosis and Luke said no. I asked about the family's background, and he said they were first-generation Mexican American immigrants living on the border of California and Baja.

I explained to Luke that it is common and culturally congruent for this family to believe in ghosts. Luke resisted: "But seeing ghosts is pathological; they don't exist. I can't reinforce these faulty beliefs." I said, "Luke, a while ago you shared with me that you are a devout Catholic. Do you believe in the virgin birth?" "Yes," he replied. I asked, "That it actually occurred? Even though, in our day and age, what we know scientifically is that a virgin birth is not possible?" I continued, "You don't need to answer that—I'm using this as an example. What matters is how our spiritual or religious beliefs, and the ways we make meaning, affect our health. Might you return to work with this young man and not see him as psychotic, but rather explore with him what it means that his grandmother is visiting him? I do not see pathology here."

As we delve into the realms of spirituality and meaning-making in the context of integrative mental health care, let's begin by defining some key terms:

- **Religious:** Believing in a god or gods and following the practices of an organized religion.

- **Spiritual:** Having a subjective experience of a sacred dimension. This also refers to the deepest values and meanings by which people live, often in a context separate from organized religious institutions.

- **Secular:** Of or relating to the physical world and not the spiritual world; not religious.

- **Agnostic:** A person who does not have a definite belief about whether a god exists, or who believes that it is impossible for us to know this.

- **Atheist:** A person who does not believe in the existence of a god or gods.

- **Transpersonal:** Experiences beyond the personal that incorporate transcendent and spiritual experiences. The transpersonal can intersect altered states of consciousness, anomalous cognition, and consciousness practices like meditation and prayer, as well as the use of entheogenic substances (psychedelics).

Spirituality and religion can play an important role in helping people cope with overwhelming events, trauma, medical and health challenges, loss, and grief. However, spirituality and religion can also reflect belief systems that reinforce shame, cause shadow projection, and maintain prejudices. There are numerous survivors of abuse at the hands of spiritual leaders from all denominations; such abuse can be devastating and often leads to a loss of hope or faith in a practice that may have previously been sustaining. As integrative clinicians, it is essential to identify how we can (or cannot) help individuals explore their spiritual or religious practices in service to their health and well-being.

AWE AND MEANING-MAKING

Post-traumatic growth is possible after the experience of trauma, whether religious-based trauma or otherwise. Post-traumatic growth has elements of spiritual transformation; it is concerned with the ultimate questions about life's meaning as it relates to the transcendent, and it leads to greater appreciation of life, changes in priorities, closer relationships with others, enhanced personal strengths, and identification of a path for one's life. Post-traumatic growth is both a process and an outcome, and it may also speak to the idea of the wounded healer.

Awe is an important emotion for post-traumatic growth, as well as in exploring spirituality and meaning-making more generally. Awe includes feelings of reverence and wonder that are experienced alongside a sense of meaning, purpose, and connection to something vaster or greater than ourselves. Experiences of awe can ameliorate the day-to-day suffering that is part of depression and chronic illness. Awe can also serve as a kickstart for trauma recovery, self-care, and a sense of "can do."

Awe can link nature with spirituality since it is often the experience of the natural world and its many wonders that helps us gain perspective and moves us forward. For example, one study found that veterans and at-risk youth had a 29 percent reduction of PTSD symptoms following a whitewater rafting experience (Anderson et al., 2018). In fact, for 25 years, I developed and facilitated awe-inspiring nature immersion adventures for learning and healing purposes. These experiences had several goals: to teach clients new skills, to test their mettle in a profoundly different environment, to develop trust and cooperation, and to immerse the senses in the natural world. The activities included climbing mountains to find specific herbal medicines, riding on horseback, soaking in jungle waterfalls, diving among coral reefs, and canoeing in streams. The physical challenges, the stunning beauty of the natural world, and the use of "trust muscles" were inevitably transforming to participants, each in the way they needed. They experienced both their capacity to change outcomes through their behaviors and their existential inability to fully control their lives.

I encourage you to consider how you could coordinate these types of events for your clients. You can also use **Ecotherapy: An Inventory** (p. 92) to help clients explore how they can spend more time in nature and create opportunities for awe in their day-to-day lives.

The exercises in this chapter explore issues of spirituality, meaning, purpose, and action, both in the inner realms and the outer world, and for the self and others. These exercises will catalyze meaning-making and spiritual growth for your clients. Because spirituality and meaning-making are deeply personal and can vary widely from one client to another, there is no "at a glance" table of recommendations for this area. To determine which activities may be beneficial, discuss with each client whether they are interested in doing work in this area and, if so, what aspects of spirituality they find meaningful.

Client Worksheet

BIOLOGICAL RESILIENCE: THE FOUNDATION OF TRANSFORMATION

PURPOSE

Overcoming mental and physical distress requires the mind-body-spirit to fire on all pistons. We need energy and sustenance to fuel the transformation. This worksheet provides integrative and nutritional methods to enhance biological resilience, which supports the energy required to recover from, transform, and transcend poor health.

BACKGROUND

Resilience is the ability to adapt to and recover from challenging life experiences. We often think of it in the psychological sense: how our mindset and coping skills help us adapt mentally and emotionally to a difficult change. But resilience is also rooted in our biology—specifically, the strength and balance of the hypothalamic-pituitary-adrenal-thyroid (HPAT) axis and the gut microbiome (Misiak et al., 2020). Restoring gut function with foods and herbs supports not only our physical health, but also our ability to cope with psychological stress.

We can see this relationship in reverse, too: Most mental illness begins with chronic stress. Long-term stress alters our ability to physically function; it even affects brain size and function. Building our biological resilience can, therefore, both prevent and treat mental distress.

INSTRUCTIONS

With your therapist, review the following list of actions that enhance biological resilience and choose some to try over the next three months.

Practices to implement daily:

- Eat ten almonds and one raw apple daily.

- Align your circadian rhythm: Obtain seven to nine hours of sleep each night, beginning with bedtime at 10 p.m.

- Nourish your body's mineral needs, which energize the HPAT axis, by eating mineral broths rich in sulfur, as well as phosphorus- and sodium-rich vegetables.

- Eat one serving of fermented food daily or take a probiotic.

- Take one to two adrenal glandular or adrenal cortex nutritional capsules at breakfast and lunch.

- Increase lean protein intake (plant and animal) to 50 percent of your daily diet for four weeks.

- Practice HeartMath methods (https://www.heartmath.com), which align heart and brain function in an envelope of self-compassion.

- Practice *bhramari* daily (see **Bumblebee Breath**, p. 294)

Practices to implement 1–3 times a week:

- Use animal glands like heart, liver, or kidneys in your meals three times a week.

- Seaweed supports thyroid function; eat nori or seaweed salad three times a week.

- Receive energy medicine or acupuncture that nourishes the triple warmer meridian, *shen men*, or "spirit gate."

Practices to implement one at a time (rotating among the four methods every three weeks):

- Drink 1 cup of licorice root tea each morning. (This is contraindicated with high blood pressure).

- Use sea salt liberally. (Adjust based on water retention or high blood pressure.)

- Identify an adaptogen you may benefit from, such as ashwagandha (at night) or ginseng (during the day).

- Use a tulsi (holy basil) tincture daily for six weeks.

REFLECTION

Did you notice any changes as you tried these methods—in your physical health, your mental health, or both? Did your experiences illustrate how the physical and the psychological are interconnected?

_____

_____

_____

_____

_____

_____

Client Worksheet

MAKING MEANING OUT OF OUR MYTHIC STORY

PURPOSE

The way you tell the story of your life can help you make sense of your past experiences, create positive changes in the present, and even determine your life's purpose and your plans for the future. This worksheet prompts you to tell your life's story.

BACKGROUND

Research has demonstrated that we benefit from taking time to rewrite the story of our lives (Pinkola Estés, 1997, 2011). By telling our tales, we can better understand our heroic triumphs, our yearning, and our efforts. We recognize our suffering, betrayal, trauma, and loss—and we see how, from this ferment, we have grown and accomplished incredible feats. As we rewrite our stories, elevate them, and transcend them, we join the pantheon of heroes, helpers, and healers who have walked the earth or who live in our imaginations.

INSTRUCTIONS

Part 1: Identify Your Favorite Hero

Begin by identifying your favorite hero. They may be real or fictional.

_____

What has influenced you about their story?

_____

_____

_____

_____

_____

_____

_____

What is it about them that you have carried as a lodestone or that you emulate?

_____

_____

_____

_____

_____

In what ways do you identify with this hero?

_____

_____

_____

_____

_____

_____

_____

Part 2: Tell Your Own Story

Write down the story of your life. You can start in the spaces provided and continue on additional sheets of paper if you need more room to write. You could also record yourself speaking aloud. Go chronologically, and be sure to include all significant events or periods of importance. You don't need to go into great detail about particular episodes, but grant yourself the space and time to tell your story.

You may want to undertake this process in stages. If you like, you could engage family members or others in this process, sharing your stories with each other and learning about the similarities and differences in your experiences and how you made meaning of them.

Once you have your story, transform it! Retell your story, this time with you as the hero (even if you didn't feel heroic at the time). You might choose to put yourself in the role of the real or fictional hero you identified in the first part of this exercise, or you can create a new heroic role for yourself—perhaps a brave adventurer, a powerful witch, or a mysterious sage. Exploring your story from this new angle will help you recognize your own heroism.

GATHERING YOUR SACRED OBJECTS

Client Exercise

PURPOSE

In this exercise, you will use an object to ground you and connect you to yourself and to a higher power (whatever you consider that to be).

BACKGROUND

Across many cultures, there is a practice of using a material object to guide mindful awareness, self-regulate, and participate in rituals. Some may consider this an energy object; in psychology, we might call it a transitional object. Anthropologists might call it a fetish. The object itself could be a crystal, an amulet, a pouch of herbs, or anything else that carries significance. Many religious practices—including Catholicism, Hinduism, Buddhism, and Islam—involve prayer beads or ropes. Some Indigenous traditions involve medicine bags or bundles, which contain sacred items that are kept private to retain their power. This exercise, which you can do on your own or with others, will help you to find or create your own sacred object.

INSTRUCTIONS

- Think about any objects that have meaning for you, or one that you would like to make or have and imbue with sacred purpose.

- Describe this object. Will you make it? Find it? Gather it? Does someone have part of it?

- Take some time to meditate, pray, or listen within. Ask for guidance in finding or creating your item.

- Once you have your item, carry it with you always as part of your healing journey. You might keep it in your pocket or bag, or wear it if the form allows.

DREAM EXPLORATION AND TRAUMA RECOVERY

Clinician Handout

PURPOSE

Many clients would like to listen to the wisdom of their dreams but are plagued by nightmares, night terrors, or trauma dreams. This handout provides a starting point for exploring dreams with your client. There are many ways to work with dreams to access the deepest wells of meaning and guidance.

BACKGROUND

Dreaming is a powerful tool for self-awareness and can enhance the meaning in people's lives. However, when clients experience trauma or have PTSD, their dream state may become disrupted, and they lose access to this critical resource. They can experience fragmented rapid eye movement (REM) and have powerful or vivid nightmares. The inability to have restorative sleep interrupts the process of healing and memory extinction (the erasure of the difficult emotional charge in memories). Or clients may be self-protective and not remember their dreams.

During healing, dreams often resume as the brain returns to its natural, synchronized state. When REM is restored by using EMDR, neurofeedback, or cranial electrical stimulation, or even in response to specific vitamins and glandulars, a client's dreams can become very vivid or include traumatic nightmares. This uptick in nightmares may mean that you need to slow down the interventions while processing the traumatic content, or else find methods to manage the nightmares. There are many integrative options to reduce and address traumatic nightmares, including canine companions, herbal medicines, yoga, breathing, and rocking (all of which are addressed elsewhere in this book).

INSTRUCTIONS

Begin by asking your client to describe their dream life to you:

- Do you remember your dreams?

- Do you have recurring dreams?

- Do you experience nightmares or night terrors?

When clients feel uncertain or unclear about their next steps or a decision, I recommend that they write down their dreams for one week. In the next session, have the client read the dream out loud in the first person. If a dream's meaning is unclear, ask the client to act out the dream as a gestalt—playing each role in the dream and giving it a voice expressing what they have to say.

The client may also find it helpful to request a dream response. Before falling asleep, they should focus on their intention of learning from their dreams and, if desired, ask a higher power or entity to send them a message through a dream. They may need to repeat this for several nights in a row before a dream response occurs.

For further exploration, you can pose the following questions to your clients:

- Name three important dreams and their themes.

- What information or guidance have you received from your dreams?

- What do you need to balance your dream life?

- Write down the story of how your dreams have affected your life and share it with someone important to you.

For more information on dreams, I highly recommend Kathryn Ridall's *Dreaming at the Gates: How Dreams Guide Us (2019)*.

LAUGHTER YOGA

Client Exercise

PURPOSE

Practicing laughter yoga is one way to remember the qualities of lightness, happiness, gratitude, and enjoyment.

BACKGROUND

Too often we get bogged down in the heaviness of distress. We can lose connection to ourselves, to others, and to the greater mysteries of life. Laughter is universal; it occurs in response to joy, jokes, and even absurdities. We can laugh mirthfully or as an expression dark humor. We may choose to laugh at ourselves and this can also lead to forgiving ourselves or others. We benefit psychologically, spiritually, and neurologically by actively laughing. It causes neurological changes that lift our mood and improve our physical well-being (Cross et al., 2022).

INSTRUCTIONS

Do this exercise every day and watch your mood change. It's simple! Close your eyes and put a big grin on your face. Now open your eyes and start laughing. Lose the inhibition!

Of course, it's fun to do this with others, but it's also fine to laugh on your own. Experiment with your laugh, change the pitch, try a guffaw, move your shoulders, and get your whole body involved. Just when you think you are all laughed out, give it another go.

ENGAGING THE TRANSFORMATION PROCESS: POST-TRAUMATIC GROWTH

PURPOSE

Talking about post-traumatic growth requires the clinical art of timing—that is, recognizing when someone is at a stage of healing from traumatic and challenging events where they are ready to consider and talk about the positive changes that have also resulted.

BACKGROUND

Post-traumatic growth occurs in response to overwhelming events that rock the self to the core. It is cultivated with support from therapists, family, and friends. Over time, it often happens as someone absorbs and integrates the loss, grieves, and reemerges with a newly re-visioned identity in response to traumatic events.

While some would suggest that resilience and post-traumatic growth are very separate, and that resilient people don't develop PTSD or need post-traumatic growth, in my clinical experience with thousands of clients, that is not my observation. Many resilient people develop PTSD and survive complex trauma; likewise, many also experience tremendous growth following this trauma. Your role as a clinician is to provide a safe place to explore that growth at the right stage of recovery.

INSTRUCTIONS

Knowing how to start a productive conversation about a person's post-traumatic growth is crucial in engaging the transformation process and fostering constructive reflection. The following sample questions will help you begin and guide this type of conversation.

- You've shared with me all the challenges, pain, and suffering that you've gone through during your experiences. I'm wondering if you've experienced what you would call positive changes—perhaps beneficial outcomes of this tragedy. What changes would you identify?

- Have the challenges you've had with your mental or physical health led to any positive changes?

- Do you feel that your outlook on life has changed? Have your priorities in life shifted?

- Have your relationships with loved ones evolved? In what ways?

- Do you allow yourself to rely on others for help when you need it? Are there new ways you rely on others?

- In what ways has your self-relationship evolved? Is there more acceptance, comfort, or confidence present?

- Do you feel better equipped to deal with everyday challenges? In what ways?

- Have you developed a new practice, hobby, or ritual?

- How do you work with, use, or appreciate the strength of your body, perhaps in new ways, to help you cope and thrive?

Before proceeding with these questions, consider the stage of recovery that a person is in. Don't ask about positive things or forgiveness amid someone's acute suffering; it's too soon. Help them process anger, rage, disappointment, and betrayal first. It is only then that forgiveness, if called for, becomes possible. Help clients focus first on forgiving themselves first, and then possibly forgiving others. Forgiving themselves is a requirement for deep resolution and healing; forgiving others is not.

GRATITUDE AND LOVING-KINDNESS MEDITATIONS

Client Exercise

PURPOSE

Compassion-based meditations focus your attention on expressing gratitude, concentrate compassion for oneself and others, open the heart, and relieve the distressed heart and mind. Many people benefit from practicing these meditations daily.

BACKGROUND

Meditations or prayers that access compassion, care, and loving-kindness open our hearts, both to ourselves and to others. This has many benefits for our mental and physical health. Gratitude directly fosters social support and hope, and protects people from stress and depression (Feng & Yin, 2021). Loving-kindness meditation has also been found to be helpful for managing chronic pain, improving social anxiety, reducing marital conflict, and coping with the stress of long-term caregiving (Graser & Stangier, 2018; Hofmann et al., 2011).

Sometimes you may feel like shutting others out, especially if you are feeling despair, betrayal, or loss. Sometimes you may even feel like shutting down yourself. In these cases, even if you don't feel like doing the meditation, it's important to do it anyway. Meditation has the power to transform your experience and shift you into feeling more open, connected, and heartful.

INSTRUCTIONS

There are many variations of sending love or compassion to oneself and others. Consider using the following examples, or you might find—or write—your own favorite version.

May You Be Well

May you be well.

May you be cleansed and purified
of all that isn't health.

May every cell in your body
wake up and fight.

May the powerful light of healing
move into every part of you.

May you return to being purely you.

May you be well.

    – Joanna Fuchs

A Meditation on Gratitude and Joy

With gratitude I remember the people, animals, plants, insects, creatures of the sky and sea, air and water, fire and earth, all whose joyful exertion blesses my life every day.

With gratitude I remember the care and labor of a thousand generations of elders and ancestors who came before me.

I offer my gratitude for the safety and well-being I have been given.

I offer my gratitude for the blessings of this earth I have been given.

I offer my gratitude for the measure of health I have been given.

I offer my gratitude for the family and friends I have been given.

I offer my gratitude for the community I have been given.

I offer my gratitude for the teachings and lessons I have been given.

I offer my gratitude for the life I have been given.

　– Jack Kornfield

Loving-Kindness Mantra

May you be happy. May you be healthy. May you be free from all pain.

May I be happy. May I be healthy. May I be free from all pain.

　– Inspired by the Buddhist practice metta bhavana

Try repeating the "may you" mantra three times while thinking of someone you love or care about deeply. Then repeat the mantra three times while thinking of someone you have neutral feelings toward—maybe someone you don't know very well. Finally, repeat the mantra three times while expanding your awareness to include the whole world, sending your warm wishes to every living being.

16

ALTERED STATES AND PSYCHEDELIC MEDICINE

THE EMERGING REVOLUTION IN PSYCHEDELIC MEDICINE

Altered states of consciousness can be healthy and healing, or less beneficial (even problematic) in our lives. Different cultures and communities define altered states in unique ways, as what is considered normal (or abnormal) in one context may not have the same connotation in another.

Though altering our state of consciousness is often demonized, many cultures deliberately use natural or synthetic mind-altering substances for healing and transcendent purposes. *Psychedelic* is the current term of reference for these substances, though a newer term—*entheogens*—reflects these substances' spiritual potential, as the word refers to beholding a god or goddess within. Examples of these substances include drugs that promote dissociation, such as ketamine and MDMA, as well as certain fungi and spirit plants, like psilocybin and peyote.

It is important to recognize that altered states of consciousness do not necessarily require psychedelic substances. For example, it is possible to achieve a trance state using hypnotherapy, drumming, or dance. Indeed, many people are already feeling altered in their daily lives, whether by dissociation or from using harmful substances, and seek balance. Throughout this book, you are exploring options for finding healthier substitutes for foods or behaviors by using exercises, herbs, nutrients, and rituals. I teach the principle of substitutions, which suggests that our behavior is partly a function of our brain chemistry. I encourage clients to ask themselves: "What state am I trying to achieve? What substance (drug, food, herb, exercise, behavior, etc.) am I doing to achieve it? Is it healthy for me or not? Are there alternatives to this substance that will address the biochemistry and the emotional needs I seek to fulfill?"

Many entheogens, spirit plants, and fungi are serotonergic agonists, meaning that they boost serotonin levels in the brain. This has implications for the pharmacological treatment of PTSD and depression, which involves enhancing the brain's serotonergic, dopaminergic, and GABA systems. Given their healing potential, psychedelics (including plants, fungi, and their chemical derivatives) are thus the subject of general empirical science, Indigenous sciences, and biomedical clinical trials. This growing research shows exciting promise for the use of psychedelics in treating PTSD, depression, anxiety, addiction, and insomnia.

The emerging revolution in psychedelic medicine for mental health mandates that you become educated about their medical, psychological, and recreational uses so you can provide evidence-based guidance to clients interested in exploring these methods and ethically facilitate these experiences. The most effective use of psychedelics or entheogens for mental health incorporates these substances as "assistants" in the psychotherapeutic and spiritual growth process. It is not advisable for clients to use substances recreationally when the purpose is psychological healing. Due diligence and research benefits both you and your clients.

CLINICAL PEARL

People raised in punitive religious settings often feel that the use of psychedelics or varied states of consciousness via ritual is pathological. This can lead to the shadow addiction to unhealthy altered states practices. It is beneficial to explore and link these experiences with their current beliefs and behaviors.

The following are definitions of some key terms that you will likely come across in your exploration of altered states and psychedelic medicine:

- **Psychedelic:** Substances capable of producing large shifts in one's state of consciousness. May also refer to alterations and enhancement of colors, patterns, music, behavior, and mental states and perceptions.

- **Hallucinogen:** Psychoactive drugs that induce hallucinations, including psychedelics; also includes dissociative drugs. Tends to be pejorative.

- **Entheogen:** From the terms *entheos* and *gen*, meaning generating the god within. Refers to a psychedelic substance, usually of plant origin, that is taken to alter consciousness for a religious or otherwise spiritual purpose.

- **Psychedelic-assisted therapy:** Includes psychotherapy that combines professionally supervised use of ketamine, MDMA, psilocybin, LSD, or ibogaine. Often used with "treatment-resistant" conditions, such as PTSD, major depression, and addictive behaviors. Evidence suggests this treatment is both efficacious and safe.

- **Microdosing:** Regularly ingesting a small dose of LSD or psilocybin, as low as one-twentieth of a typical recreational dose, every few days as an aid to mental health performance. A microdosing dose should be sub-threshold, low enough that the user does not feel at all "high."

- **Harm reduction:** Practical strategies and ideas to reduce harmful consequences associated with drug use, especially in countries where these drugs are not legal. Specific procedures are used during psychedelic "trips." Harm reduction also includes social justice analysis and actions that do not stigmatize drug use, including emphasizing the therapeutic properties of these substances when used responsibly; awareness of the damaging effects of overly punitive responses to drug possession and use; and acknowledgment of the sacred status of these substances in many Indigenous cultures and the ancient practices that facilitate responsible, productive use.

- **Harm reduction and integration therapy (HRIT):** This specific aspect of harm reduction involves therapists who provide a safe place for clients who use psychedelics to prepare thoroughly, ensure safety, and process their experience. The therapist must understand the laws in their state, including the risks inherent in this work.

CLINICAL PEARL

There is evidence that chronic use of SSRIs mutes the effects of many psychedelics, most notably psilocybin and other serotonergic psychedelics. It is advisable to discontinue from SSRIs under the guidance of a prescriber before using psychedelics.

PSYCHEDELIC THERAPY, ETHICS, AND INCLUSIVITY

Except for some synthetic and semi-synthetic drugs, most psychedelic medicines and entheogens are part of an ancient repertoire of diverse Indigenous medicinal and spiritual rituals found among cultures worldwide. Like many complementary and natural medicines, these resources and methods derive from specific locales and natural resources. In the United States, psychedelic therapies currently remain primarily within a predominantly White model of therapeutics, though awareness is shifting and action is building.

This lack of equitable access demands that you proactively create connections, accessibility, and empowerment with regard to clinical methods and research, including psychedelic therapies, and accessibility and diverse participation in research. It also requires that you thoughtfully advise clients and colleagues about all aspects of psychedelic tourism in regions involving Indigenous communities. Working with Indigenous peoples in their territories requires collaborative protocols, not cultural or natural resource appropriation or consumption.

In this chapter, I'll explore the significant psychedelic medicines in current use and explore their mind-altering qualities so you can better assess and guide appropriate referrals for clients interested in exploring these methods.

Altered States and Psychedelic Medicine at a Glance

WELLNESS TARGET	RECOMMENDATIONS
Depression	• Ketamine for depression and pain • Psilocybin, DMT, peyote, ayahuasca (with a knowledgeable guide and harm reduction and integration therapy)
Anxiety and panic	• MDMA for social anxiety • Ayahuasca
OCD	• Ketamine • Psilocybin has been studied
Bipolar disorder	• Some research suggests ketamine for the treatment of bipolar I and II • Psychedelics are contraindicated
Insomnia	• Meditation, including body scans • Daytime administration of a psilocybin • If the insomnia is related to PTSD, refer to PTSD recommendations
Stress, trauma, and PTSD	• MDMA, LSD, ketamine
ADHD	• Drumming and Sufi dancing rituals • Low dose LSD is being studied
Chronic pain	• Ketamine • Psilocin where pain is related to depression
Substance use disorder	• Peyote • Mescaline—if not taking other SSRIs or dopamine agonists • Ayahuasca—if no other psychoactive medications • Ibogaine (with a knowledgeable guide)
Cognition and memory	• MDMA for TBI • Psilocybin is under study for dementia
Autism spectrum and neurodivergence	• Serotonergics like LSD and psilocybin are being explored for specific behaviors (anxiety, depression, social behaviors) in autism
Body image and eating disorders	• MDMA is in trials for eating disorders, and psilocybin is being studied for anorexia
Digestive disorders	• Psilocybin, LSD, and ayahuasca are serotonergic agonists that affect gut motility and the microbiome and may have application in inflammatory bowel disease • Ketamine is antimicrobial and enhances gut microbiome diversity

COMMONLY USED
PSYCHEDELICS

Clinician Handout

PURPOSE

This reference sheet covers the psychedelic substances that are most used in the United States.

BACKGROUND

The following list represents the psychedelic substances most frequently used for recreational, ritual, or therapeutic/medical purposes in the United States. Psychedelics are also called *psychointegrators* because they disrupt the usual brain-mind patterns of thought and expand neuronal connections, leading to a reduction or elimination of habitual patterns of rumination and obsessiveness, as well as new ways of thinking (Winkelman, 2001).

In the following chart, *traditional* refers to traditional, Indigenous use of natural substances; *therapeutics* refers to therapeutic or medical applications; and *Schedule I* (in the "regulation" column) indicates that it is illegal to manufacture, buy, possess, process, or distribute that substance without a license from the Drug Enforcement Administration (DEA).

SUBSTANCE	NEURO-TRANSMITTERS	TRADITIONAL	THERAPEUTICS	REGULATION	CONTRAINDICATIONS
LSD (Lysergic acid diethylamide)	Serotonin	Synthetic	PTSD, anxiety associated with life-threatening illness, depression, somatic disorders	Schedule I	Do not use if suffering from psychotic disorders
Psilocybin	Serotonin	Found in over 200 fungi; psilocin is the active substance; used traditionally for millennia	Anxiety, depression, pain, nicotine withdrawal, cluster headaches	Schedule I; legal in Oregon; decriminalized in Colorado and several cities	Do not use if suffering from psychotic disorders
Peyote, Mescaline (3,4,5-trimethoxy-phenethylamine)	Serotonin, dopamine	Cactus used in traditional rituals by Indigenous peoples of North and Mesoamerica; also known as *Lophophora williamsii*, San Pedro cactus, *Trichocereus (Echinopsis pachanoi)*, or peyote buttons	Depression, alcohol or drug abuse	Schedule I; approved for use as part of the Native American Church	Do not use if taking other SSRI or dopamine agonists; often induces vomiting, so hydration and management is essential
Ayahuasca (*B. caapi* and *P. viridis*)	Serotonin, MAOI	Traditionally prepared by Indigenous shamans for spiritual purposes; traditionally made from the *B. caapi* vine and mixed with *P. viridis* and other plants containing dimethyltryptamine (DMT)	Appears to have antidepressant, anxiolytic, and anti-addictive actions	DMT is a Schedule I substance, but the plants that become ayahuasca are not regulated; the Santo Daime church and others have received religious exemptions allowing use	Not to be used with any pharmaceuticals, including SSRIs or MAOI inhibitors

SUBSTANCE	NEURO-TRANSMITTERS	TRADITIONAL	THERAPEUTICS	REGULATION	CONTRAINDICATIONS
DMT (N-dimethyl-tryptamine)	Serotonin	Occurs naturally in mammals and many plants; called the spirit molecule; associated with spiritual and near-death experiences	Depression, spiritual consciousness	Schedule I	Cardiovascular disease
Ibogaine (Tabernanthe iboga)	Serotonin, endogenous opioids, glutamate	Ibogaine is an extract from the Iboga shrub used as traditional medicine and in spiritual ritual in west Africa, especially in Gabon and Cameroon among followers of Bwiti	Opioid, alcohol, and amphetamine dependence	Schedule I; used for medical purposes in Mexico and Brazil; is studied in many countries	Must be used with a knowledgeable guide; concerns about cardiac arrhythmias have been reported
MDMA (3,4-methylene-dioxymetham-phetamine)	Dopamine, serotonin, norepinephrine	Synthetic	PTSD, TBI, social anxiety, depression	Schedule I	Psychotherapy-assisted is advised; recreational use is ill-advised
Ketamine	Glutamate	Synthetic	Pain, treatment-resistant depression, PTSD, OCD, drug and alcohol addiction	Schedule III; legal for use by registered practitioners but illegal recreationally	Do not use if afraid of dissociation; can trigger anxiety, raise heart rate and blood pressure; during pregnancy, excessive recreational use can cause neurological and bladder disorders
Salvia divinorum, salvinorin A	Endogenous opioids	Used by Indigenous shamans of Mexico for divination	Not advised for use; unstable in terms of dose or dose-related effects	Legal in some states and classified as a Schedule I substance in others	Its use is not advised for mental health purposes

Clinician Worksheet

READINESS ASSESSMENT FOR PSYCHEDELIC MEDICINE

PURPOSE

This readiness analysis will help guide your discussion with clients who are interested in the therapeutic use of psychedelic medicine, including a referral to a qualified guide or practitioner.

BACKGROUND

This interview will help you assess whether a client is ready to be referred to a psychedelic guide or practitioner and what type of psychedelic medicine may be most appropriate. It also supports a more profound exploration of treatment methods and the client's expectations, intentions, previous experiences with psychedelics, and readiness to engage in this form of treatment. While a client may fill out this form, it is best to discuss it during an interactive dialogue.

CLINICAL INTERVIEW

Client name: _____ Date of birth: _____

Intake form attached? ❑ Yes ❑ No

Mental Health History

If a mental health intake has not previously occurred, do it here; otherwise, skip to the next question.

Please list any mental health concerns that you have experienced in the past or are currently experiencing. You may include any diagnoses you have received.

_____

_____

_____

_____

_____

_____

Recreational Substance Use

Please describe your use of recreational substances (alcohol, cannabis, LSD, etc.).

_____

_____

_____

_____

_____

_____

Physical Health History

Please list any physical health conditions that you have experienced or are currently experiencing. Certain physical health conditions can affect people's experience with altered states and psychedelics. These may include, but are not limited to, the following:

❑ Hypertension   ❑ Stroke   ❑ Traumatic brain injury

❑ Cardiovascular disease ❑ Epilepsy or seizures ❑ Concussion

❑ Other: _____

_____

_____

Medications

Please list any prescriptions, nutritional supplements, and herbal medications that you are currently taking or have recently stopped taking. These may include, but are not limited to, the following:

❑ Antidepressants (SSRIs, SNRIs, MAOIs)   ❑ Benzodiazepines

❑ Mood stabilizers   ❑ St. John's wort

❑ Antipsychotic medications   ❑ Kava

❑ Other: _____

_____

_____

Previous Experiences

Please describe any previous experiences with altered states of consciousness, psychedelics, and substances. Consider the following:

Was your experience with this state/substance positive, negative, or neutral? What might have made it this way?

_____

_____

_____

_____

_____

Did you seek out an experience with this state/substance more than once? Why or why not?

_____

_____

_____

_____

What did you learn from the experience, if anything?

_____

_____

_____

_____

Are you interested in having an experience with this state/substance again? Why or why not?

_____

_____

_____

_____

Are there other states or substances that you have not previously experienced but are interested in exploring?

Altered States

- ❑ Meditation
- ❑ Hypnosis
- ❑ Trance
- ❑ Spiritual Experience

Substances

- ❑ Cannabis
- ❑ LSD
- ❑ Mushrooms/psilocybin
- ❑ DMT
- ❑ Ayahuasca
- ❑ Peyote
- ❑ MDMA
- ❑ Ketamine
- ❑ Iboga/ibogaine
- ❑ Other: _____

Further Reflection

Think about traits you have that might affect your experience with altered states and psychedelics. Consider the following:

- Are you someone who can easily let go of things?

- Is it difficult for you to reflect on your emotions and actions?

- Do you feel comfortable exploring your beliefs and values and why you hold them?

- How have you experienced healing in the past?

- Do you maintain a strong attachment to the story you have created about yourself and your life?

- What are your goals for altered states and psychedelic experiences?

_____

_____

_____

_____

_____

_____

Setting Intentions

Finish the following sentences to better understand your hopes for your healing journey.

- I hope to better understand or gain clarity about…

- I want to further my healing journey by…

- I want to be more connected to…

- My expectations for the experience of altering my consciousness include…

- I believe the following medications may be of value to my healing…

_____

_____

_____

_____

_____

_____

INTEGRATING PSYCHEDELIC MEDICINE AND HARM REDUCTION*

Clinician Worksheet

PURPOSE

This exercise allows for reflection on psychedelic medicine, harm reduction, and how you may want to integrate these into your clinical practice.

BACKGROUND

If you are considering becoming more involved in harm reduction and psychedelic-assisted therapy, use the following reflection prompts to guide your self-inquiry. In the spirit of being our own laboratory, we explore our attitudes and beliefs to inform our next steps, both clinically and personally.

REFLECTION

- What are my reasons for doing work that relates to psychedelics?

- What are three essential values that influence my interest?

- What might make it a natural fit for my next steps, clinically?

- What do I see as some obstacles or personal or professional challenges?

- Who in my caseload might be candidates?

- Have I had discussions about psychedelic medicine with clients? How did those proceed?

- Have my clients raised the inquiry, or have I?

- Is this a topic in my geographic location/local professional societies?

- Have I made a referral or wanted to?

- Do I know where to make a referral?

- Do I have positive or negative beliefs about spirituality, mysticism, the paranormal, spirits, entities, or other disembodied beings?

---

* Adapted from Pilecki, B., Luoma, J. B., Bathje, G. J., Rhea, J., & Narloch, V. F. (2021). Ethical and legal issues in psychedelic harm reduction and integration therapy. *Harm Reduction Journal, 18*, Article 40. https://doi.org/10.1186/s12954-021-00489-1.

- What influences from my religion of origin or current beliefs may influence my attitudes or my inclination to refer clients?

- How have I been influenced by my training in mental health or as an addictions counselor in considering psychedelic drugs?

- What are my experiences clinically with helping clients reduce harm or eliminate recreational drug behaviors?

- What is my level of competency in working with psychedelics and harm reduction?

- Would I like to train in this method or refer?

- What might I do to develop competency?

- What level of legal and regulatory risk am I comfortable taking on?

- What are the local laws and guidelines that may inform my choices?

- What is my level of personal experience with psychedelics?

- Are there legal ways to gain experience with non-ordinary states of consciousness, such as using holotropic breathwork, mindfulness practice, spiritual retreats, or sensory deprivation tanks? If the options in my area are limited, could I travel to obtain this experience?

- What is my privilege, and how safe is it for me to practice harm reduction and integration therapy?

- What is my level of support in the community or with a regional or national network?

- Am I interested in policy change?

- Do I see myself in the role of a public speaker, educator, or researcher influencing policies that inform laws?

- What are my next steps?

EMBRACING ALTERED STATES: A NINE-WEEK GROUP

PURPOSE

This worksheet outlines a nine-week group with the primary goal of helping people embrace and manage their capacity for altered states.

BACKGROUND

This therapeutic group will help members gain control over dissociation and explore healthy states of consciousness. Dissociation itself is neither good nor bad; it is a matter of whether it is supporting the client's health and well-being or driving discomfort and disconnection. Many people experience the adverse effects of dissociation or seek out other dissociative experiences. Most will benefit from gaining some control over their dissociation. You will teach them strategies for self-regulation, engage in harm reduction, and facilitate a safe discussion of often taboo subjects. You will also explore whether psychedelics are of value and how they can be used for trauma recovery.

CURRICULUM AND VIDEO SUPPORT

I have created a Self-Care Circuit Breaker video and guide that you may use and adapt as needed for your group. It demonstrates some of the exercises found in this book and offers additional self-regulation and self-care methods to explore with your clients. This video is available at https://drlesliekorn.com/courses/stress-self-care-circuit-breaker.

BEFORE GETTING STARTED

First, you will define the eligibility for participation in your group. You can adapt this group to the needs of teens through elders. It can focus on related issues of trauma recovery, eating disorders, self-harming, and harm reduction. It is not a psychotherapy group per se, though there may be explorative discussions about feeling states.

Include in your eligibility these parameters:

- Age, sex, or gender requirements

- Types and degree of dissociative experiences

- Stage of trauma recovery

- Client interpersonal and communication qualities

I recommend that you include no more than eight people in the group.

Assess each potential group member in a pre-screening video call or on-site interview (unless you know them well as your client) that covers the following:

- Safety: Is this client stable enough? Do they have some self-care in place?

- Setting: Define the location and atmosphere; identify potential triggers (e.g., fragrances, perceived safety of the space).

- Participation: Will this client benefit from and contribute to a group? Under what circumstances would you exclude someone from participation?

GROUP OUTLINE

Each weekly session includes self-care methods. I also recommend that you incorporate a 15-minute healthy snack at the end of each meeting as an opportunity to teach about food and herbal teas as ingredients for self-care and healthy altered moods. A healthy snack to stabilize mood can consist of a protein, a fat, and a carbohydrate. (Be sure to check whether any of the group members have food allergies.)

Week 1

- Hold space where people can talk about their experiences of dissociation and altered states.

- Make introductions and review the group process and boundaries.

- Provide definitions of dissociation and altered states that decrease shame and emphasize the ability of these methods to enhance self-regulation.

- Teach the **"Ha" Breath Wood Chopper** (p. 291) as a method to decrease anxiety and stress.

- Snack: Chamomile tea, almonds, and sliced apple.

Week 2

- Introduce a grounding exercise like **Breathing for Anxiety and Eating Disorders** parts 1 and 2 (p. 295). Anxiety often precedes dissociation; help the participants make the link between triggers for anxiety, dissociation, and risk of self-harm or reduced self-care.

- Explore the paradox of control and letting go of control for trauma survivors and its relationship to dissociation.

- Snack: Hops tea, walnuts, and sliced pear. Explain that hops is a nervine that relaxes and aids sleep.

Week 3

- Discuss methods people use to dissociate. What works, and what doesn't feel good? What are they looking for when dissociating? What does embodiment feel like?

- Explain the psychobiology of dissociation and how dissociation is useful or not.

- Practice methods of grounding with the **Bumblebee Breath** exercise (p. 294) and skin brushing.

- Snack: Lavender cocoa with stevia.

Week 4

- Explore the use of drugs and medications. Define psychedelics and substances and differentiate between recreational and therapeutic use.

- Discuss excessive exercise, self-harming, and anomalous cognition (acquiring information that appears outside of normal sensory or space-time experience, such as telepathy). People who dissociate often experience anomalous cognition; normalizing this is helpful.

- Practice the **Kinesthetic Body Exercise** (p. 251) to enhance interoceptive awareness. Have each participant do the exercise individually, then process the experience and discuss body imagery. Optionally, continue by having the participants pair up and mirror each other doing the exercise.

- Share lavender essential oil and discuss lavender as a relaxing aroma.

- Snack: Roasted salted chickpeas and grapes.

Week 5

- Focus on breathing and altered states. Teach forced-nostril breathing to consciously alter focus (**Ultradian Rhythm Exercises: "Hello, Brain"** in p. 82). Process after the exercise.

- Continue discussion of the paradox of control and not in control, in the body and out of the body, "high" states and low states.

- At the end of week 4, ask the group members to take a hot and cold shower every day (see **Hydrotherapeutic Methods for Mental Health at Home**, p. 225). After the shower, they should take a moment to sit down, rub themselves dry, use their favorite essential oils, and experience being fully in their body and how that makes them feel. They should take a few notes to share during the next group meeting.

- Snack: Raw celery, parsley, goat cheese, and a nut butter (e.g., almond or cashew).

Week 6

- Discuss hydrotherapy and altered states. Inviting sharing about the experience of the hot and cold shower.

- Teach the **Polarity Facial Massage** (p. 275).

- Check in about how their experiences of dissociation are changing.

- Snack: Fresh mixed berries or fruit-only jam, gluten-free crackers, and raw butter.

Week 7

- Explore music and altered states.

- Teach rib breathing to reduce anxiety (**Breathing for Anxiety and Fatigue: Rib Breathing with Shavasana**, p. 297), followed by the "ha" breath (**The "Ha" Breath Wood Chopper**, p. 291).

- Teach toning and listen to chanting (e.g., Gregorian chants, Bulgarian chants, Inuit throat singing, Hindu chanting). One inhales and then, on the exhale, makes a vowel sound (e.g., "ohhh" or "eeee") for the length of the breath, then repeats the cycle. You can experiment with different sounds and vowels. Participants with pain or physical discomfort can place their hands on those areas to send the sound vibration there and promote relaxation and release.

- Check in about how their experiences are evolving. For homework, have each group member identify music they repeatedly listen to that facilitates an altered state of consciousness. Can they describe what about that music evokes this state?

- Snack: Bananas or another fruit dipped in sugar-free chocolate sauce and Brazil nuts.

Week 8

- Begin discussion with some sharing and reflection on the previous weeks and ask people to check in on how they feel. Discuss how this week and the next will be the final meetings.

- Discuss psychedelics and the use of substances to alter states; educate about the benefits and challenges of different types of psychedelic medicine. Choose sections from the **Readiness Assessment for Psychedelic Medicine** (p. 326) and discuss the indications and contraindications for select medicines. Participants may wish to explore their own previous experiences.

- Introduce and practice moxibustion—the application of the burning herb mugwort (*Artemisia vulgaris*) over or on an acupuncture point. It has many applications, including increasing energy and circulation. Purchase a moxa stick for each participant and invite them to identify an acupuncture point to which they want to apply heat. Emphasize that they should not burn the skin. This can be an alternative to cutting or burning behaviors.

- Snack: Barley tea and popcorn.

Week 9

- Wrap up, process, and complete your exploration of psychedelic medicine and altered states. Continue and update the conversation from week 1 about substances.

- Consider the following prompts: Are there herbs, entheogens, or psychedelic medicine that you are interested in exploring? What are the options for exploring them? Why might you, or not? Who is a resource to help you make good decisions?

- You can also choose additional questions from the **Readiness Assessment for Psychedelic Medicine** (p. 326).

- Snack: Roselle tea and alegrías (**Taming Your Sweet Tooth with Popped Amaranth**, p. 179).

- Ask each participant to share one or two insights they have had during the group and one behavior change they will continue. Afterward, provide a positive comment on growth for each participant.

- Provide a certificate of completion and a manual with the exercises and snack menus for each group member to take home.

17
ADHERENCE STRATEGIES

Even the best health and wellness program will not work if it's not done consistently. We clinicians spend hours on an intake analysis, exploring meaning and goals, teaching exercises, explaining anatomy and function, developing protocols for herbs and nutrients, and conducting drug interactions analyses. Yet if we do not identify the potential obstacles and define adherence strategies, our clients may not achieve their goals. This chapter provides methods of engaging clients (and helping them engage with themselves) in a focused, lighthearted, and shame-free way, which will also help you define priorities, goals, tasks, and timelines.

THE FIVE BARRIERS TO CHANGE

Supporting positive behavioral change is among many of your tasks as a clinician. However, even as your clients ask for help and inquire about methods to improve their well-being, they may be ambivalent about making such changes. This ambivalence can stem from several barriers that interfere with the change process, including commitment, time/money, family, depression/learned helplessness, and religion or belief systems.

The first barrier, commitment, can arise when the client realizes that self-care requires lifelong attention. This can undercut their motivation to take actions in support of their physical, mental, emotional, and spiritual health. Acceptance and commitment therapy (ACT) can be useful here, as it can help clients identify their values and increase their ability to take values-based actions even when difficult thoughts or feelings arise. But ACT alone will not bring about nutritional change; nutritional education and counseling is also required (Järvelä-Reijonen et al., 2018.) This combination is especially useful when addressing a client's self-blaming and shaming behaviors. This is also why you must be very clear about your own unconscientious conveyance of shame, which can be rooted in ideologies about specific diets.

Time and money are another set of obstacles that can inhibit access or be perceived as a barrier to access. The reality is that not all clients have the same resources to make positive lifestyle changes. Therefore, I spend considerable time reviewing these obstacles in sessions with my clients and consider both time- and money-saving options. In this chapter, there are numerous resources for exploring affordability with clients.

Next, family has a profound influence on the client's ability to enact lifestyle changes (Gillespie & Johnson-Askew, 2009), as success is more likely when the family is on board. If one or more family members is actively against the change, it may be important to integrate nutrition and psychosocial health in the context of family therapy (Novak et al., 2021). In addition, if clients grew up in a family where they did not have a role model for self-care, you may serve as a simple step-by-step model for what it means to care for and prioritize one's own health. This is especially meaningful for parentified children, who often grew up with an ill parent or sibling, or who were abused.

Perhaps the most obvious yet overlooked obstacle to making change is depression and learned helplessness. Even as depression lifts and trauma resolves—especially during the second stage of recovery, where memories are processed and grief is experienced—a client's inability to act on their own behalf can spiral them back. The types of mind-body nutrition groups I advocate for, often co-facilitated by a therapist, a nutritionist, and a movement instructor working together, are an ideal way to address these challenges directly. The power of the group is often more effective than the one-and-one dyad. The role of positive psychology has value here as well, as focusing on a client's strengths can help them counteract the learned helplessness that often presents obstacles to engaging sustainable change.

Finally, religion and belief systems can either serve as barriers or as sources of resilience. Often, unspoken beliefs, especially those related to misinterpretations of different self-care or group rituals, can be misconstrued as threatening to or as going against a client' beliefs. This tendency can occur when discussing certain foods or practices, including bodywork, yoga, meditation, breathing, or altered states exercises. Careful use of language and exploration of these beliefs can illuminate the appropriate role or the decision to bypass a particular method that may conflict with a client's beliefs.

MOTIVATIONAL INTERVIEWING AND RELAPSE PREVENTION

At a deep level, it is essential to both care deeply and remain detached from the client's behaviors when they fail to engage in the change process. Many of my mentees in this field complain of clients who won't undertake lifestyle changes even though they say they wish to. Here is where I have found motivational interviewing helpful, it creates opportunities to explore that ambivalence compassionately. I always counsel those mentees to listen beneath the words, to understand the transference and the learned helplessness that come into play, along with the real-world obstacles like time and money. Paradoxical intention may be useful here. For example, I may agree with the client: "It may not be the right time, or you may not be ready, and that's all right."

You must also keep in mind that barriers to change may be amplified with clients in active recovery from substance use disorder, making them vulnerable to relapse. Since poor nutrition is an exacerbating influence on drug and alcohol use disorders, I advocate for the use of nutritional and herbal methods to ease the strain of detoxification by supporting brain function while addressing the emotional correlates of addiction.

In addition, the strategies of relapse prevention (Roordink et al., 2021) can be applied to nutritional relapse—especially, but not limited to, food addictions like sugar and gluten sensitivity. Relapse often begins gradually, weeks in advance of actual lapses. Helping clients identify their potential triggers or warning signs during the intake is of great value. The client may benefit from in-depth planning to name and recognize their early warning signs and create an action plan of coping strategies.

Regardless of the specific methods that you use to address a client's barriers to change, there will be ups and downs and times when greater care is needed. Your job is to provide support, good cheer, explanation, and education, along with actionable methods that help clients find a rhythm for their schedule of self-care that embraces physical, mental, emotional, and spiritual health.

Clinician Worksheet

PRACTICE PRIORITIZING

PURPOSE

Following your comprehensive assessment, you're going to have a good idea of the priorities for intervention based on your evaluation and analysis. Use this tool to enhance adherence and to align your priorities with your client's by together ranking the importance of the different integrative and nutritional methods.

BACKGROUND

How do you prioritize integrative and nutritional methods and decide what interventions to use first? Many factors will influence your choices, but the first step is to assess what the client feels is most important. You can do this by having them rank the areas of the Brainbow Blueprint. You may find that you agree with your client or feel that other methods can jump-start change more quickly. There's no right or wrong way to prioritize the Brainbow Blueprint. You will be combining the art of clinical skills and intuition with science. In any case, this prioritization exercise can serve as a basis for discussion and education with your client.

INSTRUCTIONS

For this activity, read through Julie's story and consider what activities, behaviors, and goals will affect the desired change in well-being.

Julie's Story

Julie is a 33-year-old woman who lives with her partner and their dog. She has a good social network and an established professional career. Despite this, she finds herself plagued by symptoms of depression, anxiety, insomnia, and PMS. She also has body image issues, which are tied to her previous difficulties with bulimia. While her eating disorder is mostly under control now, it can occasionally return when she finds herself under extreme stress. Julie has a history of trauma, and although she has done some work on this, there are still unresolved issues. It's also worth noting that she used to be a soccer player and has had two previous head injuries.

Julie has been on antidepressants and ADHD medications for 14 years and wants to explore coming off them. She has already done a lot of work on her mental health by spending the past three years in therapy. Now, she is ready to bring her body into the healing process—she wants to learn how to love her body better, improve her body image, and dip her toes into movement and nutrition/supplementation. However, she doesn't know how or where to start. She says that she has been trying to do yoga but gets so antsy that she can't relax and focus on the practice. Julie has identified what bothers her the most currently: She feels like she will never be able to come off her medications despite the negative impacts on her, such as weight gain.

Julie's Brainbow priorities, as she identified in numerical order, appear in the diagram here.*

What would you prioritize for Julie, and why?

_____

_____

_____

_____

_____

* A blank version of this template is included at the end of this worksheet.

Here is how I would prioritize the Brainbow Blueprint methods for Julie. Read through my notes, then consider the reflection questions that follow.

Leslie's Clinical Priorities Analysis

I agree with Julie's assessment to begin with hydrotherapy, exercise, somatics, breath, and hormones. It is important to align as much as possible with what your client feels are the major problems and their priority of methods they wish to use. This enhances rapport and adherence, leading to success. There will of course be areas of divergence, and this should be addressed with sensitivity and education.

Julie demonstrates a lot of resilience with a good social network and an established work life. However, she experiences a number of symptoms that point to ongoing dissociativity, possible body dysmorphia, and perhaps mild traumatic brain injury. This can lead to feeling disconnected from the body, challenges with self-care, and self-medicating behaviors. Julie is ready for the next steps, even as she struggles with depression, anxiety, insomnia, and PMS, common sequelae of early life trauma.

Clinical Next Steps

1. Refer her to an assessment for TBI.

2. Assess for disordered breathing, which is common in trauma and anxiety.

3. Assess imbalances in circadian rhythm, hormones, and PMS.

4. Take three months to focus on these three areas Julie prioritized:

   o Hydrotherapy

     • Apply counseling skills to identify some triggers for when she feels out of body. Introduce skin brushing and have her identify her favorite essential oil so she can use an aroma and skin brush when she feels anxious or dissociated.

     • Recommend and educate about a variety of baths: hot-cold showers, foot baths, hot baths, and added salts and aromas.

   o Exercise

     • Explore what Julie enjoys and what benefits she experiences, as well as what she doesn't enjoy and why. Julie will benefit from exercises that help bring her into the body and help her self-regulate.

- Julie mentioned that she has been trying to do yoga but gets too antsy. When a client says this, it may mean that before they do yoga they will benefit from some aerobic or high-intensity burst aerobic exercise, or even the "ha" breath, to release anxiety prior to relaxation.

- Suggest that Julie ask herself: What type of exercise would help me feel better right now? In the morning, I would suggest warm-ups, stretching, and short interval training (since she is busy). These short interval mood boosters also help sleep quality.

- Somatics

  - Teach her how to palpate and massage the diaphragm and incorporate this with special rib breathing for anxiety. Teach breath holding or bumblebee breathing.

5. Assess why she identified human-animal relationships as number 5.

She has ranked digestion, supplements, herbal medicine, and culinary medicine as a second stage (numbers 6 through 9). It makes sense that as she benefits from her initial stage of the first few areas (taking three months to solidify), she will be ready to begin incorporating nutrition and herbs and tapering medications.

She has named biological rhythms as number 10, which may be because she's not familiar with what it means. I would educate her about the role of the circadian rhythm as it relates to hormones, PMS, and getting exercise so that we can bring it in sooner as an education piece. It affects her insomnia, and that is one of her goals to improve.

I may also let her know there are nutrients that can reduce symptoms of PMS—such as magnesium, B6, and borage oil—and at an appropriate time, even though these aren't her priorities, she could add this, after starting with hydrotherapy during PMS currently. Some foods may also be exacerbating her PMS symptoms.

In conclusion, in this case, the client's goals aligned well with mine. I concurred with her goals and the order of her goals, and it was easy to construct a short, medium, and long-term plan of action based on these goals. This alignment supports her goals, and areas such as biological rhythms that could be brought in sooner as an educational component can be integrated into her areas of interest.

Compare the priorities that you identified for Julie with those that I identified. Where are they the same? Where might they differ?

_____

_____

_____

_____

_____

_____

_____

_____

_____

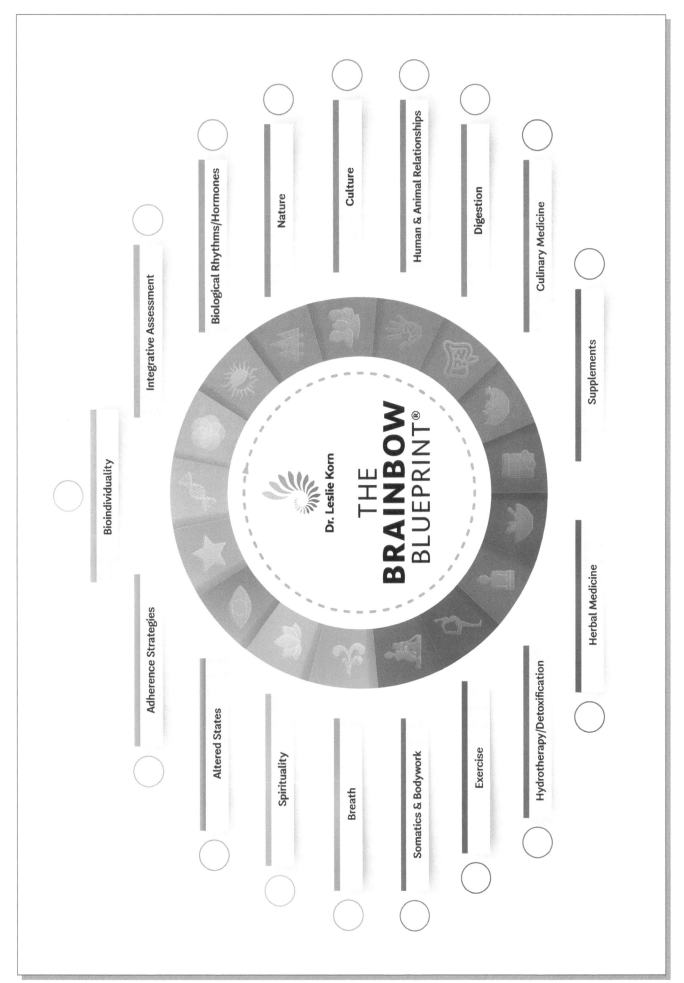

THE **BRAINBOW** BLUEPRINT®

Dr. Leslie Korn

Biological Rhythms/Hormones

Nature

Culture

Human & Animal Relationships

Digestion

Culinary Medicine

Integrative Assessment

Supplements

Bioindividuality

Herbal Medicine

Adherence Strategies

Altered States

Spirituality

Breath

Somatics & Bodywork

Exercise

Hydrotherapy/Detoxification

Clinician Handout

PURPOSE

The decision pathway provided here will help you strengthen your clients' natural antidepressants arsenal. It also serves as an example that you can follow to develop your own decision pathways.

BACKGROUND

Making informed decisions involves considering a variety of options and their contraindications. The following is one example of a decision pathway—a flowchart that is based on prior knowledge, which you can use to guide your decision-making when working with a particular client. This example focuses on natural antidepressants and will help you determine which options to recommend. Be sure to consider whether the client is on pharmaceutical antidepressants.

After you become familiar with this example, consider creating your own decision pathways. This will allow you to fine-tune and personalize other types of interventions you use with your clients.

Pathway for Incorporating Natural Antidepressants

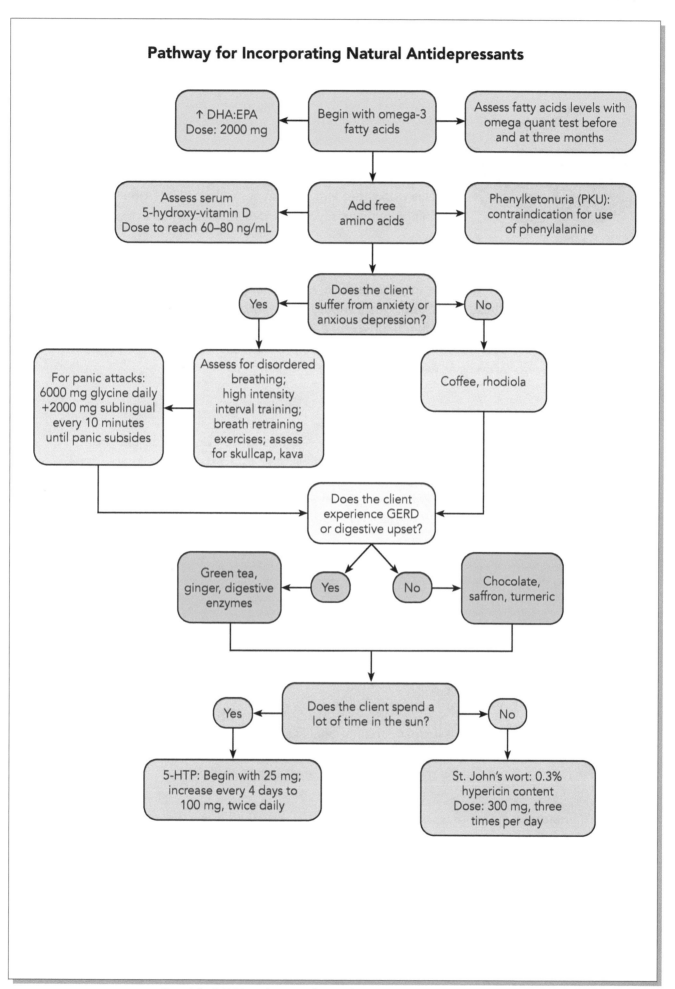

Client Worksheet

SUCCESSFULLY SETTING GOALS

PURPOSE

This worksheet introduces you to the SMART goal system. By defining your goals, you improve your ability to achieve them.

BACKGROUND

Defining goals that are important to your health and well-being is an essential step in the process of achieving these goals. Your goals should be obtainable, and to ensure this, we will use the acronym SMART, which stands for specific, measurable, attainable, relevant, and time-bound. The SMART goal framework is widely used in the business world and is an effective approach for personal goals as well.

INSTRUCTIONS

Identify one outcome you want to achieve for your health and well-being, and use the following questions to craft it into a SMART goal. It will be best to start with a simple goal that you are confident you can achieve ("I am going to go for a walk during my lunch breaks") before tackling a more difficult, long-term goal ("I am going to taper off my medications"). An example is provided for you first, followed by a blank template for you to set your own goals.

SMART GOAL EXAMPLE

My goal: *Drink chamomile tea to help with digestion and relaxation.*

What are the potential barriers to achieving my goal, and how might I overcome them? *I usually drink less healthy, sugary beverages like soda, so I may crave those instead. I can help myself stay on track by not keeping soda in the house.*

Is my goal **specific** enough? Is it clear what my goal is and what steps I need to take to achieve it? *I wasn't very specific before! I want to drink one cup of chamomile tea each evening after dinner. All I need to do to prepare is buy chamomile tea and then steep it each night.*

How will I **measure** my progress toward this goal? *I will keep a food-mood diary and record whether I drank my tea that day, along with notes about my digestive symptoms, anxiety level, and sleep. This will help me to see whether the tea is having an effect.*

Am I confident in my ability to **attain** this goal based on my current circumstances? *Yes, this is a reasonable goal for me right now. Eventually I want to decrease my sugar intake even more, but if I try to do too much at once, I'll probably fail and then feel like there's no point in trying.*

Is my goal **relevant**? Why is this goal important to me? _Yes, this goal is important to me. I want to decrease my sugar intake, and substituting chamomile tea should help with my digestive issues, insomnia, anxiety, and sugar "crashes." I'll feel a lot better if I can reduce these symptoms._

What is my **timeline** for achieving this goal? Is this timeline reasonable? _I'll pick up some chamomile tea over the weekend and start my goal on Monday. I'll plan on drinking one cup per day for three weeks, and then review my food-mood diary to see if I need to adjust my plan at all. I think this is a reasonable timeline._

Revised SMART goal: _Drink one cup of chamomile tea each evening after dinner (in place of a soda) for the next three weeks, while keeping a food-mood diary to track how it helps my digestive symptoms, insomnia, anxiety, and sugar "crashes."_

SMART Goal Template

My goal: _____

_____

What are the potential barriers to achieving my goal, and how might I overcome them?

_____

_____

_____

_____

Is my goal **specific** enough? Is it clear what my goal is and what steps I need to take to achieve it?

_____

_____

How will I **measure** my progress toward this goal? _____

_____

Am I confident in my ability to **attain** this goal based on my current circumstances? _____

_____

Is my goal **relevant**? Why is this goal important to me? _____

_____

_____

What is my **timeline** for achieving this goal? Is this timeline reasonable? _____

_____

Revised SMART goal: _____

_____

USING SHARED DECISION-MAKING TO DEFINE GOALS

Clinician Worksheet

PURPOSE

This exercise ensures that the goals established for the client align with what the client identifies as their priorities, as well as what you consider to be priorities for them. This allows you to spot signs of ambivalence, confusion, opposition, and so forth, which you can then explore with the client.

BACKGROUND

Shared decision-making invites you and your client to co-create goals and agree on a health action plan. Additional people who have a stake in the outcome—such as parents, partners, or children—may also be invited into the conversation. Shared decision-making is especially useful when there appear to be several options on the table, and choices to make about different interventions, evidence, or risk factors (Bae, 2017).

ACTIVITY

Refer to the client's intake form, where they began to identify their goals in three-month segments (or have them set these goals now). Use the following table to record the client's goals and then to take notes on the client's priorities, your priorities for the client, and any areas of contention or further exploration.

Defining Goals

Client name: _____

MONTHS	CLIENT GOALS	CLIENT PRIORITIES	CLINICIAN PRIORITIES	OTHER NOTES
1–3				
4–6				
7–9				
10–12				

OVERCOMING ADHERENCE FRUSTRATIONS

Clinician Worksheet

PURPOSE

This worksheet will help you address transference and countertransference during the goal-setting and adherence process.

BACKGROUND

It's important for you as a clinician not to get into a dynamic where the client thinks they are either disappointing or pleasing you based on their ability to carry out recommendations. It can also be frustrating to listen to reasons why someone hasn't followed through on your recommendations each week.

INSTRUCTIONS

Consider one or two clients with whom you experience adherence frustration, and reflect on the following questions:

- What are you feeling in relation to this client?

- What is it that annoys, irritates, or upsets you?

- Are you feeling helpless with this client? Angry?

- What gets in the way of feeling compassion for this client?

- Reflect on your own adherence and self-care challenges. Is there a connection between your experience and your client's?

- Are you working more at this than your client is? Are you overinvested?

- What will be your next steps in working with this client?

- What do you want to say to the client to help shift this dynamic?

SELF-CARE, ANYWHERE: EXPLORING APPS

PURPOSE

Apps can help us achieve our goals by encouraging, supporting, innovating, and keeping us on track in our self-care routine.

BACKGROUND

Many paths lead to self-care. Apps can support you in your efforts by guiding us through self-care practices, reminding you when it's time to do so, and being easily accessible—right at your fingertips, all day long! Many self-care apps are also customizable, allowing you to choose which tools you'd like to use, at what times, how often, and for how long (ranging from just a few minutes to an hour or more).

INSTRUCTIONS

Reflect on the following questions to explore your needs and options for self-care apps.

Where do you need support in your self-care routine? What obstacles are preventing you from reaching your goals? Would you benefit from guided practices (e.g., meditation, exercise)? Do you need a better way to track your self-care activities? A reminder to do them?

_____

_____

_____

Now that you've identified the type of support you're looking for, take some time to explore the apps listed in the resources section at the end of this book (your practitioner can provide you with a copy). Pick one that you think will be helpful for you, and spend a week using this app.

In what ways did this app help you? Are there ways in which this app didn't meet your expectations or needs? Would you like to keep using this app, or will you look for another?

_____

_____

_____

If you're still looking for a self-care app to use, consider the others from the list. You can find even more options by searching online or asking friends and family for recommendations.

18

BRIDGING INTEGRATIVE MEDICINE AND SOCIAL JUSTICE

Health and well-being are forged in community. So much emotional distress derives from people's lack of meaningful connection with others. Physical ailments also occur, in large part, not because of individual issues but en masse: in exposures to poor-quality food, work-life imbalance, pesticides, air pollution, and other factors that are beyond a person's individual control. As a clinician, to help individuals achieve health and healing, you must also help the whole. Therefore, this chapter will guide you in supporting social justice and equal access to health care using integrative methods.

BIOINDIVIDUALITY AND SOCIAL JUSTICE

As we explored in previous chapters, bioindividuality is the essential foundation for personalized care, and this approach should extend to the lenses we use for assessment as well. Whether conscious or not, bigotry exists in health care and leads to many injustices, such as the overdiagnosis of schizophrenia and underdiagnosis of mood disorders in the Black community, even though the actual rates of these illnesses are virtually the same across all ethnicities. This lack of mindful objectivity in diagnosis leads to overhospitalization and higher doses of medications among Black individuals. Environmental racism, food deserts, and many other injustices reveal the political and systemic forces acting on underprivileged people, who, despite these challenges, are often blamed for their poor bodily health.

Integrative medicine and nutrition is well-suited to social justice because it is rooted in the origins of self-care in cultural and nature-based methods, even if in some regions or practices it appears to be reserved for the affluent who can afford "boutique" or "concierge" health services. You can, if you choose, work toward health justice—meaning that you actively advocate for the rights of all people to optimal health, acknowledge that social factors play a fundamental role in health, and support institutions in providing equal access and compassionate and affordable care (Chao & Adler, 2018). Although it has a reputation as a luxury for the "worried well," integrative medicine holds core principles of medical pluralism and embraces diverse approaches to health and well-being.

INTEGRATIVE MEDICINE AND PLANETARY HEALTH

Health justice is one facet of a critical large-scale undertaking to restore planetary health. Planetary health is the concept that human health cannot be uncoupled from the health of natural systems within the earth's biosphere (Prescott & Logan, 2019). As Dr. Lori Arviso Alvord has said, "Human health is dependent upon planetary health and everything must exist in a delicate web of balanced relationships" (Lawson, 2000).

Calls for new ways to work together for a healthy, just, and sustainable future are burgeoning, fueled by the intersecting challenges of climate change, biodiversity loss, pollution, and profound social, economic, and environmental injustice. The COVID-19 pandemic has laid bare and further accentuated these issues. Meaningfully addressing these deep and interconnected issues is fundamentally a learning process; society at large must move beyond existing patterns and constraints toward new ways of thinking, being, and acting that restore, protect, and safeguard our shared planetary home and the living systems we depend on. This requires attending to pathways of societal, policy, and educational system change, as well as prioritizing different voices and perspectives. As an integrative clinician working with diverse methods, your perspective and work play an important part in this transformation.

TAKING ACTION

Money is often scarce for health delivery programs but abundant for conducting research that will support the introduction and delivery of care. Many integrative clinics are founded in this way. Doctors Without Borders has spurred many similar groups working locally and internationally, such as acupuncturists, herbalists, and naturopaths, all "without borders."

I have myself found many creative ways to fund my passion for serving the underserved using integrative health and nutrition. Here are some examples of pro bono health care I have undertaken to make integrative approaches more accessible:

- In 1977, I started a nonprofit center to deliver low-cost and pro bono health care to underserved populations in Mexico. I supported my pro bono work by running health retreats, continuing education programs, and internships, and in later years an accredited master's degree and certificate program.

- I ran health retreats in the United States and Mexico for 25 years, where one day of the retreat was devoted to volunteering the delivery of health care to the local population.

- I engaged volunteer massage therapists to deliver chair massage at local Indigenous elders' conferences in the Pacific Northwest. Our first goal was to provide care for elders. Our second goal was to demonstrate through federally funded research the importance of the delivery of massage therapies in tribal communities and to support policies that would lead to massage centers (and we succeeded!).

- I helped form a project called Nutrients for Natives, where we raise funds and in-kind donations to deliver health care to people who could otherwise not afford it.

- My nonprofit conducted research with tribal communities to identify food deserts as a first step toward improving the local food ecosystem.

- We offered micro business development for women to make herbal remedies and trade them within or sell them outside their communities.

- We developed different types of media—including multilingual infographics, books, websites, and videos—to support rural, urban, and Indigenous communities in the US and Mexico. Each community defined their own knowledge about health and healing and codified it in media formats that they chose and benefited from.

- We delivered medical massage to rural underserved communities and recorded videos (in Spanish and English) to document the techniques and benefits.

In this chapter, you will find space to develop your own ideas about how you might use your knowledge, skills, and passion to serve communities with integrative medicine. The other activities in this chapter focus on strengthening clinician-client communication, building awareness of historical traumas and cultural medicine, and practicing anti-bigotry—all aimed to help you provide more personalized and effective care to your clients.

Clinician-Client Exercise

PURPOSE

This worksheet helps both the client and clinician by providing strategies for improving clinician-client and doctor-patient interactions, particularly in holistic or integrative clinical settings.

BACKGROUND

This worksheet provides two improv-based exercises that are relevant to the interaction between integrative medicine practitioners and their clients. One of the exercises is for clients: It helps the client practice how they could speak up for themselves when a clinician is not listening to them and when the interaction includes microaggressions. The other exercise is directed at practitioners, to improve their listening skills and foster increased empathy toward clients whose life experiences are different from their own or toward clients who are skeptical of integrative medicine.

INSTRUCTIONS

You will need at least two chairs, whether you are doing these exercises alone, with a partner, or in a group. Position the chairs so that they face each other. If you are doing the exercises alone, sit in one chair and speak to the empty chair as if a client or clinician were sitting there. If you have a partner or group, each person should try to embody the role of client or clinician. Switch roles at least once. If the client (in real life) has struggled with claiming their voice in provider-patient interactions, have the client play themselves and the clinician play a dismissive clinician.

Clinician Exercise: Talking to an Unreceptive Client

Think back to a time when you met with a client who was unreceptive to an approach you knew would help them. Assuming the "clinician" role, face your partner or the empty "client" chair. Practice speaking to that unreceptive client.

- What would you say to them if you had a do-over?

- What would you want to know about them to understand their hesitancy better?

- How would you frame and phrase your questions to elicit this information about their background?

- How would you manage your tone of voice if you become frustrated with this client?

- Practice a scenario in which you arrive at an ideal resolution.

- Practice a scenario in which the visit is ultimately unsatisfactory.

- Can you identify specific elements of clinician-client exchanges like this one that lead to good outcomes for both parties?

- Can you identify elements that lead to unsatisfactory, frustrating outcomes?

- When do you expect your next opportunity will be to practice these skills in a real-life clinical interaction?

Client Exercise: Talking to a Dismissive Clinician

- Think back to a time when you met with a health care provider who was dismissive of your concerns. Assuming the "client" role, face your partner or the empty "clinician" chair. Practice speaking to that dismissive provider.

- What would you say in response to their dismissive attitude if you had a do-over?

- How would you convince them to respect your perspective?

- How would you behave if they refused to do this?

- How would you behave if they became more receptive?

- Would you chastise them for their attitude? If so, what words would you use? What tone of voice?

- Practice a scenario in which you arrive at an ideal resolution.

- Practice a scenario in which the visit is ultimately unsatisfactory.

- Can you identify specific elements of clinician-client exchanges like this one that lead to good outcomes for both parties?

- Can you identify elements that lead to unsatisfactory, painful outcomes?

- When do you expect your next opportunity will be to practice these skills in a real-life clinical interaction?

WORKING TOWARD ACTIVE ANTI-BIGOTRY IN CLINICAL PRACTICE

PURPOSE

This worksheet explains the importance of holding our practice in a framework of anti-bigotry.

BACKGROUND

While *anti-racism* is a more recognizable buzzword these days, the larger social justice concept I like to use is *anti-bigotry*. As we practice anti-bigotry, we engage in exploring, examining, and understanding the automatic/involuntary and voluntary responses that we have toward all types of others. To enable this depth of reflection, we must be curious about our actions and reactions, and cultivate an open mind and body that are willing, ready, and able to learn.

As integrative clinicians, active anti-bigotry can manifest as seeing no client as a stranger, educating ourselves about a client's cultural and ethnic ancestry and trauma, having empathy for all just as we would for ourselves, and questioning some of the implicit biases of Western science. For the client, active anti-bigotry can manifest as heightened body awareness and somatic inquiry, and taking the pressure off others to do the work for them.

If you would like further exercises in this area, I offer a workbook and a course on *Multicultural Awareness and Diversity: Strategies to Improve Client Rapport and Cultural Competence* (https://catalog.pesi.com/item/74878/).

INSTRUCTIONS

As you develop your knowledge and skills in anti-bigotry, you will be better able to facilitate discussion and therapeutic work related to social justice with your clients. I recommend planning an 8-week, 12-week, or ongoing anti-bigotry group practice. You can use the following table to lay out a group curriculum. Guided breathing exercises and meditations can facilitate the prerequisite body awareness and openness for working toward anti-bigotry. Some ideas for topics to explore include hypervigilance, privilege, posture, walking in public, and accessibility of foods and herbs.

Anti-Bigotry Group Curriculum

WEEK	CURRICULUM IDEAS (EXERCISES, GOALS, CONVERSATION TOPICS)
1	
2	
3	
4	
5	
6	
7	
8	

UNDERSTANDING HISTORICAL TRAUMA AND SUPPORTING RESILIENCE WITH CULTURAL MEDICINE

PURPOSE

Becoming aware of traditional cultural ways of coping with trauma can help us find better solutions for our clients in the here and now.

BACKGROUND

Dr. Maria Yellow Horse Brave Heart first coined the term *historical trauma* during her work with Native American communities. She defines historical trauma as "cumulative emotional and psychological wounding over the lifespan and across generations, emanating from massive group trauma experiences" (Brave Heart, 2003). These collective traumas can include genocide, colonization, slavery, forced relocation, destruction of cultural practices, and other forms of physical and psychological violence. Historical trauma has physical and mental health implications across many communities and cultures.

Adequately and ethically addressing historical trauma involves active, ongoing learning and the recognition that an individual experiences the intergenerational effects of the violence enacted upon their community. This worksheet supports you in interrogating your own beliefs and opening yourself to new perspectives. Those who are affected by personal or community traumas may not raise concerns about it unless you do. Learning about others' experiences and becoming aware of the limitations of your own current knowledge, even when painful, informs your work as a clinician.

INSTRUCTIONS

Part 1: Recognition

Many communities have experienced historical trauma, including the following:

- American Indians (over 500 communities)

- First Nations of Canada

- Irish colonized by Great Britain

- Africans brought as slaves to other countries

- African Americans

- Holocaust survivors and descendants (Jews, Romani, Jehovah's Witnesses, LGBT+ people, and more)

- Armenian Holocaust survivors and descendants

- Guatemalan Holocaust survivors and descendants

Think about these and other communities that have experienced historical trauma. Are you part of any of these communities? Are your friends or loved ones? Your clients?

_____

_____

_____

_____

_____

_____

_____

_____

Part 2: Your Perspective

Examine how you define and think about these significant concepts of historical trauma:

Time: Do you think of time in straightforward chronological terms? Is something frozen and the past and therefore still present for you? Do you anticipate the future often? How do you connect your perception of time to your personal history?

_____

_____

_____

_____

_____

_____

_____

_____

_____

Grief: What experiences, emotions, rituals, and supports do you associate with the grieving process? Do you experience grief as a free-flowing process, or has it had particular inflection points in your experience, or some of each? Does it feel possible for you to experience any resolution through your experience of grief?

_____

_____

_____

_____

_____

_____

_____

_____

_____

Community and family: Did your family enjoy meals together? Did they display affection physically and verbally? Were different members of the family open and forthcoming about their history? Were your parents or other elders supportive of your education and autonomy? Did you feel positively connected to a larger community?

_____

_____

_____

_____

_____

_____

_____

_____

_____

Ancestors: Who were your ancestors? In what ways did your ancestors suffer? How did your ancestors survive or build resilience? Do you know of any foods, herbs, or other strategies they used to support their survival?

_____

_____

_____

_____

_____

_____

_____

_____

_____

_____

_____

Part 3: Reading

Read one or more articles on historical trauma:

- Brave Heart, M. Y., Chase, J., Elkins, J., & Altschul, D. B. (2011). Historical trauma among Indigenous Peoples of the Americas: Concepts, research, and clinical considerations. *Journal of Psychoactive Drugs, 43*(4), 282–290. https://doi.org/10.1080/02791072.2011.628913

- DeAngelis, T. (2019, February). The Legacy of Trauma. *Monitor on Psychology, 50*(2), 36. https://www.apa.org/monitor/2019/02/legacy-trauma

- Der Sarkissian, A., & Sharkey, J. D. (2021). Transgenerational trauma and mental health needs among Armenian Genocide descendants. *International Journal of Environmental Research and Public Health, 18*(19), Article 10554. https://doi.org/10.3390/ijerph181910554

- Barak, Y., & Szor, H. (2000). Lifelong posttraumatic stress disorder: Evidence from aging Holocaust survivors. *Dialogues in Clinical Neuroscience, 2*(1), 57–62. https://doi.org/10.31887/DCNS.2000.2.1/ybarak

Part 4: Another Perspective

Next, you will revisit the prompts from part 2. This time, try to imagine how someone dealing with historical trauma might answer the same questions. (If you are personally affected by historical trauma, explore whether your previous answers align with the research findings.)

Time: Would they think of time in straightforward chronological terms? Is something frozen in the past and therefore still present for them? Would they anticipate the future often? How would they connect their perception of time to their personal history?

_____

_____

_____

_____

_____

_____

_____

_____

Grief: What experiences, emotions, rituals, and supports might they associate with the grieving process? Do they experience grief as a free-flowing process, or has it had particular inflection points in their experience, or some of each? Does it feel possible for them to experience any resolution with grief?

_____

_____

_____

_____

_____

_____

_____

Community and family: Did their family enjoy meals together? Did they display affection physically and verbally? Were different members of the family open and forthcoming about their history? Were the parents or other elders supportive of younger members' education and autonomy? Did the family feel positively connected to a larger community?

_____

_____

_____

_____

_____

_____

_____

_____

Ancestors: Who were their ancestors? In what ways did these ancestors suffer? How did their ancestors survive or build resilience? Do you know of any foods, herbs, or other strategies they used to support their survival?

_____

_____

_____

_____

_____

_____

_____

_____

Part 5: Reflection

How do your personal conceptualizations differ from those described in the research on communities affected by historical trauma? In what ways are they similar?

Your Perspective

Communities with Historical Trauma

Finally, consider and describe some ways in which you can learn to recognize different conceptualizations of historical trauma, time, grief, community, family, and ancestors in your daily life and clinical practice. Keep in mind that cultural presentations of emotional distress may be somatic.

_____

_____

_____

_____

_____

_____

_____

CLINICAL PEARL

I first learned about the use of foods and plants for healing when I lived in western Mexico's jungle, where there were no doctors. I relied on the women of the village to help me navigate the numerous diseases I encountered, along with accidents, bites, and mysterious maladies. Later, as I sat with my own grandmother back in the United States, I learned that I came from a long line of Dacian Jewish women who used their hands for healing. They healed with herbs, foods, and cupping, which is widely practiced throughout the Middle East, Europe, and by Indigenous peoples of the Americas, as well as by acupuncturists and massage therapists.

My great-grandmother brought her traditions with her, along with her borscht and brisket, when she left the Old World—yet, like most immigrants, her diet and habits changed in the new culture. New kinds of physical activity and diseases also arose, setting the stage for the intergenerational epigenetic changes that we continue to see among all immigrants (and Indigenous peoples) today. Just as I discovered my cultural medicine and became empowered by it, you may discover your own cultural medicine or help clients discover theirs.

Clinician Worksheet

BUILDING COMMUNITY CONNECTIONS

PURPOSE

Integrative medicine and nutrition, like all forms of health care, should be accessible to everyone—not just the affluent or insured. This worksheet will help you understand the needs of the community where you practice in order to build meaningful community connections and increase access to health care.

BACKGROUND

For many years, I have observed the link between poor-quality nutrition and mental and physical health concerns. What I feel has been lacking in discussions of accessibility, poverty, and food deserts is the root of the issue: what I call *nutrition trauma*. I define nutrition trauma as the introduction of foodstuffs into communities that people are biologically unable to process and digest, leading to deleterious effects, including addictions, on their body, mind, and spirit (Korn and Rÿser, 2006).

Beyond simply introducing unwholesome foods, the food delivery systems developed by transnationals also overwhelm an individual community's capacity to generate their own food resources and define and control accessibility, which contributes to food insecurity. As integrative clinicians, we must recognize that nutrition is a social justice issue.

INSTRUCTIONS

Identify five unmet needs of the community in which you practice. Use your prior knowledge, draw on issues your clients have brought up to you, and do further research as needed.

_____

_____

_____

_____

_____

_____

_____

_____

What initiatives are present in your community that are working to address these needs?

_____

_____

_____

_____

_____

_____

Here are some ideas about how to work with your community. Put a check mark by those you are interested in, and add your own ideas to the list.

- ❑ Connect with other community-facing practitioners and organizations around you and discuss ways to collaborate.

- ❑ Create a list of resources to provide to people who are interested in integrative medicine and nutrition.

- ❑ Form a network within the community for referrals or host community-building educational events together.

- ❑ Contact your local herb shop and discuss potentials for partnership. When you buy wholesale or refer clients at a discounted rate, it can make herbal medicine more affordable while keeping money and resources within the community.

- ❑ Compile resources of easy-to-follow recipes and exercises that anyone can do. Make them available to community members online, or create free booklets.

- ❑ Attend community events, especially those that center marginalized members of the community. Take time to listen to and reflect on what these members of the community are bringing up.

- ❑ Provide space for clients who wish to involve their family members in the healing process.

- ❑ Work with other people and organizations to start a food pantry and teaching kitchen.

- ❑ Offer group fitness, yoga, or creative classes to your community bi-weekly or monthly.

- ❑ _____

- ❑ _____

- ❑ _____

Choose three ideas to focus on first, and create an action plan to hold yourself accountable. In the table provided, list your three goals in order of priority, then identify what you need to do to achieve each one. Set a timeline, define what resources you will need, and outline the actionable steps you will take to achieve your goals.

ACTIONABLE STEPS			
RESOURCES		
TIMELINE		
GOAL		

19

PRACTICE DEVELOPMENT, COLLABORATION, AND LEGAL SCRIPTS

A LEGAL AND ETHICAL FOUNDATION FOR A HEALTHY PRACTICE

Whether you decide to integrate methods into an existing counseling or psychology practice or have a stand-alone practice, you'll want to identify the forms and procedures that will support your work and provide a legal and ethical foundation for a healthy practice. In this chapter, I provide a variety of resources that you can use for this purpose. These are merely examples that you need to adapt for your own use, since your needs for your practice in your particular state will be different and require consultation with an attorney.

Before deciding on forms and procedures, I encourage you to complete the integrative health competency self-evaluation to help you gauge the degree of expertise that you have gained from this book and other resources, such as my certification programs. The evaluation includes space to reflect on your professional experience, your personal "laboratory" explorations, and your defined goals.

I also encourage you to reflect on which types of clients you plan to work with. Many clinicians, especially those who work for an agency or a group practice, fall into their practices rather than intentionally defining who they want to see and how they want to function. Whether you are bringing integrative methods into an existing practice or striking out on your own, it is essential to consider which clients will (or will not) be good candidates for your methods. For example, I worked with suicidal and severely self-harming clients for many years; however, once I went into private practice full-time, I no longer wanted that responsibility. I now refer people with suicidal ideation or risk and individuals with psychotic disorder.

You may wish to do outreach to better serve the clients you wish to work with. This might involve creating integrative groups, offering workshops, writing articles or blog posts, or giving talks at a local public library or mental health association. Consider seeking the expertise of a co-facilitator or co-speaker—for instance, when creating an integrative group on nutrition and culinary medicine for mental health, you might work with a registered dietitian who is savvy about mental health.

As you begin doing this work with clients, accurate documentation is essential. If a patient files a lawsuit, documentation may prevent the case from proceeding. Your records can be used to prove that you provided reasonable care and made careful judgments when treating your patient.

Mark's Story

Mark, a 38-year-old man, came to me for help with depression. The state in which I was practicing allowed nutritional and herbal counseling, and Mark and I explored nutrition for his mental health. I recommended that he take fish oil and use 5-HTP. He improved considerably as a result of his self-care and our work together, and we terminated therapy. Six months later, a board of health investigator contacted me. Mark had died of thromboembolism, and they were researching all of his previous practitioners. I was so saddened to learn of Mark's passing. I was also confident that my records were detailed, and I had evidence that neither fish oil nor 5-HTP was a risk factor. The medical examiner determined this was a genetic abnormality. The board of health agreed and complimented me on my recordkeeping.

To whatever extent you finally develop an integrative medicine practice, this type of work by its very nature bridges the boundaries between contemporary disciplines. In a careerist society, such a creative approach is an act of courage. I advise you to be confident and patient.

My own experience can illustrate why these qualities are so important. I had already been working as a clinician for eight years when, in 1985, I introduced somatic therapies into outpatient psychiatry at a major teaching hospital. This was before somatic therapies, yoga, meditation, and mindfulness were well integrated into care, and even though all my patients improved, there was a lot of hesitation and fear about using methods that were considered controversial. Today, these many years later, that teaching hospital routinely refers their patients for these methods and is part of a major hospital system that researches these methods.

The lesson? You may find yourself blazing trails for the next person. Trust your instincts, your curiosity, and your interests in this and any number of innovative approaches to helping your clients. Don't be afraid of being the first one on your block, and if you are, find the others who are also interested but "only half out of the closet." Join together and explore the variety of methods that bring promise of hope and change for clients.

INTEGRATIVE HEALTH COMPETENCY SELF-EVALUATION

Clinician Worksheet

PURPOSE

This self-evaluation will help you understand where you are and what you need in your journey of education as an integrative medicine and nutrition clinician.

BACKGROUND

The field of integrative medicine and nutrition for mental health is as broad and deep as the field of counseling and psychotherapy. This book will help you launch or expand your current practice. However, you did not become a competent counseling practitioner with just a few books or courses. Through this self-assessment, you can locate where you are on the journey and what your next steps for study might include.

Bioindividuality

❑   I know that different people need different types of foods based on their genomic profile.

❑   **Professional experience:** I understand the influence of methylation and the COMT gene on depression.

❑   **Personal laboratory:** I have experimented with different food groups to determine what is the best source of nourishment for me.

❑   **Defining goals:** I want to:

    ❑   Learn more about genomic influences on mental health

    ❑   Obtain my own genomic health report

    ❑   Enroll with a lab to obtain genomic reports for my clients

Notes: _____

_____

_____

_____

Culture

❑   I am familiar with different cultural health and healing practices in the communities to which my clients belong.

❑   **Professional experience:** I can competently ask an individual about their use of traditional medicine or culture-specific healing practices, and I have an open mind about these methods.

❑   **Personal laboratory:** I have explored at least two traditional medicine or cultural healing practices for my own health.

❑   **Defining goals:** I want to learn more about traditional medicine and cultural healing:

   ❑   For myself

   ❑   For my clients

Notes: _____

_____

_____

Integrative Assessment

❑   I am comfortable conducting an assessment about mental health and physical health.

❑   **Professional experience:** I understand how to read a blood test showing low levels of vitamins D and B-12.

❑   **Personal laboratory:** I have conducted, with a professional or on my own, a comprehensive mind-body-spirit assessment of my health and have made decisions based on my analysis.

❑   **Defining goals:** I want to deepen my understanding about how to conduct a mind-body-spirit assessment, including the following:

   ❑   Self-report

   ❑   Clinical assessments

   ❑   Analyzing serum/saliva/hair/tissue

Notes: _____

_____

_____

Biological Rhythms

- ❑ I am aware that the light and the dark are nature's way of balancing our mood and energy.

- ❑ **Professional experience:** I can discuss the biological underpinnings of why sleep deprivation therapy works for depression.

- ❑ **Personal laboratory:** I have identified my personal circadian rhythm and attempt to align myself with it as much as possible.

- ❑ **Defining goals:** I am interested in:

    - ❑ Learning more about chronotherapeutics

    - ❑ Going to bed earlier

    - ❑ Incorporating chronotherapeutics, including light boxes, into my clinical practice

Notes: _____

_____

_____

_____

Hormones

- ❑ I realize that hormones are crucial for regulating health.

- ❑ **Professional experience:** I can recognize when a referral for bioidentical hormone therapy is appropriate.

- ❑ **Personal laboratory:** I have engaged in balancing my own hormones for my health.

- ❑ **Defining goals:** I want to seek out a bioidentical hormone prescriber for potential collaboration:

    - ❑ For my clients

    - ❑ For myself

Notes: _____

_____

_____

_____

Nature

- ❑   I am aware that ecotherapy has a profound influence on well-being.

- ❑   **Professional experience:** I can discuss the ways in which the blue-green spectrum of nature influences mood.

- ❑   **Personal laboratory:** I have explored the effects of nature on my well-being and have had the opportunity to benefit from immersion in nature.

- ❑   **Defining goals:** I want to:

  - ❑   Learn more about the science of ecotherapy

  - ❑   Personally experience the benefits of nature more often

Notes: _____

_____

_____

_____

Human-Animal Relationships

- ❑   I recognize the importance of companion animals and their impact on people's well-being.

- ❑   **Professional experience:** I can explain what happens to oxytocin levels in the body when touching an animal companion.

- ❑   **Personal laboratory:** I have had companion animals or have engaged in animal-assisted therapy.

- ❑   **Defining goals:** I want to:

  - ❑   Learn more about animal-assisted therapies

  - ❑   Incorporate animal-assisted therapies into my clinical practice

Notes: _____

_____

_____

_____

Digestion

- ❑ I can explain the process of digestion, the organs involved, and its relevance.

- ❑ **Professional experience:** I can define the function of each organ of digestion, including the biochemistry, and how foods and moods affect the digestive process.

- ❑ **Personal laboratory:** I support my own digestive process through the use of foods, herbs, and belly massage as needed.

- ❑ **Defining goals:** I want to:

  - ○ Learn more about each organ of digestion

  - ○ Learn more about the relationship between mental health and gastrointestinal illnesses

  - ○ Introduce digestion and self-care into my clinical practice

Notes: _____

_____

_____

_____

Culinary Medicine

- • I know that food, and how it is prepared, influences people's health and mood.

- • **Professional experience:** I can define the names of antioxidants and polyphenols found in different plant colors.

- • **Personal laboratory:** I like to cook and consider it an important part of my health.

- • **Defining goals:** I want to:

  - ○ Study more about culinary medicine

  - ○ Conduct culinary medicine groups in my practice

  - ○ Cook and prepare food more often for myself

Notes: _____

_____

_____

_____

Supplementation

- ❑ I am aware that supplements can be a useful tool in bettering health.

- ❑ **Professional experience:** I can define the essential amino acids and assess the correct dose for omega-3 fatty acids.

- ❑ **Personal laboratory:** I use or have used vitamins and minerals for my health and consider them valuable.

- ❑ **Defining goals:** I want to learn more about:

  - o Nutrients for mental health
  - o Omega-3 fatty acids and amino acids
  - o Drug-nutrient-herb interactions
  - o My own health needs for supplementation

Notes: _____

_____

_____

_____

Herbal Medicine

- ❑ I recognize that herbs influence health and well-being.

- ❑ **Professional experience:** I know how to evaluate herb interaction with the P450 enzyme.

- ❑ **Personal laboratory:** I have grown or foraged for herbs and used herbal teas or extracts for my well-being.

- ❑ **Defining goals:** I want to:

  - o Read or take a course on herbal medicine
  - o Study pharmacognosy
  - o Make herbal teas and extracts
  - o Use herbs and spices in my culinary and health practice

Notes: _____

_____

_____

_____

Hydrotherapy and Detoxification

- I understand the importance of water and detoxification as health improvement strategies.

- **Professional experience:** I am familiar with the appropriate principles of application for hot and cold water to pain.

- **Personal laboratory:** I use water as a healing agent or have personally undergone some detoxification routines.

- **Defining goals:** I want to explore the scientific literature about:

  o Hydrotherapy

  o Detoxification

Notes: _____

_____

_____

_____

Exercise

- ❑ I know that certain exercises can help target specific health concerns.

- ❑ **Professional experience:** I can explain the role of exercise on BDNF levels, or I can recommend appropriate exercises to reduce anxiety, depression, and pain.

- ❑ **Personal laboratory:** I engage in varied exercise routines for my health and well-being.

- ❑ **Defining goals:** I want to:

  o Teach different exercises to my clients

  o Read the literature about the benefits of exercise

Notes: _____

_____

_____

_____

Somatics and Bodywork

- I understand that bodywork and somatic therapies are a valuable tool to improve people's health and well-being.

- **Professional experience:** I can define three reasons why I would refer a client for a specific type of bodywork.

- **Personal laboratory:** I have personally experienced bodywork or energy medicine.

- **Defining goals:** I want to:

    - Experiment with different types of somatic therapies for my personal well-being

    - Learn a somatic therapy for clinical application

    - Reach out to somatic practitioners in my community to establish a collaborative relationship

Notes: _____

_____

_____

_____

Breath

- ❑ I understand the role breath plays in anxiety, mood, and health.

- ❑ **Professional experience:** I can discuss the science of hyperventilation and anxiety.

- ❑ **Personal laboratory:** I practice several different types of breathing exercises to enhance my health and well-being.

- ❑ **Defining goals:** I want to:

    - Routinely incorporate breathing exercises with my clients

    - Build my skills in applying numerous breathing methods to specific forms of mental and physical distress

    - Dedicate more time to my own breathing practice

Notes: _____

_____

_____

Spirituality and Meaning-Making

- I am comfortable with my belief system and understand that belief systems influence people's perceptions and interpretations about their health and well-being.

- **Professional experience:**

  - I routinely incorporate questions, discussions, and processes about spirituality and religion in my clinical practice.

  - I am comfortable with clients who are atheists.

- **Personal laboratory:** I have:

  - A spiritual practice

  - Explored in depth the influence of religion in my life

- **Defining goals:** I'd like to:

  - Learn more about the role of spirituality in health

  - Incorporate spirituality or religion into my clinical practice

  - Incorporate more options for spirituality or transpersonal experiences in my life

Notes: _____

_____

_____

_____

Altered States and Psychedelic Medicine

- I realize that altered states and psychedelic medicine can have profoundly positive effects on people's lives and are an integral part of some communities' cultural practices. I can differentiate between the use of substances as addictions and their therapeutic potential.

- **Professional experience:** I can discuss the psychobiology and healing potential of altered states as a result of psychedelic medicine or various cultural rituals.

- **Personal laboratory:** I have experienced altered states that have:

  - Been under my control

  - Not been under my control

  - Been due to using psychedelic medicine

- **Defining goals:** I want to:

    o   Explore psychedelic medicine's use and benefits

    o   Engage in rituals that alter my consciousness

Notes: _____

_____

_____

_____

Adherence Strategies

- I understand the benefits and challenges of adhering to a self-care plan.

- **Professional experience:** I understand how personality interacts with the success of adherence to self-care plans.

- **Personal laboratory:** I have experience adhering to my own self-care plan.

- **Defining goals:** I want to:

    ❑   Adjust my adherence to a self-care plan

    ❑   Explore motivational interviewing and other methods to enhance adherence

    ❑   Enhance my awareness of how personality influences adherence to self-care

Notes: _____

_____

_____

_____

LANGUAGE FOR INTEGRATIVE PRACTITIONERS

Clinician Worksheet

PURPOSE

This worksheet will enable you to define and introduce your work as an integrative mental health clinician to new or existing clients.

BACKGROUND

Clients are not always aware of the mental health benefits of body therapies, meditation, nutrition, herbal medicine, and exercise. Because of this, it can be challenging to inform them about the integrative aspects of the work you do. Along with feeling confident about your new area of work, having a script to practice before initiating these conversations is key to successful communication. As you educate clients about how "everything is connected to everything" in mental health, you can also help them identify their readiness for change and prioritize the methods they prefer.

SCRIPT FOR NEW CLIENTS

I am trained and licensed as a [*e.g., mental health counselor, psychologist*]. I specialize in helping people who experience [*e.g., depression, anxiety, the after-effects of trauma*].

In my clinical experience, I have found that in addition to counseling, integrative methods such as [*e.g., breathwork, yoga, exercise, nutrition*] are essential to getting the best benefits and overcoming the symptoms you describe. Therefore, in addition to my work in [*e.g., CBT, EMDR, ACT*], I am trained in [*e.g., integrative medicine and nutrition*].

Would you be interested in learning about and applying some of these methods? I can also share the research supporting this work. In addition to our work together, if we need to bring in another clinician or consultant, I have an excellent network of caring and highly skilled practitioners we can draw on.

Please note that I am not a [*e.g., registered dietitian, medical prescriber*], and I do not bill insurance for these services. If you have insurance for these types of services, I am happy to coordinate with a provider to ensure you receive the most up-to-date care.

SCRIPT FOR EXISTING CLIENTS

We have been working together for [*e.g., weeks, months, years*]. During this time, we have been focusing on your recovery from [*e.g., depression, early life trauma*], and you've made tremendous gains. I am so honored to be working with you.

I wanted to share with you some additional options we might explore that support the therapy we've been doing. In addition to my licensure, I work in the area of integrative approaches, including nutrition and culinary medicine for mental health. There's a great deal of research that suggests that improvements in [*e.g., nutrition, breathwork, exercise*] can improve the symptoms you've been experiencing. I am a great believer and have seen excellent results when people combine counseling along with some small changes in these areas.

Is this something that would be of interest to you? Would you like to talk about this more? Does this feel like the right time to introduce some additional methods?

SCRIPT FOR INTEGRATIVE GROUPS

We've been working together for [*e.g., weeks, months, years*] now, and you have really thrown yourself into your self-care. I'm excited for all the changes and benefits you're experiencing.

As you may know from my self-disclosure, I work in the area of integrative approaches, including nutrition and culinary medicine for mental health. I am starting a [*e.g., 9-week, 12-week*] group that will address a range of methods, including [*e.g., movement, yoga, mindfulness, culinary and nutritional approaches*].

I think this group would be a great complement to the work you're already doing. Would you like to learn more about this group?

SCRIPT FOR REFERRALS

We've been working together now for [*e.g., weeks, months, years*] to address your [*e.g., anxiety, depression*], and you've made wonderful progress. I notice that you often share with me some of your physical complaints, and I wanted to let you know that there's a great deal of research and clinical knowledge that some of the complaints you're discussing related to [*e.g., digestion and discomfort*] are related to the mental health issues we've been exploring.

As you may know from my self-disclosure, I also work in the area of integrative methods and nutrition—and in my professional opinion, you would benefit physically and emotionally from a consultation with [*e.g., a nutrition expert, a bodywork practitioner*]. I believe you could feel a lot better with some gentle changes to your current self-care regime. Would you be interested in such a referral? I work with someone who I think you'd enjoy meeting and is very compassionate and knowledgeable.

NUTRITIONAL PRACTICE GUIDELINES

Clinician Handout

PURPOSE

This worksheet will help you consider your role with clients as you support their connection between mental health and nutrition.

BACKGROUND

The two most important determinants of integrating nutrition into your practice are what your state allows and your level of competency. As of this writing, there are 12 states in which nutritional counseling must be done by registered dietitians. The American Nutrition Association's website (https://theana.org/advocate) maps legislative changes and is an excellent resource for keeping up-to-date with the laws in your state of practice. It also provides information about opportunities to lobby for legislative changes.

NUTRITIONAL PRACTICE ISSUES TO CONSIDER

Some states have an "exclusive scope of practice nutrition law," in which it is illegal for a mental health therapist without a nutrition or dietetics license to provide nutrition counseling unless one of the following applies:

- The practitioner has a state license or state certification that recognizes nutrition counseling as part of the legal scope of practice

- The practitioner's nutrition guidance is covered under an exemption to the nutrition/dietetics licensing law

If you are not able to practice nutritional therapies in your state, you still have options. With insurance-based practices, you can team up with a kindred licensed nutritionist or dietitian, co-create a psychoculinary group, and run it together. The group can combine mental health and psychoeducation about food and mood, along with fulfilling the requirements for insurance-based medical nutrition groups.

In addition, I recommend following these basic guidelines when incorporating nutrition into your practice:

- Create a separate legal entity and obtain liability insurance if you are practicing as an independent contractor. It may be beneficial with an integrative practice or parallel practice to have more than one type of insurance to cover your activities. Make sure they are clearly delineated and you seek the advice of an attorney.

- Educate your clients about healthy nutrition choices and provide reputable sources for that information. Avoid "Dr. Google."

- Keep your competency levels high to provide high-quality services. Licensing boards want to know you are addressing the standard of care and are following or aware of best practices.

- Recognize what you know, what you don't know, and when to refer. Collaborative work benefits you, the other provider, and the client.

- Provide easy-to-understand forms, including disclosure and informed consent forms, that define your expectations, services, credentials, and mediation options if the client is unhappy with your services.

- Offer a money-back guarantee. If someone is not satisfied with my services, I want to either address the client's concerns or offer a full refund, regardless of time spent.

- Understand the limitations of your methods. Always discuss options and offer a conventional approach or referral.

- Always make sure you are trained and have references—including textbooks, peer-reviewed journal articles, and continuing education courses—on the areas you teach and treat.

CONSENT FOR CARE AND DISCLAIMERS

Clinician Handout

PURPOSE

This handout outlines a variety of disclaimers that may be relevant to your practice. Remember, you should always seek legal advice on the specific type of content you require.

BACKGROUND

There are many types of consent forms and disclaimers you can use for an integrative medicine and nutrition practice. After you consult an attorney about your practice needs, you may decide to add some integrative methods to your existing licensure practice or develop a separate, parallel practice as a health coach, herbalist, or nutritional practitioner. The following is a sample consent form, including disclaimers, that may be of relevance to your practice or clinic.

SAMPLE CONSENT FORM

Consent for Care

I voluntarily give my consent to receive treatment from [*therapist name*] and authorize care that we mutually define and decide upon. This includes assessment methods, review of test results and forms completed at the request of [*therapist name*], and recommendations for health and wellness activities.

[*Therapist name*] does not practice medicine, and if they deem it necessary or beneficial for my health program will request from me the opportunity to consult in collaboration with my prescriber. The methods that [*therapist name*] may suggest or recommend for self-care or referral may include:

- Health coaching, such as lifestyle counseling and exercise recommendations

- Herbs and natural substances, including plant, mineral, and animal materials; substances may be recommended in the form of teas, pills, powders, tinctures (may contain alcohol), topical creams, pastes, plasters, washes, suppositories, or other forms

- Manual therapies and therapeutic use of heat and cold, including massage, stretching, resistance, joint manipulation, and hydrotherapy

- Dietary advice and nutrition, including the use of food and nutritional supplements for treatments

I acknowledge and consent to the following:

- I understand that potential risks exist. While not common, risks occur with any form of therapy. Examples include but are not limited to pain or discomfort, allergic reactions from prescribed herbs or supplements, and aggravation of pre-existing symptoms.

- I understand that potential benefits exist. Benefits include restoration of health and the body's maximal functional capacity, relief of pain and symptoms, assistance in recovery, and prevention of progression.

- I understand that by signing this form, I am authorizing care from [*therapist name*] until I withdraw my consent in writing.

_____ Consent for treatment (please initial here)

Notice to Pregnant Clients

I understand that if I know or suspect that I am pregnant, I must alert [*therapist name*], since some of the therapies could present a risk to the pregnancy.

No Guarantee of Results

[*Therapist name*] cannot guarantee any specific result(s). I release [*therapist name*] from any liability for any accident or injury that is not directly caused by the negligence of [*therapist name*] or their employees. If I have any questions concerning any assessments or recommended health programs, I will ask [*therapist name*] to provide me with additional information.

_____ Consent for treatment (please initial here)

Disclaimers

I understand that [*therapist name*] is certified as a [area of certification] specializing in integrative mental health and physical well-being as it relates to mental health. While [*therapist name*] is a licensed [area of licensure], they do not provide these services for clients outside of [state name].

[*Therapist name*] does not dispense medical advice nor prescribe treatment. Rather, [*therapist name*] provides education to enhance my knowledge of health as it relates to foods, dietary supplements, and behaviors associated with eating and mental wellness. While nutritional and botanical support can be an important complement to my care, I understand nutrition counseling is not a substitute for diagnosis, treatment, or care of disease by a medical provider.

If I am under the care of a health care professional or currently using prescription medications, I acknowledge that I should discuss any dietary changes or potential dietary supplement use with my primary care physician, and should not discontinue any prescription medications without first consulting my primary care physician.

I acknowledge that the care I receive during my nutrition and health coaching sessions is separate from the care that I receive from any medical facility and that the nutrition coaching sessions are in no way intended to be construed as medical advice or care. I should continue regular medical supervision and care by my primary care physician.

Personal Responsibility and Release of Health Care–Related Claims

I acknowledge that I take full responsibility for my life and well-being, as well as the lives and well-being of my family and children (where applicable), and all decisions made during and after the duration of my nutrition and wellness coaching sessions.

I expressly assume the risks of nutrition and wellness coaching sessions, including the risks of trying new foods, and the risks inherent in making lifestyle changes.

I release [*therapist name*] from any and all liability, damages, causes of action, allegations, suits, sums of money, claims, and demands whatsoever, in lay or equity, which I have ever had, now have, or will have in the future against [*therapist name*] arising from my past or future participation in, or otherwise with respect to, the clinical coaching sessions, unless arising from the gross negligence of [*therapist name*].

Confidentiality

[*Therapist name*] will keep my information private and will not share my information to any third party unless compelled to do so by law or with my consent.

Payments and Refunds

Payments are due at the time of service. If I am dissatisfied with service, I may request a full refund.

No-Show/Cancellation Policy

In the event that I do not show up to an appointment or cancel within 24 hours of a scheduled appointment, [*therapist name*] reserves the right to charge me 50 percent of the session payment fee. The above may be disregarded in the event of an emergency.

_____

Client Signature

PUTTING IT ALL TOGETHER: THE BRAINBOW BLUEPRINT REPORT

Clinician Handout

PURPOSE

This handout illustrates the Brainbow Blueprint in action with a sample report for a client.

BACKGROUND

The previous forms can help provide the parameters for your work with clients. Once you have the legal and ethical foundation in place, using the Brainbow Blueprint will allow for a breadth and depth of client-clinician collaboration that will lead to greater healing results than most mainstream providers are able to help their clients work toward. After doing a comprehensive intake assessment with your client, reviewing their tests and forms, and prioritizing areas of the Brainbow Blueprint to work on, you should compile a Brainbow Blueprint report to give your client as a roadmap for your work together.

SAMPLE REPORT: INEZ

Dear Inez,

It was a pleasure to meet you, talk with you, and learn about you and your health goals. Below I will review the major principles we discussed and some initial recommendations.

The major focus of our discussion focused on your experience of IBS, depression, anxiety, insomnia, and some bodily pain. We discussed that you are experiencing significant biochemical sensitivities to sugar, alcohol, and grains. Unfortunately, there is no such thing as moderation in their use for you. Sugar and fast foods are toxic and addictive to your brain, and they underlie depression and pain. There is also evidence they can exacerbate endometriosis and are a major factor in IBS. These items underlie many of the challenges you face, so my suggestion is to quit them cold turkey or take three months to reduce and eliminate them from your diet. I will work with you to define ways to do this.

Given your symptoms, it may also be that you are sensitive to gluten; we can test that or eliminate it to ascertain its effects on your health. We can also test for additional food allergies in later stages of treatment. In the meantime, I suggest using the Coca pulse test (which I can teach to you) to explore your reactions to certain foods. I will work with you and support you in your health, whatever you decide to do.

I know you also love coffee, so let's find a way to make it work for you, not against you. Instead of eliminating coffee altogether, we can reduce your caffeine intake to improve symptoms of insomnia and anxiety. It is easy to start making cold-brewed coffee using half-decaf beans. This will reduce the acid and have beneficial effects on your digestive system (while still tasting delicious). As you increase the amount of protein in your diet and reduce refined foods, you will find that your energy also increases.

You identified reducing alcohol as a goal, so I will identify some herbal combinations that will help you relax at night instead of alcohol. These herbs cannot be used with alcohol, so when you are ready for those, we will evaluate you to determine which protocol suits you best. As you sleep better, this sets the stage for your goal to eliminate Seroquel.

In addition to making changes to your diet, I suggest you find 90–120 minutes every day just for you. This is a sacred, inviolable time for self-care. You might decide to take a walk, do a few yoga exercises, listen to binaural beats, make a healthy meal, sit back and read a novel with a hot (or cold) pack on your body, take a nap, or do nothing at all and explore how it feels to be and not do. I also want to explore some simple feel-good methods that can be part of your at-home healing "spa," including skin brushing, aromatherapy with essential oils, or foot baths. As you begin to feel better, housework is good exercise to consider because of how it helps you stretch and move.

You said that a 3-to-6-month timeline would work for you to achieve these goals, where you can detox from the substances we've identified (and all the products that contain them). When we meet next, we will review how you have organized monthly and quarterly tasks to meet your goals. This will be the first set of changes we have discussed, and we will plan to tackle your goals in several phases, since you are concerned about feeling overwhelmed. I have no doubt that in 12 to 24 months you can feel excellent physically and emotionally. It's wonderful your partner is so supportive. Bring her in on the plan and ask her to help you.

We also discussed the challenges of your early life and its effects on your health. Our work together will complement the work you are doing in therapy. We discussed being compassionate with yourself in how you are using foods to soothe yourself when triggered. We explored how to identify what you need in these initial moments of distress. You made a list of comfort foods and herbal teas that you enjoy that will not exacerbate your digestion or pain symptoms. We discussed your options for movement during these stressor moments and your options for doing shavasana, the corpse pose, or going for a vigorous power walk. Your self-care and self-soothing muscle gets stronger the more you use it, so take the time to explore what you need in these moments.

Below are some specific suggestions based on our discussions. As you make these changes, as questions come up feel free to drop me a quick email or ask them at our scheduled appointments.

Bioindividuality

- You are currently a pescatarian and do not eat dairy.

- **Proposed:** We will discuss your ethnic, cultural, and genomic background. I also recommend that you receive a hair analysis to ascertain your metabolic type and assess your mineral level. (I suspect from the intake that it is slow, which means you need more protein, moderate carbs, no sugar, and less fat in your diet.)

Integrative Assessment

- We will identify sources of xenoestrogens (i.e., foreign chemicals that mimic estrogen) and explore how to eliminate plastics and pesticides from your life.

- You will undertake self-guided Coca pulse testing.

- Over time, we can consider checking 24-hour cortisol levels to assess your biological stress response and circadian rhythm; using pharmacogenomic testing to evaluate which medications are not harmful and which to avoid; and MTHFR and COMT genetic testing.

- **Proposed:** Since you noted concerns with money, it would be beneficial for you to explore elimination of gluten on your own versus seeking out expensive testing.

Biological Rhythms and Hormones

- Your circadian rhythm is out of balance due to working irregular and long hours.

- You have endometriosis.

- **Proposed:** You will take the Automated Morningness-Eveningness Questionnaire (AutoMEQ) to better understand your circadian rhythm chronotype. We will make a plan to help you consider taking a day job that does not require working a night shift. We'll assess for the length of your sleep disruption, and you'll learn about the role of stimulants and sedatives in circadian rhythm. For your endometriosis, we will discuss hormones and the liver and consider referring you to a prescriber for bioidentical hormones.

Nature

- You live in a city, so you don't get to be in nature frequently. But you do go on walks with your dog, sometimes to a small local park.

- **Proposed:** We will discuss additional options for accessing nature in urban areas.

Human-Animal Relationships

- You live with your long-term partner. You feel overwhelmed in social settings and find it difficult to maintain relationships and set boundaries.

- You have a dog who is very important to you.

- **Proposed:** Invite your long-term partner in for a session to educate her about how she can best support you when you are feeling overwhelmed. We can also conduct role-plays in session to help you develop and practice your own phrases for setting boundaries. Given the importance of your dog, you'll learn more about how canine therapy can be helpful.

Digestion and Culinary Medicine

- Packaged foods and sugar can contribute to depression.

- Reducing sugar and caffeine can help with your endometriosis.

- **Proposed:** Eliminate gluten, sugar, and alcohol from your diet (in that order). As you eliminate glutenous grains and sugar, you will benefit from incorporating more proteins, healthy fats, vegetables, and fruits with some fiber. Increase animal protein, focusing on eggs daily. Incorporate more cruciferous vegetables into your diet—these are good for helping the liver detoxify estrogen. Fiber is important for your IBS, so slowly integrate lightly cooked fruits and vegetables and work your way toward consuming them raw. Making some chia puddings (sweetened with stevia) will also help constipation. Don't go hungry, especially as you reduce gluten. Read labels and eat whole, natural foods (not packaged or fast).

Supplements

- Among the most important supplements to address your symptoms of endometriosis are black currant seed oil, B-complex vitamins, and magnesium. Start with 200 mg of magnesium glycinate during the day with breakfast, and 200 mg at night before bed. If you find your fecal elimination getting too loose, decrease the magnesium.

- **Proposed:** Take MygranX™ (2 capsules per day), Phytolens® (2 capsules twice a day), DIM (200 mg. per day, added to your smoothie), and Pycnogenol (60 mg. per day).

Herbal Medicine

- Cannabis can help reduce anxiety and promote falling asleep some nights.

- **Proposed:** You'll benefit from a 1:1 ratio of THC:CBD at night. You can use CBD orally and topically. Polarity tea and licorice root tea can also help balance circadian rhythm. To help with endometriosis pain, drink a mixture of fresh ginger, chamomile, cramp bark, and skullcap tea three days before menstruation begins, and continue to drink this throughout the duration of menstruation. Add cinnamon to foods during menstruation to help with pain as well. Use slippery elm bark tea to aid digestion.

Hydrotherapy and Detoxification

- You would like to explore coming off psychotropic medication (100 mg Seroquel for sleep and 75 mg Zoloft for anxiety and depression). To get off these medications, you will first need to implement this integrative health program for a solid 12 weeks to give your body a chance to recover from alcohol and sugar and to be sleeping well.

- There are specific tapering methods you can explore with your prescriber, and we can discuss those when you are ready.

- Hydrotherapy can be very helpful for pain in your uterus, colon, and intestines.

- **Proposed:** We will adjust your nutrient and herbal protocol every three months (or as needed) as your progress in your taper to detox from psychotropic medication (prioritizing good exercise, taking nutrients, and eating well). You will contact your prescriber and begin to engage with your partner about detox to help alleviate any fears. We will discuss the use of coffee enemas (which aid liver function) and hot-water bottle packs over the abdomen and the application of CBD cream (which help with bodily pain).

Exercise

- You do yoga once or twice a week and go on daily walks with your dog.

- **Proposed:** Increase your daily walks to 45 minutes per walk, five times a week. We will discuss building up to HIIT workouts for mood and pain management. I also suggest incorporating resistance and weight training to help with your body dysmorphia. I will demonstrate how different yoga poses can release pelvic pain.

Somatics and Bodywork

- You are interested in energy work.

- You've gone to a massage therapist a few times and are interested in self-massage techniques for chronic pain management.

- **Proposed:** We will discuss body awareness and identify where different organs are located. I will teach you how to do a belly self-massage, which will help with pain related to both digestion and endometriosis. I will also teach you to apply moxibustion for this abdominal pain (specifically, moxi points CV 3, 4, and 5; ST 25 and 36; GV 20; LI 4; LV 3; KI 3; and SP 6 and 9). We can also explore cranial sacral and Japanese acupuncture.

Breath

- We explored why you didn't prioritize breathing, and you said that you didn't know much about it. But following our discussion, you agreed that you would like to do one exercise and changed the priority to do it right away. It is something that you will share with your partner.

- You feel that you are a shallow chest breather because of anxiety. You have panic attacks infrequently, but when they do happen, you tend to hyperventilate.

- Breathing during yoga helps relieve tension in the chest by breathing into your belly.

- **Proposed:** We will explore some balanced pranayama exercises that activate the left and right hemispheres of the brain. I will teach you the "ha" breath and discuss the benefits of putting a one-pound bag of rice on your chest while you lie down during breathing exercises.

Spirituality

- You're not religious but grew up in a Christian household.

- **Proposed:** No suggestions because you are not interested.

Altered States

- You are interested in tapering off alcohol.

- **Proposed:** See the earlier sections for details on our plan to taper off alcohol and prescription medications. Because medical cannabis is legal in your state, I have recommended cannabis to alleviate your anxiety and insomnia, which was also described earlier.

- You asked me whether I think you are a candidate for ketamine; in my opinion we might revisit this question in 3–6 months, after you have undertaken these initial changes.

Adherence Strategies

- You've been able to stick to a consistent exercise routine.

- You feel less able to engage in regular self-care because of your busy schedule and stress levels.

- Your doctor made you feel hopeless by telling you that you will be on psychotropic medication your whole life.

- **Proposed:** I will provide you with strategies to counteract learned helplessness, reframe shame about your perceived ability to be self-efficacious, and help you achieve your goals. The goal is to prioritize what you feel is doable right now and link that to your goals for coming off psychotropic medication. I will also explore concrete ways that your partner can help you stay on track. Please drop me a note weekly with any questions you have and to let me know how you are doing. We will schedule a brief live check-in every week or two as you prefer. I look forward to supporting your next steps to health.

CONCLUSION

The development of this book has been a labor of love born from a passion for supporting clinicians and others in exploring nonpharmaceutical and integrative methods for mental health.

It is apparent in our lived experiences and clinical observations that when we practice techniques and provide interventions that nourish the needs of the mind and the body and promote balance, we achieve exponential results.

The methods I suggest in this book are all rooted in nature and the natural process of change—nature is slow but sure. These methods will not be for everyone, as they are often challenging and time-consuming. Our role as clinicians is to bring the fine art of rapport, empathy, and insight to engage our beloved clients on the right path for them as individuals and guide them toward their definition of wholeness.

RESOURCES

INTRODUCTION

General Resources on Integrative Medicine

- Academic Consortium for Integrative Medicine & Health (https://imconsortium.org): This consortium works to advance the principles and practices of integrative health care within academic institutions.

- Integrative Mental Health Plan (http://integrativementalhealthplan.com/index.php?main_page=page&id=5): This list of online resources on mental health care, compiled by the integrative psychiatrist Dr. James Lake, contains links to valuable databases and other online resources on both Western mental health care and complementary and alternative medicine, including expert resources on specific CAM modalities.

- International Society for Nutritional Psychiatry Research (http://www.isnpr.org): ISNPR is a membership organization supporting the generation of high-quality evidence for nutritional approaches to the prevention and treatment of mental disorders, as well as knowledge-sharing.

- International Society for Traditional, Complementary, and Integrative Medicine Research (https://iscmr.org): ISCMR is an international, multidisciplinary scientific organization that fosters the development and dissemination of new knowledge regarding whole-person healing and whole-systems health care research, including all traditional, holistic, alternative, complementary, and integrative forms of medicine.

- National Center for Complementary and Integrative Health (https://nccih.nih.gov): The center conducts research and provides information about integrative health products and practices.

- National Directory of Integrative Health & Medicine Centers (https://fonconsulting.com/resources/integrative-medicine-centers): This directory is maintained by FON Consulting, which supports the long-term growth of integrative health organizations while advancing evidence-based integrative medicine as the standard of care.

CHAPTER 1: THE BRAINBOW BLUEPRINT

Foundational Books on Integrative Medicine

- Belenky, M. F., Clinchy, B. M., Goldberger, N. R., & Tarule, J. M. (1986). *Women's ways of knowing: The development of self, voice, and mind.* Basic Books.

- Boon, S., Steele, K., & van der Hart, O. (2011). *Coping with trauma-related dissociation: Skills training for patients and therapists.* Norton.

- Edwards, B. (1989). *Drawing on the right side of the brain: A course in enhancing creativity and artistic confidence.* J. P. Tarcher.

- Fisher, J. (2021). *Transforming the living legacy of trauma: A workbook for survivors and therapists.* PESI Publishing.

- Houston, J. (1982). *The possible human: A course in extending your physical, mental, and creative abilities.* J. P. Tarcher.

CHAPTER 2: BIOINDIVIDUALITY

Further Study

- Food as Medicine: Food and Our Genome (https://www.monash.edu/medicine/scs/nutrition/short -courses/food-as-medicine-food-and-our-genome): This two-week online course is offered by the Department of Nutrition and Dietetics at Monash University for health care professionals.

- Introduction to Clinical Nutrigenomics (https://training.nutritiongenome.com): Nutrition Genome's free, short course discusses high-impact nutrigenomic concepts, and its advanced paid course covers numerous health disorders and comprehensive analysis of 149 clinically relevant SNPs. Both courses can support you to leverage Nutrition Genome's DNA testing services in your clinical practice.

- Personal Genomics and Your Health (https://online.stanford.edu/courses/xgen205-personal -genomics-and-your-health): This is an elective course in Stanford Medical School's Genetics and Genomics Program and can be taken for CEUs.

Specific Bioindividuality Resources

Both of these web pages, from two of the largest direct-to-consumer genetic testing companies, provide an overview of genetic variability in caffeine metabolism and references to relevant research:

- Caffeine Consumption, AncestryDNA® Traits Learning Hub (https://www.ancestry.com/c/traits -learning-hub/caffeine-consumption)

- Caffeine Consumption & Genetics, 23andMe (https://www.23andme.com/topics/wellness/caffeine -consumption)

CHAPTER 3: INTEGRATIVE ASSESSMENT

Testing Resources

- Rupa Labs (https://www.rupahealth.com): A one-stop shop for over 30 lab companies conducting all types of health tests. Requires an NPI number to enroll and physician support is available.

- DiagnosTechs, Inc. (https://www.diagnostechs.com): This lab focuses on testing food allergies, adrenal stress, and sex hormone panels.

- Great Plains Laboratory (https://www.greatplainslaboratory.com/home): Great Plains provides specialized testing, including for organic acids, gluten, casein, vitamin D, amino acid levels (urinary and blood), urinary/serum peptides, and a zinc taste test. The lab also offers mycotoxin testing for 172 different toxic chemicals, including organophosphate pesticides, phthalates, benzene, xylene, vinyl chloride, pyrethroid insecticides, acrylamide, perchlorate, diphenyl phosphate, ethylene oxide, and acrylonitrile. Tests are available for glyphosate herbicide (Roundup) and tiglylglycine (TG), a marker for mitochondrial disorders caused by exposure to toxic chemicals, infections, inflammation, and nutritional deficiencies.

- Kashi Lab (https://kashilab.com/mood-profile): The Kashi Mood Profile Panel identifies genomics that may contribute to susceptibility to mood disorders.

- Life Extension (https://www.lifeextension.com/vitamins-supplements/blood-tests): Life Extension Blood Testing Services provide requisitions for client-ordered blood tests for a variety of markers, including inflammatory markers, homocysteine, high-sensitivity C-reactive protein (hs-CRP), fibrinogen and micronutrient tests (blood), hormones (urine and serum), omega index, and a thyroid antibody panel.

- Testing.com (https://www.testing.com): Formerly known as Lab Testing Online, this site offers a variety of tests, including interleukin-6 for monitoring inflammatory responses, high-sensitivity C-reactive protein (hs-CRP) for assessing risk of developing cardiovascular disease, fibrinogen, and a gastrointestinal pathogens panel.

CHAPTER 4: BIOLOGICAL RHYTHMS AND HORMONES

Biological Rhythms Resources

- Center for Environmental Therapeutics (https://cet.org): The center focuses on the role of light, darkness, and air in mental and physical health. They offer assessments and resources for professionals and others.

- Mind-Eye Institute (https://mindeye.com): The institute's research is centered around neuro-optometric rehabilitation for people with brain injuries, autism, learning disorders, and neurodegenerative diseases.

Hormones Resources

- Edinburgh Postnatal Depression Scale (https://womensinternational.com/wp-content/uploads/2019/09/Edinburgh-Postnatal-Depression-Scale.pdf): This self-assessment supports individuals to determine the existence and severity of postnatal depression.

- Hormone Imbalance Symptom Chart (https://womensinternational.com/wp-content/uploads/2019/09/DaltonSymptomChart.pdf): This printable chart allows individuals to track symptoms occurring cyclically that may be related to hormone imbalances.

- Women's International Pharmacy (https://www.womensinternational.com): This pharmacy focuses on custom compounding bioidentical hormone solutions for patients across the continental United States, Hawaii, Puerto Rico, Guam, and the US Virgin Islands.

CHAPTER 5: NATURE

Further Study

- Association of Nature and Forest Therapy Guides and Programs (https://www.natureandforesttherapy.earth): A leading provider of forest therapy training, the association provides a combination of remote and in-person training.

- Center for Nature Informed Therapy (https://www.natureinformedtherapy.com/training): CNIT provides training to individuals to cultivate healing reconnection with the natural world. For mental health professionals, they also offer CE and a three-month training to become a certified nature-informed therapist.

General Nature Resources

Both of these sites can help individuals find parks and trails in their area:

- All Trails (https://www.alltrails.com)

- Find Your Park (https://findyourpark.com)

CHAPTER 6: HUMAN-ANIMAL RELATIONSHIPS

General Human-Animal Relationship Resources

- Assistance Dogs International (https://assistancedogsinternational.org): This is a worldwide coalition of not-for-profit programs that train and place assistance dogs.

- Camp Gone to the Dogs (http://www.camp-gone-tothe-dogs.com): These camps offer a wide range of sessions, seminars, and more so participants can explore and experience new activities with their dogs.

- Pet Partners (https://petpartners.org): This organization is focused on demonstrating and promoting the health and wellness benefits of animal-assisted therapy, activities, and education.

- Professional Association of Therapeutic Horsemanship International (https://www.pathintl.org): PATH International promotes safe and effective therapeutic horseback riding throughout the United States and Canada, with more than 800 member centers and 7,000 individual members globally, who help and support children and adults (including veterans) with special needs through a variety of equine-assisted services.

- Therapy Dog International (https://tdi-dog.org): TDI is a volunteer organization dedicated to the regulating, testing, and registration of therapy dogs and their volunteer handlers for the purpose of visiting nursing homes, hospitals, and wherever else therapy dogs are needed.

Specific Resources

- Dognition (https://www.dognition.com): Dognition offers a series of fun games to do with your dog to identify their learning and interaction style.

- Insureon (https://www.insureon.com/therapy-counseling-business-insurance/animal-assisted -therapists): provides business insurance for animal-assisted therapists.

CHAPTER 7: DIGESTION

Further Study

- Gehringer, L., & Gehringer, N. (2019). *From chewing to pooing: Food's journey through your body to the potty.* Authors.

- Mayer, E. (2016). *The mind-gut connection: How the hidden conversation within our bodies impacts our mood, our choices, and our overall health.* HarperCollins.

CHAPTER 8: CULINARY MEDICINE

Further Study

My Courses with PESI

- Certified Integrative Mental Health Professional (CIMHP) Training Course: Nutritional and Integrative Medicine for Mental Health Professionals (https://catalog.pesi.com/sales/bh_c _001278evg_nimcert_012320_organic-105450)

- Create a Successful Telehealth Practice for Nutrition and Integrative Medicine (https://catalog.pesi .com/item/59563)

- Integrative Medicine and Nutrition for PTSD and Complex Trauma Certification Course (https:// catalog.pesi.com/sales/bh_c_001533_integrativemedicinenutritionptsdtrauma_organic-266353)

- Nutrition Essentials for Mental Health: Strategies to Enhance Mood and Well-Being (https://catalog .pesi.com/item/45331)

- Nutrition and Integrative Medicine for Cognitive Decline, Alzheimer's Disease and Diabetes (https://catalog.pesi.com/sales/bh_c_001384_nimcognitivedecline_organic-138824)

Other Institutions

- Maryland University of Integrative Health (https://muih.edu): MUIH educates leaders in health and wellness with more than 20 different programs—including those in nutrition and herbal medicine—that integrate ancient wisdom and contemporary science. MUIH offers graduate degrees and certificates in a wide range of wellness fields, as well as individual courses for professional and personal development.

- Nutritional Therapy Association (https://nutritionaltherapy.com): NTA's Nutritional Therapy Practitioner program is a 10-month, instructor-led, and fully online course of study in a foundational and bioindividual approach to functional, holistic nutrition.

- Saybrook University (https://www.saybrook.edu): Saybrook offers a certificate, an MS, and a PhD in integrative and functional nutrition, as well as degrees in mind-body medicine.

- University of Western States (https://www.uws.edu/human-nutrition-functional-medicine): UWS offers online master's, doctoral, and graduate certificate programs in human nutrition and functional medicine.

My Books

- Korn, L. E. (2016). *Nutrition essentials for mental health: A complete guide to the food-mood connection.* W. W. Norton & Company.

- Korn, L. E. (2017a). *Eat right, feel right: Over 80 recipes and tips to improve mood, sleep, attention & focus.* PESI Publishing & Media.

- Korn, L. E. (2017b). *The good mood kitchen: Simple recipes and nutrition tips for emotional balance.* Norton Professional Books.

- Korn, L. E. (2023). *Rhythms of recovery: Integrative medicine for PTSD and complex trauma* (2nd ed.). Routledge.

Other Books

- Lake, D. (2015). *Integrative mental health care: A therapist's handbook.* Norton Professional Books.

Other Resources

- Champion Juicer (http://championjuicer.com): Champion Juicer is a very high-quality juicer.

- Excalibur Dehydrator (excaliburdehydrator.com): The Excalibur has temperature control, is fan operated, and is easy to clean.

- Kalustyan's (kalustyans.com): Hard-to-find foods from around the world can be ordered from this specialty food store.

CHAPTER 9: NUTRITIONAL SUPPLEMENTS

General Resources

- Micronutrient Information Center (https://lpi.oregonstate.edu/mic): The Linus Pauling Institute's Micronutrient Information Center is a source for scientifically accurate information regarding the roles of vitamins, minerals, phytochemicals, and other dietary factors, including some foods and beverages, in preventing disease and promoting health.

- NIH Center for Complementary and Integrative Health (https://www.nccih.nih.gov/health/dietary -and-herbal-supplements): This site provides the federal definitions of dietary supplements and links to the NCCIH Clearinghouse, where information on NCCIH and complementary and integrative health approaches may be found, including publications and searches of federal databases of scientific and medical literature.

- NIH Office of Dietary Supplements (https://ods.od.nih.gov): ODS is the lead federal government entity addressing the scientific exploration of dietary supplements.

Specific Resources

- Allergy Research (https://www.allergyresearchgroup.com)

- Arthur Andrew Medical (https://arthurandrew.com)

- Biotics Research, Inc. (https://www.bioticsresearch.com)

- Designs for Health (https://www.designsforhealth.com)

- Fullscript (https://fullscript.com)

- Integrative Therapeutics (https://www.integrativepro.com)

- Jarrow Formulas (https://jarrow.com)

- Klaire Labs (https://klaire.com)

- Nordic Naturals (https://www.nordic.com)

- Quicksilver Scientific (https://www.quicksilverscientific.com)

CHAPTER 10: HERBAL MEDICINE

Further Study

- American Herbalists Guild herbal education schools (https://www.americanherbalistsguild.com/ school-profilesHerbal Education Programs)

- Korn, L. (2019). *Natural woman: Herbal remedies for radiant health at every age and stage of life.* Shambhala.

General Resources

- American Botanical Council (https://www.herbalgram.org): ABC is an independent, nonprofit research and education organization dedicated to providing accurate and reliable information.

- American Herbalists Guild (https://www.americanherbalistsguild.com): AHG is a nonprofit, educational organization that represents the goals and voices of herbalists specializing in the medicinal use of plants. Members receive access to monthly webinars and discounted rates on intensive courses and archives. They also have a registry of practitioners who have met the criteria for Registered Herbalist (https://www.americanherbalistsguild.com/member-profiles).

- American Herbal Pharmacopoeia (https://herbal-ahp.org): This organization provides extensive information on different Ayurvedic, Chinese, and Western herbs used in the United States.

- Botanical Adulterants Prevention Program (https://www.herbalgram.org/resources/botanical -adulterants-prevention-program): Three leading nonprofit organizations initiated this large-scale program to educate members of the herbal and dietary supplement industry about ingredient and product adulteration.

- Gaby, A. R., & Healthnotes, Inc. (Eds.). (2006). *A–Z guide to drug-herb-vitamin interactions, revised and expanded 2nd edition*. Harmony.

Specific Resources

- Bear Wallow Herbs (https://bear-wallow-herbs.myshopify.com)

- Gaia Herbs (https://www.gaiaherbs.com)

- Herb Pharm (https://www.herb-pharm.com)

CHAPTER 11: HYDROTHERAPY AND DETOXIFICATION

General Resources

- Body Sense (www.bodysenseinc.com): This company offers hot/cold aromatherapy products and hot/cold pads made by hand in the United States.

- Nidra (https://www.nidragoods.com): Nidra makes high-quality, contoured sleep masks that aid deep rest.

- Traditional Tobacco (https://keepitsacred.itcmi.org): This is a national network of tribes, tribal organizations, and health programs working to decrease commercial tobacco use and cancer health disparities among American Indians and Alaska Natives (AI/AN) across the United States.

- Warm Buddy (https://www.warmbuddy.com): This company creates natural hot/cold therapy products for adults and children.

- Yerba Prima (https://yerba.com): Yerba Prima is a good source for supplies for detoxification, including skin brushes, bentonite, and psyllium husk powder.

- Quit That! (https://cozyapps.com/quitthat): This app helps you track habits to quit smoking, drinking alcohol, using drugs, or consuming caffeine.

CHAPTER 12: EXERCISE

Specific Resources

- Autoimmune Strong (https://www.getautoimmunestrong.com): This online fitness program is designed for people with chronic pain and offers videos, community support, and coaching; there is also a free trial available.

- The Class (https://www.theclass.com): This digital fitness studio offers diverse exercise classes for everyone, ranging from prenatal to children to adults, including high-intensity and mindfulness exercises.

- Fitness Blender (https://www.fitnessblender.com): This site offers diverse types of workouts, including free options.

- FitOn (https://fitonapp.com): This app can be linked to an Apple watch and includes live and on-demand fitness classes.

- Nike Training Club (https://www.nike.com/ntc-app): Nike's fitness app tailors training programs for you.

- Yoga for Everyone (https://www.yogaforeveryone.tv): Dianne Bondy is the instructor for these wide-ranging, body-positive yoga, Pilates, and yin yoga classes.

- Yoga with Adrienne (https://www.youtube.com/user/yogawithadriene): Adriene offers low-key yoga classes that are 10–30 minutes long.

CHAPTER 13: SOMATICS AND BODYWORK

General Resources

- United States Association for Body Psychotherapy (https://usabp.org/): USABP's mission is to develop and advance the art, science, and practice of body psychotherapy and somatic psychology in a professional, ethical, and caring manner.

Specific Resources

- Alpha-Stim (http://www.alleviahealth.com): The Alpha-Stim is a cranial electrotherapy stimulation device, a drug-free treatment option for pain, anxiety, insomnia, and depression. Practitioners may be eligible for a 60-day loan of an Alpha-Stim machine for use by patients to try out the device.

- Mindfulness Activities (https://positivepsychology.com/mindfulness-for-kids/): This site contains videos and quotations for children and teens to help explain, illustrate, and teach a variety of mindfulness practices.

- Sommerfly (sommerfly.com): Sommerfly offers weighted blankets and vests.

- Unyte (https://unyte.com/): Unyte is a neurotech company that serves a community of more than 10,000 mental health and neurodevelopmental professionals in over 50 countries. Their products aim to help people find effective mind-body solutions and guidance to become more aware, regulated, and resilient.

CHAPTER 14: BREATH

Apps

- Breathe2Relax (https://onemindpsyberguide.org/apps/breathe2relax/): Breathe2Relax is a portable stress management tool that provides detailed information on the effects of stress on the body and instructions and exercises to help users learn diaphragmatic breathing.

- iBreathe (https://www.jadelizardsoftware.com/ibreathe): This is a simple and easy-to-use app for breathing exercises.

Specific Resources

- Buteyko Breathing Association (https://www.buteykobreathing.org/): Buteyko exercises promote nose-breathing and taking in an effective amount of air, which may be useful for individuals who are habituated to overbreathing or hyperventilating. The technique is named after Ukrainian doctor Konstantin Buteyko, who first developed the techniques in the 1950s.

- Deep Breathing Exercises for Kids (https://copingskillsforkids.com/deep-breathing-exercises-for-kids): This site offers a child therapist's favorite ways to help children learn to take a deep breath, and it includes quick explanations and videos of deep breathing techniques.

- Komuso (https://www.komusodesign.com/): This is an elegant tool to reduce anxiety via improved breathing. Based on the Zen tradition of the blowing meditation of the shakuhachi flute, this small steel straw-like breathing necklace can be worn and used throughout the day to enhance mindful breathing and reduce anxiety.

CHAPTER 15: SPIRITUALITY AND MEANING-MAKING

Further Study

- Burris, M. (2021). *Latinx heroes: A to Z*. Author.

- Ford, C. (1999). *The hero with an African face: Mythic wisdom of traditional Africa*. Bantam.

- Hamby, Z. (2021). *World mythology for beginners: 50 timeless tales from around the globe*. Rockridge Press.

- Harris, R. (2001). *The hero's journey and brain-based teaching*. The Hero's Journey. https://www.yourheroicjourney.com/the-heros-journey-and-brain-based-teaching-2/

- *Heroes' stories*. (n.d.). Home of Heroes: Medal of Honor & Military History. https://homeofheroes.com/heroes-stories/

- Murdock, M. (1990). *The heroine's journey*. Shambhala.

- The works of Clarissa Pinkola Estés (https://www.clarissapinkolaestes.com/works.htm)

- Ridall, K. (2019). *Dreaming at the gates: How dreams guide us*. DreamGate Press.

- Sicardi, A. (2019). *Queer heroes: Meet 53 LGBTQ heroes from past and present!*. Wide Eyed Editions.

- Spence, L. (2019). *The myths of the North American Indians*. Dover Publications.

Specific Resources for Children

- Le, M., Pak, G., Wong, A., Tamaki, M., Kuhn, S., Ansari A. A., Pichetshote, P., Yang, G. L., V., R., Nguyen, D., Chu, A., Wheeler, A., Johns, S., Maines, N., Ayala, V., Grace, S., Lore, D., Andreyko, M., Orlando, S., & Tynion, J. (2021). *DC festival of heroes (2021–) #1: The Asian superhero celebration*. DC Comics.

- Norwood, A. (2020). *Black heroes: A Black history book for kids: 51 inspiring people from ancient Africa to modern-day U.S.A.* Rockridge.

CHAPTER 16: ALTERED STATES AND PSYCHEDELIC MEDICINE

General Resources

- Pilecki, B., Luoma, J. B., Bathje, G. J., Rhea, J., & Narloch, V. F. (2021). Ethical and legal issues in psychedelic harm reduction and integration therapy. *Harm Reduction Journal, 18,* Article 40. https://doi.org/10.1186/s12954-021-00489-1

Training and Research Programs

- Berkeley Center for the Science of Psychedelics (https://bcsp.berkeley.edu/): BCSP examines the short- and long-term effects of psychedelics in healthy volunteers, trains clinicians to facilitate psychedelic experiences, and advances public understanding of psychedelic substances.

- California Institute of Integral Studies (https://www.ciis.edu/): CIIS offers a diverse range of graduate degrees, including Integrative Health Studies (MA), Integral and Transpersonal Psychology (PhD), and Integral Counseling Psychology (MA, MFT prep). Many of these degrees are fully online.

- The Center for Psychedelic and Consciousness Research at Johns Hopkins (https://hopkinspsychedelic.org/): The leading psychedelic research institute in the United States, the center at Johns Hopkins explores psychedelics as pharmacological compounds. It was the first in the United States to reinitiate approved psychedelic research in healthy, psychedelic-naive volunteers.

- The Center for Psychedelic Psychotherapy and Trauma Research (https://icahn.mssm.edu/research/center-psychedelic-psychotherapy-trauma-research): Located at Mount Sinai and the James J. Peters Department of Veterans Affairs Medical Center, the center investigates the utility of psychedelic compounds, particularly MDMA and psilocybin, for treating PTSD. The center launched a training program for future MDMA psychotherapists in 2020 and hosts a monthly lecture series on psychedelic topics.

- Chacruna Institute of Psychedelic Plant Medicines (https://chacruna.net/): Chacruna collects academic research articles and other media exploring all aspects of psychedelic use.

- The Fireside Project (https://firesideproject.org/): The Fireside Project is a peer support call-in line for those currently undergoing psychedelic experiences and those seeking to integrate past experiences.

- Fluence (https://www.fluencetraining.com/): Fluence offers courses, workshops, and certificate programs in psychedelic-assisted psychotherapy, harm reduction, and integration for prescribing clinicians, psychotherapists, and wellness practitioners.

- Multidisciplinary Association for Psychedelic Study (https://maps.org/): MAPS produces research on psychedelic medicine, including public policy.

- Naropa University (https://www.naropa.edu/academics/extended-campus/psychedelic-assisted-therapies-certificate/): Naropa University offers a 200-hour, 10-month, hybrid online training program in psychedelic-assisted therapies. This certificate program is intended for licensed and certified clinicians.

- Psychedelic Research and Training Institute (https://pratigroup.org/): PRATI offers experiential training in ketamine-assisted psychotherapy.

- Zendo Project (https://zendoproject.org/): This is a volunteer-based peer support network for those undergoing psychedelic experiences. It originated at Burning Man in 2012. The Zendo Project puts forth guiding principles for psychedelic experiences and provides comprehensive harm reduction education.

CHAPTER 17: ADHERENCE STRATEGIES

Apps

For Meditation, Sleep, and Relaxation

- Breathe+: Delivers guided and customizable pranayama sessions to help you relax and train your breath through regular practice.

- Insight Timer: Offers an extensive catalog of music, guided meditations, and yoga practices to reduce stress and support sleep, mindfulness, self-compassion, mindful eating, and more.

- Pzizz: Provides psychoacoustic tracks based in clinical sleep science to guide your brain through nap and night-time sleep cycles and wake you up refreshed.

- Shine: Offers a daily meditation, a gratitude log, and a daily self-care article. Created by women of color, this app focuses on representation in the wellness world, the workplace, and more, while acknowledging the unique mental health challenges faced by people of color, women, and LGBTQ+ individuals.

- Tide: Offers sound scenes, meditations, and customizable timers to help you focus, relax, fall asleep, and wake up refreshed.

For Digital Journaling and Mood and Habit Tracking

- Daylio: Generates charts and graphs to help you visualize the way your mood and activities influence each other.

- Done: Provides a simple interface for tracking habits and goals, with options to view weekly, monthly, and yearly summaries of your progress.

- Grateful: A prompt-based digital gratitude journal. You can create your own daily prompts or use the ones provided.

- Happify: Choose from over 65 "tracks" to improve your outlook using the tools of positive psychology. Topics include coping with stress, connecting socially, happy parenting, strengthening friendships, and more.

- Moodfit: Tracks any number of daily activity variables—from mood-related medications to socializing to breathing exercises—and plots them against daily mood to help you identify patterns. The app analyzes data you input from multiple angles to answer questions about how daily, weekly, and monthly choices affect your mood.

- Strides: Create customized trackers for good habits you want to build and bad habits you want to break.

For Disordered Eating Recovery

- Brighter Bite: Helps you understand, track, and recover from disordered eating. Features mood and food logs, tools to help you name your emotions, and a collection of relaxing, therapeutic alternatives to disordered eating behaviors.

- Rise Up + Recover: An eating disorder recovery tool based in CBT. Offers fillable meal, behavior, and emotion logs that you can share with your treatment team, along with a collection of coping activities and homework assignments that support self-monitoring.

Digital Therapeutics

- Pear reSET: A prescription digital therapeutic designed for people with substance use disorder, this FDA-authorized treatment offers CBT lessons, trigger and craving tracking, and an evidence-based reward system.

- Sanvello: Combines CBT, mindfulness meditation, and mood and habit tracking to address mild to moderate depression and anxiety. The premium version of this app may be in-network for some forms of insurance.

For PTSD, Veterans, and First Responders

- VetTriage: Allows you to "triage" your moods, stressors, and daily activities in order to rate the severity of their impact on your overall health and wellness. Designed to connect veterans and first responders to a community of peers seeking to improve their mental health.

For Neuro-Rehabilitation

- Clock Yourself: Balance and hemisphere integration

- Dexteria: Fine motor skills and handwriting readiness

- Flow Free and Flow Free Hexes: Puzzle games

- Kami 2: Puzzle game

- Train Your Brain – Memory: Memory games

- Visual Attention Therapy Lite: Cognitive training for elders and kids

- WordBubbles!: Word search

Other Resources

- BrainMaster Technologies (https://brainmaster.com/): BrainMaster offers training, products, and resources regarding contemporary neurofeedback and qEEG.

- MindEd (https://www.minded.org.uk/Component/Details/447268): This e-learning session for counselors and therapists focuses on setting therapeutic goals.

- Next Step Cards (http://www.nextstepcards.co.uk/): This goal-based tool helps young people to communicate on their own terms, in their own environment.

- PTSD Coach Online (https://www.ptsd.va.gov/apps/ptsdcoachonline/tools_menu.htm): The National Center for PTSD created this toolkit of videos and handouts to help with the many facets of PTSD.

CHAPTER 18: BRIDGING INTEGRATIVE MEDICINE AND SOCIAL JUSTICE

General Resources

- Anti-Racist Guide (https://www.antiracistguide.org/the-guide): This resource is for anyone looking to broaden their understanding of anti-racism and get involved to combat racism, specifically as it relates to anti-Blackness.

- Association of Asian Pacific Community Health Organizations (http://www.aapcho.org/): AAPCHO is a national association representing community health organizations dedicated to promoting advocacy, collaboration, and leadership that improves the health status and access of Asian Americans and Native Hawaiians and other Pacific Islanders.

- Black Emotional and Mental Health (https://www.beam.community/): BEAM is a collective of advocates, yoga teachers, artists, therapists, lawyers, religious leaders, teachers, psychologists, and activists committed to the emotional and mental health and healing of Black communities.

- Center for World Indigenous Studies (https://www.cwis.org/): CWIS is a global community of activist scholars advancing the rights of Indigenous peoples through the application of traditional knowledge. It is also a leading Indigenous peoples' think tank, ensuring that communities can safeguard their rights and resources.

- Curanderismo (https://curanderismo.unm.edu/coursera.html): These free online courses sponsored by the University of New Mexico provide information on the history, traditions, rituals, herbs, and remedies of Curanderismo, a folk healing tradition of the southwestern United States, Latin America, and Mexico.

- Identifying Critical Moments and Healing Complex Trauma (https://learn.nctsn.org/course/index.php?categoryid=78): This series of webinars from the National Child Traumatic Stress Network provides clinicians, counselors, and other helpers with insights on recognizing and dealing with the most difficult crises and turning points that occur in therapy with traumatized children and families.

- Institute for Research and Education on Human Rights (https://www.irehr.org/category/c19-irehr/): IREHR is a social justice organization dedicated to standing against bigotry and defending democracy and human rights.

- Integrative Medicine for the Underserved (https://im4us.org/): IM4US is a collaborative, multidisciplinary group committed to affordable, accessible integrative health care for all. Through outreach, education, research, and advocacy, they work to shift the current paradigm toward equity, wellness, prevention, patient empowerment, and self-care.

- National Queer and Trans Therapists of Color Network (https://nqttcn.com/en/): A healing justice organization, NQTTCN is committed to transforming mental health for queer and trans people of color.

- Racial Equity Terminology Glossary (https://www.racialequitytools.org/glossary): The meanings of many words used in discussions of race are not universally agreed upon. Even frequently used words can easily cause confusion, controversy, or hostility. This glossary can help achieve some degree of shared understanding.

- Rochester Racial Justice Toolkit (https://thetoolkit.wixsite.com/toolkit): This toolkit is a compilation of articles, guides, news, videos, social media, and other tools from several online sources on racial justice and Black Lives Matter activism.

CHAPTER 19: PRACTICE DEVELOPMENT, COLLABORATION, AND LEGAL SCRIPTS

General Resources

- Cohen, M. H. (1998). *Complementary and alternative medicine: Legal boundaries and regulatory perspectives.* Johns Hopkins University Press.

- NOLO (https://www.nolo.com/): This helpful website is devoted to DIY legal forms, business contracts, and so forth.

- Person Centered Tech (https://personcenteredtech.com): PCT has a wealth of high-quality resources related to teletherapy practices and the role of technology in mental health, including teletherapy practice rules by state (https://personcenteredtech.com/teletherapy-practice-rules-by-state).

REFERENCES

Amon, K. L., & Campbell, A. J. (2008). Can children with AD/HD learn relaxation and breathing techniques through biofeedback video games? *Australian Journal of Educational and Developmental Psychology, 8*, 72–84. https://www.newcastle.edu.au/__data/assets/pdf_file/0014/100337/v8-amon -campbell.pdf

Andre, L., Gallini, A., Montastruc, F., Montastruc, J.-L., Piau, A., Lapeyre-Mestre, M., & Gardette, V. (2019). Association between anticholinergic (atropinic) drug exposure and cognitive function in longitudinal studies among individuals over 50 years old: A systematic review. *European Journal of Clinical Pharmacology, 75*(12), 1631–1644. https://doi.org/10.1007/s00228-019-02744-8

Anjum, I., Jaffery, S. S., Fayyaz, M., Samoo, Z., & Anjum, S. (2018). The role of vitamin D in brain health: A mini literature review. *Cureus, 10*(7), Article e2960. https://doi.org/10.7759/cureus.2960

Bailly, M., Evrard, B., Coudeyre, E., Rochette, C., Meriade, L., Blavignac, C., Fournier, A.-C., Bignon, Y.-J., Dutheil, F., Duclos, M., & Thivel, D. (2022). Health management of patients with COVID-19: Is there a room for hydrotherapeutic approaches? *International Journal of Biometeorology, 66*(5), 1031–1038. https://doi.org/10.1007/s00484-022-02246-w

Bayer, L., Constantinescu, I., Perrig, S., Vienne, J., Vidal, P.-P., Mühlethaler, M., & Schwartz, S. (2011). Rocking synchronizes brain waves during a short nap. *Current Biology, 21*(12), R461–R462. https://doi .org/10.1016/j.cub.2011.05.012

Beans, D. R. (2009). *Integrative endocrinology: The rhythms of life.* Routledge.

Bevilacqua, D., Davidesco, I., Wan, L., Chaloner, K., Rowland, J., Ding, M., Poeppel, D., & Dikker, S. (2019). Brain-to-brain synchrony and learning outcomes vary by student-teacher dynamics: Evidence from a real-world classroom electroencephalography study. *Journal of Cognitive Neuroscience, 31*(3), 401–411. https://doi.org/10.1162/jocn_a_01274

Birke, L., & and Thompson, K. (2019). *(Un)stable relations: Horses, humans and social agency.* Routledge.

Böbel, T. S., Hackl, S. B., Langgartner, D., Jarczok, M. N., Rohleder, N., Rook, G. A., Lowry, C. A., Gündel, H., Waller, C., & O. Reber, S. (2018). Less immune activation following social stress in rural vs. urban participants raised with regular or no animal contact, respectively. *PNAS, 115*(20), 5259–5264. https://doi.org/10.1073/pnas.1719866115

Borrega-Mouquinho, Y., Sánchez-Gómez, J., Fuentes-García, J. P., Collado-Mateo, D., & Villafaina, S. (2021). Effects of high-intensity interval training and moderate-intensity training on stress, depression, anxiety, and resilience in healthy adults during coronavirus disease 2019 confinement: A randomized controlled trial. *Frontiers in Psychology*, 12, Article 643069. https://doi.org/10.3389/fpsyg.2021.643069

Brave Heart, M. Y. (2003). The historical trauma response among natives and its relationship with substance abuse: A Lakota illustration. *Journal of Psychoactive Drugs, 35*(1), 7–13. https://doi.org/10.1080 /02791072.2003.10399988

Brown, R. P., Gerbarg P. L., & Muench, F. (2013). Breathing practices for treatment of psychiatric and stress-related medical conditions. *Psychiatric Clinics of North America, 36*(1), 121–140. https://doi.org /10.1016/j.psc.2013.01.001

Callahan, G. N. (2003). Eating dirt. *Emerging Infectious Diseases, 9*(8), 1016–1021. https://doi.org/10.3201 /eid0908.ad0908

Castaneda, D., Popov, V. B., Wander, P., Thompson, C. C. (2019). Risk of suicide and self-harm is increased after bariatric surgery—A systematic review and meta-analysis. *Obesity Surgery, 29*(1), 322–333. https://doi.org/10.1007/s11695-018-3493-4

Chao, M. T., & Adler, S. R. (2018). Integrative medicine and the imperative for health justice. *Journal of Alternative and Complementary Medicine, 24*(2), 101–103. https://doi.org/10.1089/acm.2017.29042.mtc

Chevalier, G., Sinatra, S. T., Oschman, J. L., Sokal, K., & Sokal, P. (2012). Earthing: Health implications of reconnecting the human body to the earth's surface electrons. *Journal of Environmental and Public Health*, 2012, Article 291541. https://doi.org/10.1155/2012/291541

Childers, N. F., & Margoles, M. S. (1993). An apparent relation of nightshades (Solanaceae) to arthritis. *Journal of Neurological and Orthopedic Medical Surgery, 12*, 227–231.

Cho, K. K. A., Davidson, T. J., Bouvier, G., Marshall, J. D., Schnitzer, M. J., & Sohal, V. S. (2020). Cross-hemispheric gamma synchrony between prefrontal parvalbumin interneurons supports behavioral adaptation during rule shift learning. *Nature Neuroscience, 23*, 892–902. https://doi.org/10.1038/s41593-020-0647-1

Choi, J. M., Yang, J. I., Kang, S. J., Han, Y. M., Lee, J., Lee, C., Chung, S. J., Yoon, D. H., Park, B., & Kim, Y. S. (2018). Association between anxiety and depression and gastroesophageal reflux disease: Results from a large cross-sectional study. *Journal of Neurogastroenterology and Motility, 24*(4), 593–602. https://doi.org/10.5056/jnm18069

Cohen, M. (2020). Turning up the heat on COVID-19: Heat as a therapeutic intervention. *F1000Research, 9*, Article 292. https://doi.org/10.12688/f1000research.23299.2Cross, M. P., Acevedo, A. M., Leger, K. A., & Pressman, S. D. (2022). How and why could smiling influence physical health? A conceptual review. *Health Psychology Review*. Advance online publication. https://doi.org/10.1080/17437199.2022.2052740

D'Aquili, E. G., Laughlin, C. D., & McManus, J. (Eds.) (1979). *The spectrum of ritual: A biogenetic structural analysis*. Columbia University Press.

Della Vecchia, A., Mucci, F., Pozza, A., & Marazziti, D. (2021). Negative air ions in neuropsychiatric disorders. *Current Medicinal Chemistry, 28*(13), 2521–2539. https://doi.org/10.2174/0929867327666200630104550

Donadon, M. F., Martin-Santos, R., & de Lima Osório, F. (2018). The associations between oxytocin and trauma in humans: A systematic review. *Frontiers in Pharmacology, 9*, Article 154. https://doi.org/10.3389/fphar.2018.00154

Ellingsen, D. M., Isenburg, K., Jung, C., Lee, J., Gerber, J., Mawla, I., Sclocco, R., Jensen, K. B., Edwards, R. R., Kelley, J. M., Kirsch, I., Kaptchuk, T. J., & Napadow, V. (2020). Dynamic brain-to-brain concordance and behavioral mirroring as a mechanism of the patient-clinician interaction. *Science Advances, 6*(43), Article eabc1304. https://doi.org/10.1126/sciadv.abc1304

Evans, S. S., Repasky, E. A., & Fisher, D. T. (2015). Fever and the thermal regulation of immunity: The immune system feels the heat. *Nature Reviews Immunology, 15*(6), 335–349. https://doi.org/10.1038/nri3843

Fabio, R. A., & Towey, G. E. (2018). Long-term meditation: The relationship between cognitive processes, thinking styles and mindfulness. *Cognitive Processing, 19*, 73–85. https://doi.org/10.1007/s10339-017-0844-3

Feng, L., & Yin, R. (2021). Social support and hope mediate the relationship between gratitude and depression among front-line medical staff during the pandemic of COVID-19. *Frontiers in Psychology, 12*, Article 623873. https://doi.org/10.3389/fpsyg.2021.623873

Fisher, P. W., Lazarov, A., Lowell, A., Arnon, S., Turner, J. B., Bergman, M., Ryba, M., Such, S., Marohasy, C., Zhu, X., Suarez-Jimenez, B., Markowitz, J. C., & Neria, Y. (2021). Equine-assisted therapy for posttraumatic stress disorder among military veterans: An open trial. *Journal of Clinical Psychiatry, 82*(5). https://doi.org/10.4088/JCP.21m14005

Geoffroy, P. A., & Palagini, L. Biological rhythms and chronotherapeutics in depression. *Progress in Neuro-Psychopharmacology and Biological Psychiatry, 106,* Article 110158. https://doi.org/10.1016/j.pnpbp.2020.110158

Gershon, M. D. (1998). *The second brain: A groundbreaking new understanding of nervous disorders of the stomach and intestine.* HarperCollins.

Gershon, M. D., & Margolis, K. G. (2021). The gut, its microbiome, and the brain: Connections and communications. *Journal of Clinical Investigation, 131*(18), Article e143768. https://doi.org/10.1172/JCI143768

Gharbi-Meliani, A., Dugravot, A., Sabia, S., Regy, M., Fayosse, A., Schnitzler, A., Kivimäki, M., Singh-Manoux, A., & Dumurgier, J. (2021). The association of APOE ε4 with cognitive function over the adult life course and incidence of dementia: 20 years follow-up of the Whitehall II study. *Alzheimer's Research & Therapy, 13*(1), Article 5. https://doi.org/10.1186/s13195-020-00740-0

Gillespie, A. M., & Johnson-Askew, W. L. (2009). Changing family food and eating practices: The family food decision-making system. *Annals of Behavioral Medicine, 38*(Suppl. 1), S31–36. https://doi.org/10.1007/s12160-009-9122-7

Grahn, J. A., Bauer, A.-K. R., & Zamm, A. (2021). Is neural entrainment to rhythms the basis of social bonding through music? *Behavioral and Brain Sciences, 44,* Article e73. https://doi.org/10.1017/s0140525x20001296

Graser, J., & Stangier, U. (2018). Compassion and loving-kindness meditation: An overview and prospects for the application in clinical samples. *Harvard Review of Psychiatry, 26*(4), 201–215. https://doi.org/10.1097/HRP.0000000000000192

Groves, N. J., McGrath, J. J., & Burne, T. H. J. (2014). Vitamin D as a neurosteroid affecting the developing and adult brain. *Annual Review of Nutrition, 34,* 117–141. https://doi.org/10.1146/annurev-nutr-071813-105557

Harmer, C. J., Charles, M., McTavish, S., Favaron, E., & Cowen, P. J. (2012). Negative ion treatment increases positive emotional processing in seasonal affective disorder. *Psychological Medicine, 42*(8), 1605–1612. https://doi.org/10.1017/S0033291711002820

He, S., Zheng, X., Zeng, D., Luo, C., & Zhang, Z. (2016). Exploring entrainment patterns of human emotion in social media. *PLOS ONE, 11*(3), Article e0150630. https://doi.org/10.1371/journal.pone.0150630

Hersey, M., Samaranayake, S., Berger, S. N., Tavakoli, N., Mena, S., Nijhout, H. F., Reed, M. C., Best, J., Blakely, R. D., Reagan, L. P., & Hashemi, P. (2021). Inflammation-induced histamine impairs the capacity of escitalopram to increase hippocampal extracellular serotonin. *The Journal of Neuroscience, 41*(30), 6564–6577. https://doi.org/10.1523/JNEUROSCI.2618-20.2021

Hodges, R. E, & Minich, D. M. (2015). Modulation of metabolic detoxification pathways using foods and food-derived components: A scientific review with clinical application. *Journal of Nutrition and Metabolism, 2015,* Article 760689. https://doi.org/10.1155/2015/760689

Hofmann, S. G., Grossman, P., & Hinton, D. E. (2011). Loving-kindness and compassion meditation: Potential for psychological interventions. *Clinical Psychology Review, 31*(7), 1126–1132. https://doi.org/10.1016/j.cpr.2011.07.003

Houston, J. (1997). *The possible human: A course in enhancing your physical, mental, and creative abilities.* TarcherPerigee.

Hu, H., Lei, Y., Zhang, W., Xiong, P., Song, L., Luo, X., Jia, B., & Zhang, F. (2022). Anti-inflammatory activity and safety of compound glycyrrhizin in ulcerative colitis: A systematic review and meta-analysis of randomized controlled trials. *Journal of Functional Foods, 91,* Article 105004. https://doi.org/10.1016/j.jff.2022.105004

Jackson, J. R., Eaton, W. W., Cascella, N. G., Fasano, A., & Kelly, D. L. (2012). Neurologic and psychiatric manifestations of celiac disease and gluten sensitivity. *Psychiatric Quarterly, 83*(1), 91–102. https://doi.org/10.1007%2Fs11126-011-9186-y

Järvelä-Reijonen, E., Karhunen, L., Sairanen, E., Muotka, J., Lindroos, S., Laitinen, J., Puttonen, S., Peuhkuri, K., Hallikainen, M., Pihlajamäki, J., Korpela, R., Ermes, M., Lappalainen, R., & Kolehmainen, M. (2018). The effects of acceptance and commitment therapy on eating behavior and diet delivered through face-to-face contact and a mobile app: A randomized controlled trial. *International Journal of Behavioral Nutrition and Physical Activity, 15*(1), Article 22. https://doi.org/10.1186/s12966-018-0654-8

Kempuraj, D., Selvakumar, G. P., Thangavel, R., Ahmed, M. E., Zaheer, S., Raikwar, S. P., Iyer, S. S., Bhagavan, S. M., Beladakere-Ramaswamy, S., & Zaheer, A. (2017). Mast cell activation in brain injury, stress, and post-traumatic stress disorder and Alzheimer's disease pathogenesis. *Frontiers in Neuroscience, 11,* Article 703. https://www.frontiersin.org/article/10.3389/fnins.2017.00703

Kim, T., Song, B., Cho, K. S., & Lee, I.-S. (2020). Therapeutic potential of volatile terpenes and terpenoids from forests for inflammatory diseases. *International Journal of Molecular Sciences, 21*(6), Article 2187. https://doi.org/10.3390/ijms21062187

Kitamura, A., Torii, K., Uneyama, H., & Niijima, A. (2010). Role played by afferent signals from olfactory, gustatory and gastrointestinal sensors in regulation of autonomic nerve activity. *Biological and Pharmaceutical Bulletin, 33*(11), 1778–1782. https://www.jstage.jst.go.jp/article/bpb/33/11/33_11_1778/_pdf

Korn, L. E. (2016a). *Multicultural counseling workbook: Exercises, worksheets & games to build rapport with diverse clients.* PESI Publishing & Media.

Korn, L. E. (2016b). *Nutrition essentials for mental health: A complete guide to the food-mood connection.* W. W. Norton & Company.

Korn, L. E. (2017a). *Eat right, feel right: Over 80 recipes and tips to improve mood, sleep, attention & focus.* PESI Publishing & Media.

Korn, L. E. (2017b). *The good mood kitchen: Simple recipes and nutrition tips for emotional balance.* Norton Professional Books.

Korn, L. E. (2019). *Natural woman: Herbal remedies for radiant health at every age and stage of life.* Shambhala.

Korn, L. E. (2022). *Rhythms of recovery: Trauma, nature, and the body* (Classic ed.). Routledge. (Original work published 2013)

Korn, L. E., Logsdon, R. G., Polissar, N. L., Gomez-Beloz, A., Waters, T., & Rÿser, R. (2009). A randomized trial of a CAM therapy for stress reduction in American Indian and Alaskan Native family caregivers. *Gerontologist, 49*(3), 368–77. https://doi.org/10.1093/geront/gnp032

Korn, L. E., & Rÿser, R. C. (2006). Burying the umbilicus: Nutrition trauma, diabetes and traditional medicine in rural west Mexico. In M. L. Ferreira & G. C. Lang (Eds.), *Indigenous peoples and diabetes*. Carolina Academic Press.

Kumar, R., Kumar, A., Nordberg, A., Långström, B., & Darreh-Shori, T. (2020). Proton pump inhibitors act with unprecedented potencies as inhibitors of the acetylcholine biosynthesizing enzyme—A plausible missing link for their association with incidence of dementia. *Alzheimer's & Dementia, 16*(7), 1031–1042. https://doi.org/10.1002/alz.12113

LaChance, L. R., & Ramsey, D. (2018). Antidepressant foods: An evidence-based nutrient profiling system for depression. *World Journal of Psychiatry, 8*(3), 97–104. https://doi.org/10.5498/wjp.v8.i3.97

La Puma, J. (2016). What is culinary medicine and what does it do? *Population Health Management, 19*(1), 1–3. https://doi.org/10.1089/pop.2015.0003

Lawson, M. (2000, February 19). Walking in beauty for greater harmony. *Marshfield News-Herald*, A14.

Levinta, A., Mukovozov, I., & Tsoutsoulas, C. (2018). Use of a gluten-free diet in schizophrenia: A systematic review. *Advances in Nutrition, 9*(6), 824–832. https://doi.org/10.1093/advances/nmy056

Lobay, D. (2015). Rauwolfia in the treatment of hypertension. *Integrative Medicine, 14*(3), 40–46. https://www.ncbi.nlm.nih.gov/pmc/articles/PMC4566472/pdf/40-46.pdf

Lustig, R. H. (2020). Ultraprocessed food: Addictive, toxic, and ready for regulation. *Nutrients, 12*(11), Article 3401.

Ma, X., Yue, Z.-Q., Gong, Z.-Q., Zhang, H., Duan, N.-Y., Shi, Y.-T., Wei, G.-X., & Li, Y.-F. (2017). The effect of diaphragmatic breathing on attention, negative affect and stress in healthy adults. *Frontiers in Psychology, 8*, Article 874. https://doi.org/10.3389/fpsyg.2017.00874

Maintz, L., & Novak, N. (2007). Histamine and histamine intolerance. *The American Journal of Clinical Nutrition, 85*(5), 1185–1196. https://doi.org/10.1093/ajcn/85.5.1185

Maroo, N., Hazra, A., & Das, T. (2013). Efficacy and safety of a polyherbal sedative-hypnotic formulation NSF-3 in primary insomnia in comparison to zolpidem: A randomized controlled trial. *Indian Journal of Pharmacology, 45*(1), 34–39. https://doi.org/10.4103/0253-7613.106432

Marx, W., Moseley, G., Berk, M., & Jacka, F. (2017). Nutritional psychiatry: The present state of the evidence. *Proceedings of the Nutrition Society, 76*(4), 427–436. https://doi.org/10.1017/s0029665117002026

McCraty, R., Atkinson, M., & Tomasino, D. (2001). *Science of the heart: Exploring the role of the heart in human performance*. Institute of HeartMath.

McCraty, R., & Zayas, M. (2014). Intuitive intelligence, self-regulation, and lifting consciousness. *Global Advances in Health and Medicine, 3*(2), 56–65. https://doi.org/10.7453/gahmj.2014.013

McDonald, R. I., Biswas, T., Sachar, C., Housman, I., Boucher, T. M., Balk, D., Nowak, D., Spotswood, E., Stanley, C. K., & Leyk, S. (2021). The tree cover and temperature disparity in US urbanized areas: Quantifying the association with income across 5,723 communities. *PLOS ONE, 16*(4), Article e0249715. https://doi.org/10.1371/journal.pone.0249715

Menigoz, W., Latz, T. T., Ely, R. A., Kamei, C., Melvin, G., & Sinatra, D. (2020). Integrative and lifestyle medicine strategies should include Earthing (grounding): Review of research evidence and clinical observations. *Explore, 16(3), 152–160. https://doi.org/10.1016/j.explore.2019.10.005*

Misiak, B., Łoniewski, I., Marlicz, W., Frydecka, D., Szulc, A., Rudzki, L., & Samochowiec, J. (2020). The HPA axis dysregulation in severe mental illness: Can we shift the blame to gut microbiota? *Progress in Neuro-Psychopharmacology and Biological Psychiatry, 102*, Article 109951. https://doi.org/10.1016/j.pnpbp.2020.109951

Moskowitz, D. (2006). A comprehensive review of the safety and efficacy of bioidentical hormones for the management of menopause and related health risks. *Alternative Medicine Review, 11*(3), 208–223.

Mumtaz, H., Ghafoor, B., Saghir, H., Tariq, M., Dahar, K., Ali, S. H., Waheed, S. T., & Syed, A. A. (2022). Association of vitamin B12 deficiency with long-term PPIs use: A cohort study. *Annals of Medicine and Surgery, 82,* Article 104762. https://doi.org/10.1016%2Fj.amsu.2022.104762

Ng, Q. X., Venkatanarayanan, N., & Ho, C. Y. X. (2017). Clinical use of *Hypericum perforatum* (St John's wort) in depression: A meta-analysis. *Journal of Affective Disorders, 210,* 211–221. https://doi.org/10.1016/j.jad.2016.12.048

Novak, J. R., Robinson, L. P., & Korn, L. E. (2021). What MFTs should know about nutrition, psychosocial health, and collaborative care with nutrition professionals. *Journal of Marital and Family Therapy.* Advance online publication. https://doi.org/10.1111/jmft.12540

Ooi, S. L., Henderson, P., & Pak, S. C. (2018). Kava for generalized anxiety disorder: A review of current evidence. *Journal of Alternative and Complementary Medicine, 24*(8), 770–780. https://doi.org/10.1089/acm.2018.0001

Pagliai, G., Dinu, M., Madarena, M. P., Bonaccio, M., Iacoviello, L., Sofi, F. (2021). Consumption of ultra-processed foods and health status: A systematic review and meta-analysis. *British Journal of Nutrition, 125*(3), 308–318. https://doi.org/10.1017%2FS0007114520002688

Pan, S.-Y., Litscher, G., Chan, K., Yu, Z.-L., Chen, H.-Q., & Ko, K.-M. (2014). Traditional medicines in the world: Where to go next? *Evidence-Based Complementary and Alternative Medicine* 2014, Article 739895. https://doi.org/10.1155/2014/739895

Parletta, N., Zarnowiecki, D., Cho, J., Wilson, A., Bogomolova, S., Villani, A., Itsiopoulos, C., Niyonsenga, T., Blunden, S., Meyer, B., Segal, L., Baune, B. T., & O'Dea, K. (2019). A Mediterranean-style dietary intervention supplemented with fish oil improves diet quality and mental health in people with depression: A randomized controlled trial (HELFIMED). *Nutritional Neuroscience, 22*(7), 474–487. https://doi.org/10.1080/1028415X.2017.1411320

Perrault, A. A., Khani, A., Quairiaux, C., Kompotis, K., Franken, P., Mühlethaler, M., Schwartz, S., & Bayer, L. (2019). Whole-night continuous rocking entrains spontaneous neural oscillations with benefits for sleep and memory. *Current Biology, 29*(3), 402–411. https://doi.org/10.1016/j.cub.2018.12.028

Pilecki, B., Luoma, J. B., Bathje, G. J., Rhea, J., & Narloch, V. F. (2021). Ethical and legal issues in psychedelic harm reduction and integration therapy. *Harm Reduction Journal, 18*(1), Article 40. https://doi.org/10.1186/s12954-021-00489-1

Pinkola Estés, C. (1997). *Women who run with the wolves: Myths and stories of the wild woman archetype.* Ballantine Books.

Pinkola Estés, C. (2011). *Untie the strong woman: Blessed mother's immaculate love for the wild soul.* Sounds True Books.

Prescott, S. L., & Logan, A. C. (2019). Planetary health: From the wellspring of holistic medicine to personal and public health imperative. *Explore, 15*(2), 98–106. https://doi.org/10.1016/j.explore.2018.09.002

Price, W. A. (1939). *Nutrition and physical degeneration.* P. B. Hoeber.

Pouso, S., Borja, Á., Fleming, L. E., Gómez-Baggethun, E., White, M. P., & Uyarra, M. C. (2021). Contact with blue-green spaces during the COVID-19 pandemic lockdown beneficial for mental health. *Science of the Total Environment, 756,* Article 143984. https://doi.org/10.1016/j.scitotenv.2020.143984

Quintana, D. S., Lischke, A., Grace, S., Scheele, D., Ma, Y., & Becker, B. (2021). Advances in the field of intranasal oxytocin research: Lessons learned and future directions for clinical research. *Molecular Psychiatry, 26*(1), 80–91. https://doi.org/10.1038/s41380-020-00864-7

Ramirez, F. E., Sanchez, A., & Pirskanen, A. T. (2021). Hydrothermotherapy in prevention and treatment of mild to moderate cases of COVID-19. *Medical Hypotheses, 146,* Article 110363. https://doi.org/10.1016/j.mehy.2020.110363

Rao, M., Afshin, A., Singh, G., & Mozaffarian, D. (2013). Do healthier foods and diet patterns cost more than less healthy options? A systematic review and meta-analysis. *BMJ Open, 3*(12), Article e004277.

Rao, N. Z., & Fuller, M. (2018). Acidity and antioxidant activity of cold brew coffee. *Scientific Reports, 8,* Article 16030. https://doi.org/10.1038/s41598-018-34392-w

Reinold, J., Braitmaier, M., Riedel, O., & Haug, U. (2021). Anticholinergic burden: First comprehensive analysis using claims data shows large variation by age and sex. *PLOS ONE, 16*(6), Article e0253336. https://doi.org/10.1371/journal.pone.0253336

Reissig, C. J., Strain, E. C., & Griffiths, R. R. (2009). Caffeinated energy drinks—A growing problem. *Drug and Alcohol Dependence, 99*(1–3), 1–10. https://doi.org/10.1016/j.drugalcdep.2008.08.001

Ridall, K. (2019). *Dreaming at the gates: How dreams guide us.* DreamGate Press.

Roordink, E. M., Steenhuis, I. H. M., Kroeze, W., Schoonmade, L. J., Sniehotta, F. F., & van Stralen, M. M. (2021). Predictors of lapse and relapse in physical activity and dietary behaviour: A systematic search and review on prospective studies. *Psychology & Health.* https://doi.org/10.1080/08870446.2021.1981900

Roslund, M. I., Puhakka, R., Grönroos, M., Nurminen, N., Oikarinen, S., Gazali, A. M., Cinek, O., Kramná, L., Siter, N., Vari, H. K., Soininen, L., Parajuli, A., Rajaniemi, J., Kinnunen, T., Laitinen, O. H., Hyöty, H., Sinkkonen, A., & ADELE Research Group. (2020). Biodiversity intervention enhances immune regulation and health-associated commensal microbiota among daycare children. *Science Advances, 6*(42), Article eaba2578. https://doi.org/10.1126/sciadv.aba2578

Rucklidge, J. J., Johnstone, J. M., & Kaplan, B. J. (2021). Nutrition provides the essential foundation for optimizing mental health. *Evidence-Based Practice in Child and Adolescent Mental Health, 6*(1), 131–154. https://doi.org/10.1080/23794925.2021.1875342

Rucklidge, J. J., & Kaplan, B. J. (2016). Nutrition and mental health. *Clinical Psychological Science, 4*(6), 1082–1084. https://doi.org/10.1177%2F2167702616641050

Sarris, J. (2018). Herbal medicines in the treatment of psychiatric disorders: 10-year updated review. *Phytotherapy Research, 32*(7), 1147–1162. https://doi.org/10.1002/ptr.6055

Sasano, T., Satoh-Kuriwada, S., Shoji, N., Iikubo, M., Kawai, M., Uneyama, H., & Sakamoto, M. (2014). Important role of umami taste sensitivity in oral and overall health. *Current Pharmaceutical Design, 20*(16), 2750–2754. https://doi.org/10.2174/13816128113199990577

Schlote, S. (2018). Integrating somatic experiencing and attachment theory into equine-facilitated trauma recovery. In K. Trotter and J. Baggerly (Eds.), *Equine-assisted mental health for healing trauma* (pp. 3–18). Routledge.

Scotland-Coogan, D. (2019). Anxiety symptoms and sleep disturbance in veterans with posttraumatic stress disorder: The impact of receiving and training a service dog. *TQR, 24*(10), 2655–2674. https://doi.org/10.46743/2160-3715/2019.3573

Serlin, I. A. (2014). Kinaesthetic imagining. In B. Thompson & R. Neimeyer (Eds.), *Grief and the expressive therapies: Practices for creating meaning* (pp. 116–119). Routledge.

Siddiqui, M. J., Saleh, M. S., Basharuddin, S. N., Zamri, S. H., Mohd Najib, M. H., Che Ibrahim, M. Z., Mohd Noor, N. A., Mazha, H. N., Mohd Hassan, N., & Khatib, A. (2018). Saffron (*Crocus sativus* L.): As an antidepressant. *Journal of Pharmacy & Bioallied Sciences, 10*(4), 173–180. https://doi.org/10.4103/JPBS.JPBS_83_18

Smith, L. C., Tieu, L., Suhandynata, R. T., Boomhower, B., Hoffman, M., Sepulveda, Y., Carrette, L. L. G., Momper, J. D., Fitzgerald, R. L., Hanham, K., Dowling, J., Kallupi, M., & George, O. (2021). Cannabidiol reduces withdrawal symptoms in nicotine-dependent rats. *Psychopharmacology, 238*(8), 2201–2211. https://doi.org/10.1007/s00213-021-05845-4

Sokal, K. & Sokal, P. (2011). Earthing the human body influences physiologic processes. *Journal of Alternative and Complementary Medicine, 17*(4), 301–308. https://doi.org/10.1089%2Facm.2010.0687

Sorriento, D., Di Vaia, E., & Iaccarino, G. (2021). Physical exercise: A novel tool to protect mitochondrial health. *Frontiers in Physiology, 12,* Article 660068. https://doi.org/10.3389/fphys.2021.660068

Trasande, L., Shaffer, R. M., Sathyanarayana, S., Council on Environmental Health, Lowry, J. A., Ahdoot, S., Baum, C. R., Bernstein, A. S., Bole, A., Campbell, C. C., Landrigan, P. J., Pacheco, S. E., Spanier, A. J., & Woolf, A. (2018). Food additives and child health. *Pediatrics, 142*(2), Article e20181408. https://doi.org/10.1542/peds.2018-1408

Uhlhaas, P. J., & Singer, W. (2006). Neural synchrony in brain disorders: Relevance for cognitive dysfunctions and pathophysiology. *Neuron, 52*(1),155–68. https://doi.org/10.1016/j.neuron.2006.09.020

Ulrich, R. S. (1984). View through a window may influence recovery from surgery. *Science, 224*(4647), 420–421. https://doi.org/10.1126/science.6143402

Wahl, S., Engelhardt, M., Schaupp, P., Lappe, C., & Ivanov, I. V. (2019). The inner clock—Blue light sets the human rhythm. *Journal of Biophotonics, 12*(12), Article e201900102. https://doi.org/10.1002/jbio.201900102

Walser, S. H., MacDonald, M., & Udell, M. A. R. (2021). Dog–human behavioral synchronization: Family dogs synchronize their behavior with child family members. *Animal Cognition, 24,* 747–752. https://doi.org/10.1007/s10071-020-01454-4

Weir, E. K., Thenappan, T., Bhargava, M., & Chen, Y. (2020). Does vitamin D deficiency increase the severity of COVID-19? *Clinical Medicine, 20*(4), e107–e108. https://doi.org/10.7861/clinmed.2020-0301

Winkelman, M. (2001). Psychointegrators: Multidisciplinary perspectives on the therapeutic effects of hallucinogens. *Complementary Health Practice Review, 6*(3), 219–237.

Woodford, K. B. (2021). Casomorphins and gliadorphins have diverse systemic effects spanning gut, brain and internal organs. *International Journal of Environmental Research and Public Health, 18*(15), Article 7911. https://doi.org/10.3390/ijerph18157911

Yarnell, E. (2017). Herbal medicine and migraine. *Alternative and Complementary Therapies, 23*(5), 192–201. http://doi.org/10.1089/act.2017.29131.eya

Yuan T. F., Chen, W., Shan, C., Rocha, N., Arias-Carrión, O., Machado, S. (2015). Activity-dependent neurorehabilitation beyond physical trainings: "Mental exercise" through mirror neuron activation. *CNS & Neurological Disorders - Drug Targets, 14*(10), 1267–1271. http://dx.doi.org/10.2174/1871527315666151111130956

Zhang, H., Liu, P., Wu, X., Zhang, Y., & Cong, D. (2019). Effectiveness of Chinese herbal medicine for patients with primary insomnia: A PRISMA-compliant meta-analysis. *Medicine, 98*(24), Article e15967. https://doi.org/10.1097/md.0000000000015967

Leslie Korn, PhD, MPH, LMHC, ACS, RPP, NTP, NCBTMB, specializes in integrative medicine and nutrition to treat complex trauma and chronic physical illness. She has provided over 70,000 hours of treatment in private practice in psychotherapy and somatic psychotherapy for diverse populations. She completed her graduate education in psychiatry and public health at Harvard Medical School, cross-cultural health psychology at Lesley University, and behavioral medicine at the Union Institute. She received her life training in the jungle of Mexico, where she lived and worked alongside local healers for over 25 years and directed a pro bono natural medicine clinic.

Dr. Korn is licensed in mental health counseling and certified in functional nutritional therapy, massage and bodywork, and clinical supervision. She was previously a faculty member at the National College of Naturopathic Medicine and at the New England School of Acupuncture, where she also served as clinical director. She was a founder of the National Certification Board for Therapeutic Massage and Bodywork, a Fulbright research scholar on herbal medicine, and an NIH-funded research scientist in mind/body medicine.

Currently, Dr. Korn is the research director at the Center for World Indigenous Studies. She provides supervision and career coaching for clinicians incorporating nutrition and integrative medicine into their practices and agencies. Dr. Korn has authored ten books, including the *Eat Right, Feel Right* cookbook. She lives with her husband and two dogs in Mexico.